Current Topics in Bioenergetics

Volume 10

Current Topics in Bioenergetics

Edited by
D. RAO SANADI

Boston Biomedical Research Institute
Boston, Massachusetts

VOLUME 10

1980

ACADEMIC PRESS

A Subsidiary of Harcourt Brace Jovanovich, Publishers

New York   London   Toronto   Sydney   San Francisco

ACADEMIC PRESS, INC.
111 Fifth Avenue, New York, New York 10003

United Kingdom Edition published by
ACADEMIC PRESS, INC. (LONDON) LTD.
24/28 Oval Road, London NW1 7DX

LIBRARY OF CONGRESS CATALOG CARD NUMBER: 66–28678

ISBN 0–12–152510–4

Contents

Application of Fluctuation Spectroscopy to Muscle Contractility

JULIAN BOREJDO

Respiration-Linked H⁺ Translocation in Mitochondria: Stoichiometry and Mechanism

MÅRTEN WIKSTRÖM AND KLAAS KRAB

Uptake and Release of Bivalent Cations in Mitochondria

NILS-ERIK SARIS AND KARL E. O. ÅKERMAN

Role of Subunits in Proton-Translocating ATPase (F_0-F_1)

MASAMITSU FUTAI AND HIROSHI KANAZAWA

Control of Mitochondrial Substrate Oxidation

RICHARD G. HANSFORD

Electrochemistry of Nitrogenase and the Role of ATP

ROBERT V. HAGEMAN AND R. H. BURRIS

List of Contributors

Numbers in parentheses indicate the pages on which the authors' contributions begin.

KARL O. E. ÅKERMAN (103), *Department of Medical Chemistry, University of Helsinki, Siltavuorenpenger 10, SF 00170, Helsinki 17, Finland*

JULIAN BOREJDO (1), *Polymer Department, Weizmann Institute of Science, Rehovot, Israel, and Cardiovascular Research Institute, University of California, San Francisco, California 94143*

R. H. BURRIS (279), *Department of Biochemistry, College of Agricultural and Life Sciences, University of Wisconsin—Madison, Madison, Wisconsin 53706*

MASAMITSU FUTAI (181), *Department of Microbiology, Faculty of Pharmaceutical Sciences, Okayama University, Okayama 700, Japan*

ROBERT V. HAGEMAN (279),[1] *Department of Biochemistry, College of Agricultural and Life Sciences, University of Wisconsin—Madison, Madison, Wisconsin 53706*

RICHARD G. HANSFORD (217), *Laboratory of Molecular Aging, Gerontology Research Center, National Institute on Aging, National Institutes of Health, Baltimore City Hospitals, Baltimore, Maryland 21224*

HIROSHI KANAZAWA (181), *Department of Microbiology, Faculty of Pharmaceutical Sciences, Okayama University, Okayama 700, Japan*

---

[1] Present address: Department of Chemistry, Stanford University, Stanford, California 94305

KLAAS KRAB (51), *Department of Medical Chemistry, University of Helsinki, Siltavuorenpenger 10, SF 00170 Helsinki 17, Finland*

NILS-ERIK SARIS (103), *Department of Medical Chemistry, University of Helsinki, Siltavuorenpenger 10, SF 00170 Helsinki 17, Finland*

MÅRTEN WIKSTRÖM (51), *Department of Medical Chemistry, University of Helsinki, Siltavuorenpenger 10, SF 00170, Helsinki 17, Finland*

Preface

Areas in bioenergetics that are of increasing interest are included in this volume. Borejdo introduces our readers to developments in the study of dynamic mechanisms in functioning muscle by following fluctuations in kinetic states. The method permits analysis of cyclic rotational motions in cross-bridge formation, and has considerable potential in other bioenergetic systems. The bioenergetic aspects of nitrogen fixation, an important topic not previously reviewed in this series, is examined by Hageman and Burris. The regulation of the *in vivo* activity of organelles is a complex phenomenon and no doubt is multifactorial. Hansford critically reviews one aspect of it, namely, the regulation of mitochondrial activities at the level of substrate. The article by Saris and Åkerman is of particular interest, since Saris is one of the pioneers in the field of calcium transport and has maintained an objective viewpoint. Wikström and Krab discuss the status of the controversial findings on the proton–oxygen ratios in mitochondria and the mechanism of H^+ pumping in oxidative reactions. There has been rapid progress in our understanding of the structure and mechanism of F_1-ATPase, but its function in association with the membrane segment of the proton translocating ATPase is still obscure. Futai and Kanazawa point to the usefulness of bacterial mutants in the study of this key process in cell metabolism.

D. Rao Sanadi

xi

Contents of Previous Volumes

Application of Fluctuation Spectroscopy to Muscle Contractility

JULIAN BOREJDO

Polymer Department
Weizmann Institute of Science
Rehovot, Israel, and Cardiovascular Research Institute
University of California
San Francisco, California

I. Introduction

The development of critical concepts about the structure and function of muscle has covered a period of the last 25 years. Since the postulation of the sliding filament hypothesis by Huxley and Niedergerke (1954) and Hanson and Huxley (1954), very definite ideas have been gathered as to how the relative motion of the two kinds of filaments takes place. It is no longer disputed that it is the hydrolysis of ATP by myosin that fuels the relative motion of filaments (Cain and Davies, 1962; Kushmerick, 1977), and it becomes increasingly clear how this motion is affected by the cyclic operation of appendages of myosin molecules known as cross-bridges (cf. Morales, 1975). Although the detailed mechanism is still hotly debated, it is mostly agreed that the cross-bridges cyclically deliver mechanical impulses to the actin filaments and that the time average of such impulses constitutes the contractile force. Combined efforts of a number of laboratories has led to the formulation of a self-consistent picture of how cyclic mechanical motions of cross-bridges may be coupled to the enzymic chemistry proceeding simultaneously at the hydrolytic site [cf. Taylor (1979) for a recent review]. Figure 1, which is the distillation of these concepts, is reproduced here to set the stage for the subsequent discussion. In brief, it is presumed that the myosin cross-bridge with the bound ATP molecule [in the current terminology the subfragment 1 (S-1) moiety of myosin] assumes roughly a 90° attitude with respect to the actin (and muscle fiber) axis (i, Fig. 1). Biochemical experiments, utilizing S-1 or a double-headed proteolytic fragment of myosin, heavy meromyosin (HMM), have made it clear that the cross-bridge, bearing the hydrolytic products ADP and P_i, attaches to actin (ii, Fig. 1) only after it has hydrolyzed the ATP molecule (e.g., Chock et al., 1976); polarization of fluorescence experiments suggested that it does so while still at an angle of 90° (Dos Remedios et al., 1972b). Physiological experiments of Huxley and Simmons (1971) utilizing high time resolution perturbation techniques pioneered by Podolsky (1960) and Civan and Podolsky (1966) showed how, after the attachment, the elasticity residing in the cross-bridge may allow it to "roll" on actin, passing perhaps through a succession of attitudinal states. The final attitude (iii, Fig. 1) is likely to be that of rigor, where a cross-bridge forms a 45° angle with actin as suggested by electron microscopic work of Reedy et al. (1965). The binding of a new ATP molecule and rapid dissociation (Lymn and Taylor, 1971; Sleep and Taylor, 1976) of the cross-bridge from actin completes the cycle. In a series of theoretical papers, Hill (1968, 1974, 1977) and Hill et al. (1975) developed a rigorous link between free-energy changes of myosin cross-bridge and the physiological parameters of contracting muscle and thus provided a formal basis for the cycling cross-bridge models.

   While these major contributions significantly advanced progress toward unraveling the great esoteric question of how muscle works, some fundamental difficulties stand in the way of a thoroughly satisfying explanation of muscle contractility. A major difficulty has been to establish the cycling cross-bridge theory by decisive experimentation. Specifically, one would like to obtain firm experimental evidence that the cross-bridges indeed execute mechanical cycles suggested in Fig. 1. Clearly, if the distinctive events depicted in Fig. 1 are correct, then the principal components of cross-bridge motion are the rotations of the S-1 moieties, and it is such rotations that one would like to visualize. Further, if the mechanical intermediates are coupled to the enzymic chemistry progressing at the cross-bridges, one would like to see evidence for the time correlation

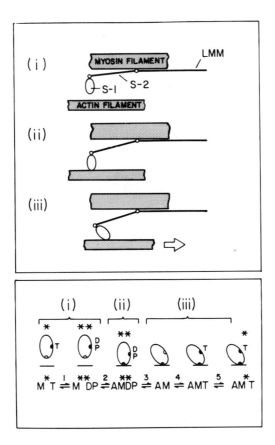

FIG. 1. The mechanical and enzymic cycle of myosin cross-bridge as envisaged by most current theories of contraction. In the upper figure mechanical states of a cross-bridge are emphasized. Small circles represent the "hinge" regions of myosin (Mendelson *et al.*, 1973; Highsmith *et al.*, 1977). Dissociation (i) is followed by binding of the cross-bridge to actin at perpendicular attitude (ii) and by the "power stroke" (iii), which translates the two sets of filaments. The bottom part of the figure emphasizes the chemical states of subfragment 1 (S-1), namely, nucleotide and actin site occupancy. The nucleotide site (circle on the side of S-1) can be either free (open circle) or occupied (filled circle). ATP, ADP, and P_i are represented by T, D, and P, respectively. Actin binding site is represented by the circle at the tip of S-1. The asterisks indicate the fluorescing condition of the nearby tryptophan residue. The brackets lump together intermediates in the mechanically equivalent states, consistent with the notations in the top part of the figure. The sequence of enzymic states (bottom figure) is identical with the sequence proposed by Johnson and Taylor, 1978. The tight binding of ATP to S-1 (AMT ⇄ AM*T) and the dissociation of S-1 from actin (AM*T ⇄ M*T) are probably very rapid. For simplicity, free actin, T, D, and P are not depicted. After hydrolysis on the free S-1, the cross-bridge is shown to recombine with actin. It is entirely plausible, however, that binding is preceded by the rate-limiting transition to another product intermediate, the so-called nonrefractory state (not shown), which in turn binds to actin (Eisenberg *et al.*, 1972; Chock *et al.*, 1976). After Morales and Borejdo (1978), with permission.

between the two. Finally, one would ideally want to know the *in vivo* characteristic times of various kinetic transitions depicted in Fig. 1.

It is not difficult in principle to construct experimental schemes in which the cyclic operation of one cross-bridge may be sensed *in vivo*. X-Ray diffraction or fluorescence polarization methods are sensitive to positional information and have been shown to be fast enough to monitor the dynamic behavior of cross-bridges (Podolsky *et al.*, 1976; Yagi *et al.*, 1977; Matsubara *et al.*, 1979; Huxley, 1979; Dos Remedios *et al.*, 1972a). Similarly, by a chemical probe one may record the cyclic reappearance of a particular enzymic intermediate. The fundamental difficulty associated with this approach is that practical instruments are insensitive to single molecules, and, when one reverts to observing large ensembles of cross-bridges operating asynchronously, one records ensemble averages conveying no information allowing one to deduce the presence of underlying cyclic events.

In what follows, a new class of experimental procedures designed to overcome these difficulties is discussed. The distinguishing feature of these approaches is that they monitor spontaneous fluctuations of cross-bridge-related parameters under conditions of thermodynamic equilibrium or steady state. Amplitudes and time dependence of fluctuations are related (through fundamental theorems of statistical physics) to the molecular concentrations and the kinetic or diffusive characteristics of cross-bridges, and they connect the fluctuation approach with the conventional relaxation (perturbation) methods.

The experimental technique relying on the extraction of kinetic information from the random fluctuations of measured signals is called fluctuation, or correlation, spectroscopy, and it has been increasingly recognized as an important biophysical tool. The measurements of fluctuations in the intensity of quasi-elastically scattered light have in fact been used for many years to determine diffusion constants of macromolecules (for reviews, see Pecora, 1972; Carlson, 1975b; Schurr, 1977). Voltage and current fluctuations have been used routinely to study the behavior of ionic channels in membranes (Varveen and DeFelice, 1974), and more recently the measurement of concentration fluctuations has been successfully adapted to the study of the kinetics of chemical reactions (Feher and Weissman, 1973; Elson and Magde, 1974; Magde *et al.*, 1974). The principal advantages of the fluctuation approach is that the time-dependent behavior of the individual contributor can be determined from the macroscopic signal (asynchrony problem is avoided), that no perturbation of the system is necessary, and that the methods are usually applicable to the *in vivo* situation.

The theoretical work of Chen and Hill (1973) and Hill (1974, 1975) has paved the way for the application of fluctuation analysis to active muscle.

The following discussion of these applications centers around different probes that translate fluctuations in cross-bridge parameters into measurable signals. The centrality of the different probes (indicators) in fluctuation analysis stems from the fact that their availability and choice entirely defines experimental conditions. The discussion begins with a description of sources of occupation number fluctuations, i.e., the fluctuations in the number of molecules occupying a given intermediate state in a kinetic system, and continues with the survey of methods—mainly correlation analysis—for characterizing these fluctuations. I attempt to define the vocabulary used in the field to familiarize those not acquainted with the fluctuation terminology. The first indicator discussed—the fluorescence of molecules—has not yet found application to muscle fibers, but its potential value in monitoring the enzymic cycle of the cross-bridge is emphasized. An account of its application to the study of *in vitro* motion of myosin fragments is given. It also sets the stage for the second indicator, polarization of fluorescence, which, it is argued, reflects the attitudinal state of the cross-bridge. The discussion of the tension as an indicator is followed by a brief survey of other indicators with possible application to contractility. Whenever applicable, the comparison with alternative kinetic methods is made. The second part of the review deals with the quasi-elastic light scattering (QELS), an approach technically related but conceptually sufficiently different to warrant separate treatment. The description of the fundamental concepts of QELS is followed by the summary of the up-to-date applications to muscle contractility.

II. Occupation Number Fluctuations

A. Basic Concepts

The fundamental concept underlying "number fluctuation" techniques is that in a classical kinetic system the amplitude and the time course of fluctuations in the number of molecules (n) occupying a given state are defined by the thermodynamic and rate parameters of this system. Both amplitude and time dependence of fluctuations are described by fundamental theorems of statistical physics (Elson and Webb, 1975): the equipartition theorem assigns the energy associated with each distinct mode of fluctuation as equal to thermal energy $k_B T$, where k_B is the Boltzmann constant. It is a consequence of this theorem that the root mean square (rms) amplitude of fluctuations in the number of molecules in a given state $\langle (\delta n)^2 \rangle^{1/2}$ is equal to $\langle n \rangle^{1/2}$ and, therefore, that the relative rms amplitude is (cf. Reif, 1965)

$$\langle (\delta n)^2 \rangle^{1/2} / \langle n \rangle = \langle n \rangle^{-1/2} \tag{1}$$

This important result pronouncing the inverse proportionality between relative fluctuation amplitude and square root of the number of molecules under observation underlies the design of all occupation number experiments. In fact, the number of molecules in a given volume (and hence the molecular weight) can be determined either by measuring n (e.g., by light scattering; cf. Debye, 1947), or by measuring fluctuation amplitude $(\delta n)^2$ and obtaining n from Eq. (1) (Weissman *et al.*, 1976).

The time dependence of fluctuations, in contrast to their amplitude, is a reflection of the kinetic parameters of the system. The autocorrelation function of fluctuations (see below) quantifies this time dependence in terms of the mean persistence time of fluctuations. The fluctuation–dissipation theorem states that the autocorrelation function of fluctuations describes relaxation of the system to steady state after it has been perturbed. In other words, the relaxation of the imposed perturbation back to the steady state and the autocorrelation function of number fluctuations at the steady-state exhibit identical time dependence. Thus, in principle, the analysis of the autocorrelation functions from actively contracting muscle fiber should yield the same information as the perturbation–relaxation methods (Eigen and DeMaeyer, 1963). When applied to actomyosin ATPase this means that the analysis of autocorrelation functions should provide enzymic kinetic data; the point of importance here is that one should be able to gather such data from working muscle fibers, a clear advantage over *in vitro* studies, to which relaxation methods have been usually applied. When applied to mechanical measurements, this means that the autocorrelation functions carry the same information as those experiments in which the muscle is perturbed by step changes in tension (Civan and Podolsky, 1966), by changes in muscle length (Huxley and Simmons, 1971; Ford *et al.*, 1977), by sinusoidal length vibrations (cf. White and Thorson, 1973; Kawai *et al.*, 1977), or by random noise oscillations (Halpern and Alpert, 1971).

The Autocorrelation Function

Because the concept of autocorrelation function is central in the subsequent discussion, I shall attempt to picture its physical meaning in the specific example that follows. Consider one of the reactions of Fig. 1,

$$M*T \underset{k_b}{\overset{k_f}{\rightleftharpoons}} M**DP \tag{2}$$

and suppose for the moment that the other paths through which either intermediate can decay are inoperative. We are dealing then with a single unimolecular isomerization reaction describing, in this case, the hydrolysis of ATP to its products (Pr). Suppose further that we have at our disposal a technique allowing us to follow (without specifying at present how)

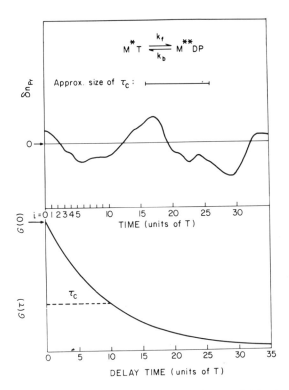

FIG. 2. A simple chemical reaction (hydrolysis of ATP by myosin) (top) and associated hypothetical occupation number fluctuations (center). Characteristic time of fluctuations τ_0 is related to the kinetic constants in this type of chemical reaction by $1/\tau_c = k_f + k_b$. The autocorrelation function (bottom curve) in such a case decays with the delay time like $\exp(-\tau/\tau_c)$. T is the sampling internal (bin width).

the time evolution of the number n_{Pr} of cross-bridges in, say, state M**DP during steady state (Fig. 2). Clearly, the rapidity with which the fluctuations in the number of cross-bridges n_{Pr} occur, and which is characterized by the mean persistence time of the individual fluctuation, τ_c, is a function of the rate constants k_f and k_b. (If, on the other hand, the process responsible for the change in the number of molecules is not a chemical reaction, but diffusion of molecules in and out of the strictly defined experimental volume, then the persistence time τ_c will depend on the diffusional properties of the molecules.) Suppose that the signal in Fig. 2 is sampled at regular time intervals T that are short compared to the characteristic time τ_c. From the sequence of experimental points $n_{Pr}(T)$, $n_{Pr}(2T)$, . . . , $n_{Pr}(NT)$ where $T \ll \tau_c$ and $NT \ll \tau_c$, we construct a function

$$G(\tau) = \lim_{N \to \infty} (1/N) \sum_i \delta n_{\mathrm{Pr}}(iT)\delta n_{\mathrm{Pr}}(iT + \tau) \qquad (3)$$

where the fluctuation in n_{Pr} at time iT

$$\delta n_{\mathrm{Pr}}(iT) = n_{\mathrm{Pr}}(iT) - \langle n_{\mathrm{Pr}} \rangle \qquad (4)$$

is defined in terms of the average value $\langle n_{\mathrm{Pr}} \rangle$

$$\langle n_{\mathrm{Pr}} \rangle = 1/N \sum_{i=1}^{N} n_{\mathrm{Pr}}(iT) \qquad (5)$$

$G(\tau)$ is called an autocorrelation function, and it provides a statistical characterization of the time course of fluctuation. The choice of this particular function to characterize dynamics of fluctuations is motivated by the fluctuation–dissipation theorem, as discussed above, but it is not the only possible choice (see below). For a system at equilibrium or in the steady state, the result of the multiplications and additions prescribed by Eq. (3) is independent of the absolute time when the operations are begun, and $G(\tau)$ is a function of "delay time," $\tau = jT$ only. In other words, the fluctuations are stationary and the autocorrelation function of fluctuations in, e.g., the number of dissociated cross-bridges bearing the hydrolytic products is independent of the time in the steady state when the measurement has begun.

To get a "feeling" for the meaning of the delay time τ, consider what happens when $j = 0$, i.e., $\tau = 0$. Then

$$G(0) = \lim_{N \to \infty} (1/N) \sum_{i=1}^{N} [\delta n_{\mathrm{Pr}}(iT)]^2 = \langle (\delta n_{\mathrm{Pr}})^2 \rangle = n_{\mathrm{Pr}} \qquad (6)$$

i.e., the value of the autocorrelation function at the delay time $\tau = 0$ is equal to the mean square (otherwise known as variance or average power) of the signal. Note now what happens when the value of τ increases from 0 (Elson and Webb, 1975). When $\tau = T(j = 1)$, the number of molecules in state $M^{**}DP$ will have little time to change from its initial value at $\tau = 0$, because we take care to sample the signal often enough ($T \ll \tau_c$, Fig. 2). In other words, most of the products $\delta n_{\mathrm{Pr}}(iT)\delta n_{\mathrm{Pr}}(iT + T)$ will be positive, and close to the value $[\delta n_{\mathrm{Pr}}(iT)]^2$ except at the points when the signal intercepts the mean value (i.e., the fluctuations cross zero, e.g., for $i = 2$, 12 on Fig. 2). The average of the sum of the products (the autocorrelation function) will therefore be smaller, but not significantly so, from G(O). On the other hand, for the delay times close to the characteristic time τ_c, the products $\delta n_{\mathrm{Pr}}(iT)\delta n_{\mathrm{Pr}}(iT + \tau_c)$ will differ substantially from those calculated before. Reference to Fig. 2 shows that many more of those products will be negative—for example, for $i = 0, 1, 2, 6, 7, 8$ (but not for $i = 3, 4, 5, 12$). The average of the sum of the products will therefore be less

G(0). Finally, when the delay time $jT = \tau \gg \tau_c$ there will be no correlation at all between various products. For a given value of $\delta n_{Pr}(iT)\delta n_{Pr}(iT + jT)$, there will be another product, $\delta n_{Pr}(i'T)\delta n_{Pr}(i'T + jT)$, which is of equal amplitude and of opposite sign (for example, in Fig. 2 when $\tau = 20\ T$, then the negative product for $i = 0$ will be matched by the positive one for $i' = 4$). In the limit when τ is very large all the products will cancel each other and $\lim_{\tau \to \infty} G(\tau) = 0$. As a result, the autocorrelation function of the fluctuations in the number of molecules in state M**DP will look something like the function shown in the bottom part of Fig. 2: it will have a maximum at $\tau = 0$, assume intermediate values for the delay times close to the characteristic time of fluctuations τ_c, and vanish for long τ.

The preceding description presumes random character of the kinetic reaction; at any given time it is impossible to predict when the next ATP molecule will be hydrolyzed. The only information available is that the hydrolysis events have Gaussian probability distribution with the mean rate $f = 1/\tau_c$. Indeed, if the process were not random in this sense, the autocorrelation function would not necessarily vanish in the limit of very large τ.

So far we have limited ourselves to the description of the variations in the number n_{Pr} in terms of the characteristic time of fluctuations. It is equally valid, and often more convenient, to describe time variations in terms of various frequencies $\omega = 2\pi\nu$ underlying the fluctuations. The experimental trace, such as that shown in Fig. 2, can be thought of as a superposition of various frequencies that can be uncovered by harmonic analysis. The mathematical apparatus for such analysis is well known and centers around construction of what is known as a power spectrum of fluctuations, which is a representation of the relative importance of various frequencies contained in the signal. An important theorem, named after Wiener and Khintchine (cf. Lee, 1960), pronounces the equivalence of the autocorrelation and power spectrum approaches by a claim that the two constitute a Fourier transform pair related through

$$G(\tau) = (\tfrac{1}{2}\pi)^{1/2} \int_{-\infty}^{\infty} G(\omega)e^{i\omega\tau}d\omega \tag{7}$$

and

$$G(\omega) = (\tfrac{1}{2}\pi)^{1/2} \int_{-\infty}^{\infty} G(\tau)e^{-i\omega\tau}d\tau \tag{8}$$

The choice between the two representations is a question of taste or prejudice only. In keeping with the practice adopted by Magde $et\ al.$ (1974) and by Elson and Magde (1974), I have opted for correlation function representation when describing fluorescence experiments, but have used autocorrelation and power spectrum representations alternatively in other cases.

In summary then, we have seen how the "noise"-like signal (Fig. 2) can be manipulated to determine the characteristic time of fluctuations in the system under study. In the analysis we have relinquished the idea of following the individual behavior of any of the great number of molecules inevitably contributing to the signal, and instead have paid attention only to its statistical properties, such as amplitude of fluctuations, and their average time dependence, as expressed by the autocorrelation function.

In the fluctuation experiments, it is a task of the experimenter to measure the fluctuations in the occupation number n and to compute the autocorrelation functions. As a rule the fluctuations in the number itself cannot be directly detected—there is no way of counting the number of molecules in a given state at fixed time intervals. It is necessary instead to find a convenient indicator of the occupation number—a quantity that is both straightforwardly related to the instantaneous number of molecules and can be simply converted into a practical signal, such as voltage or current.

Once such an indicator has been found and the correlation function has been measured, it is necessary to relate amplitude and the characteristic time of fluctuations to the phenomenological coefficients for diffusion or the chemical reaction, or both. This relationship can be achieved in one of two ways (Stevens, 1975). In the first, analytical, approach one explicitly solves for the autocorrelation function of fluctuations in the concentration of given species by making use of Eq. (3) and expressing δn_{Pr} as a solution of an appropriate set of differential equations describing the system. Often this approach is complicated by the fact that the chemical reactions are coupled to diffusion, but with ingenuity the analytical solution can still be found (Elson and Magde, 1974). However, in the systems that consist of more than one chemical reaction, the autocorrelation function becomes a polynomial containing complex exponential terms and it is practically impossible to extract kinetic coefficients. In such cases it is convenient to resort to the second approach that connects the autocorrelation function with the phenomenological parameters of the system through mechanistic theories. In this approach one constructs a model of the system that includes all phenomenological coefficients and supplies stochastic methods to compute its average response (i.e., macroscopic behavior) and the autocorrelation function. Clearly, this method of approach suffers from the fact that any inference about the properties of the system is accurate insofar as the original model used to describe it is correct; in other words, the interpretation of the autocorrelation function depends entirely on the correct representation of the underlying mechanism.

The following discussion begins with the description of various indicators of fluctuations, with particular emphasis on those that have found application in the study of muscle contractility. Whenever possible, an account is given of the attempts to relate the autocorrelation functions or power spectra to the phenomenological coefficients through either of the two approaches described above.

Several indicators of fluctuations have so far found application in the study of biological materials. They are (a) fluorescence of molecules in a light beam; (b) polarized fluorescence of molecules; (c) contractile tension; (d) light scattering from particles; (e) conductance of ionic solution through a capillary tube; and (f) ionic currents flowing across excitable membranes. Excellent reviews of some of these techniques have been published (Elson and Webb, 1975; Magde, 1977; Ehrenberg and Rigler, 1976; Varveen and DeFelice, 1974). Out of the listed indicators, only the first three have been utilized in the study of general problems of contractility. In what follows, I will therefore discuss in some detail these three and limit myself to the outline of general principles and to the discussion of possible applications to muscle in the remaining cases.

B. FLUORESCENCE OF MOLECULES

1. General Principles

An obvious way to translate the time-dependent fluctuations in the occupation number n into a measurable quantity is to confine fluorescently labeled molecules in a well defined volume V, to illuminate them with a stable light source, and to detect the fluctuations in the emitted light intensity. The fluctuations arise then either because of the diffusion of molecules in and out of the illuminated volume or because chemical reaction continuously changes the number of monitored molecules. If the illuminated volume has thickness l and if the total radiant power incident on the volume is P, then the current of a photomultiplier that detects the fluorescence is

$$\langle i \rangle = g \epsilon Q \overline{C} P l \tag{9}$$

where $\overline{C}$ is the mean concentration of monitored molecules, g is the overall collection efficiency of the electrooptical system, and ϵ and Q are the extinction coefficient and quantum efficiency of the fluorophore, respectively. The photocurrent is thus proportional to the concentration of molecules (and hence to their number). The relative rms fluctuation in photocurrent is given by Eq. (1) with $n = \pi \omega^2 l \overline{C}$, where ω is the effective beam radius.

Elson and Magde (1974) have applied an analytical (as opposed to mechanistic) method to relate the autocorrelation function of fluctuations in the fluorescent light intensity to the phenomenological coefficients for a number of kinetic systems. For the case of diffusion of a single fluorescent solute and a laser beam defining the experimental volume having a Gaussian intensity profile, the autocorrelation function of photocurrent fluctuations was shown to be of the form

$$G(\tau) = g\epsilon Q P \overline{C}[1/(1 + \tau/\tau_c)] \tag{10}$$

where τ_c, the characteristic time of fluctuations, is related to the diffusion coefficient D of fluorescent molecules by $\tau_c = \omega^2/4D$. It is important to point out that $G(\tau)$ does not decay exponentially with τ. This property, which holds true also for more complex cases (Elson and Magde, 1974), results from the convolution of the exponential Fourier components of diffusion with the Gaussian laser beam intensity profile. A further point that distinguishes number fluctuations from the more familiar scattered light intensity fluctuations (see Section III) is that the characteristic time τ_c is long, approximately equal to the time it takes the molecule to diffuse across a macroscopic distance of beam diameter, which for $\omega = 10 \ \mu m$ and $D = 10^{-7} \ cm^2$ per second is as large as 2.5 seconds.

The cases in which the fluctuations dissipate through diffusion coupled to uniform translation, flow, or both, has been recently examined by Magde et al. (1978). A much more complex situation prevails in the case (relevant to the subsequent discussion), in which fluctuations can relax both through diffusion and chemical reaction. The general differential equation governing such a case has been treated by Elson and Magde (1974), who showed that the solution is a sum of relaxation processes, each of which is a "normal mode" of relaxation describing different paths of decay of fluctuation. The autocorrelation function was shown to be composed of the sum of terms $A_{jl}^{(\alpha)}$, which represent the contributions from correlations between interacting species j and l belonging to given mode of relaxation (α). For a simple one-step reaction, such as binding of a small molecule (e.g., myosin moiety, M) to a large one (e.g., actin, A) to give AM complex (C),

$$A + M \underset{k_b}{\overset{k_f}{\rightleftharpoons}} C \tag{11}$$

the physical meaning of the correlation function can be grasped, providing certain simplifying assumptions are met. Thus, when the chemical reaction expressed by its characteristic rate R is rapid compared to diffusion, when the diffusion coefficient $D_A = D_C \ll D_M$, and when mean concentrations $\overline{C}_M \simeq \overline{C}_c \ll \overline{C}_A$, then the autocorrelation function is (Elson and Magde, 1974)

$$G(\tau) = \frac{(g\epsilon QP)^2 \overline{l} \overline{C_c}}{\pi \omega^2} [A^\circ(\tau) + A^+(\tau) + A^-(\tau)] \qquad (12)$$

where

$$A^\circ(\tau) = [K\overline{C_M}](1 + \tau/\tau_A)^{-1} \qquad (13a)$$

$$A^+(\tau) = [K\overline{C_A}/(1 + K\overline{C_A})](1 + \tau/\tau_+)^{-1} \qquad (13b)$$

$$A^-(\tau) = [1/(1 + K\overline{C_A})]\exp(-R\tau)(1 + \tau/\tau_-)^{-1} \qquad (13c)$$

and the modified diffusion times are

$$\tau_+ = \tau_M(1 + K\overline{C_A}) \qquad (14a)$$

$$\tau_- = \tau_M(1 + K\overline{C_A})/K\overline{C_A} \qquad (14b)$$

and τ_M is the characteristic time of freely diffusing species M. The physical meaning of A° is that it characterizes the diffusive motion of slowly moving macromolecule A; and A^+ represents motion of the small molecule as it is slowed down through its interaction with the large one, while A^- is dominated by the exponential decay of the chemical reaction. We shall see later how this formalism can be further simplified to be of practical value in the study of binding of HMM and S-1 to actin in the presence of MgATP.

2. Experimental Realization

An experimental apparatus for practical implementation of the fluorescence correlation spectroscopy was first described by Magde et al. (1974). A similar instrument is diagrammed in Fig. 3. A laser beam is directed through mirrors to the microscope objective, which focuses the light into the sample solution and collects the fluorescent signal. A dichroic mirror serves as a beamsplitter and a filter, passing vertically only fluorescent light. The barrier filter further blocks light of the excitation frequency, and the field diaphragm decreases depth of focus and so helps to discriminate against background fluorescence (Koppel et al., 1976). A photomultiplier tube serves as a detector and is followed by an amplifier and a discriminator arranged so that a single pulse is obtained when a single photon is detected at a photocathode. A monitor photodiode provides a digital signal proportional to laser light intensity and is used to compensate for laser intensity variations. A scaler counts the photomultiplier and monitor pulses over a period of time T (cf. Fig. 2), referred to here as bin width. A computer compensates for laser power variations and then applies standard signal processing techniques to evaluate the autocorrelation function of fluorescent light intensity fluctuations. [In practice the computer determines the power spectrum by applying Fourier decomposition known as

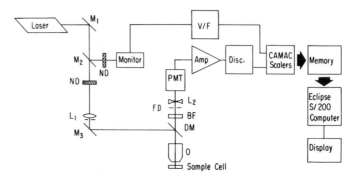

FIG. 3. Schematic diagram of the fluorescence correlation spectrometer. M, mirrors; ND, neutral density filters; L_1, spatial filter; O, microscope objective; DM, dichroic mirror; BF, barrier filter; FD, field diaphragm; L_2, negative lens; PMT, photomultiplier tube; Amp, amplifier: Disc., discriminator. From Borejdo (1979a), with permission.

the fast Fourier transform (FFT), an algorithm that decreases the amount of time necessary for calculations by making ingenious use of the properties of digital computers (Rabiner and Gold, 1975). It then applies Eq. (7) to yield the autocorrelation function.] The performance of apparatus of this kind is governed by the parameter $\langle n \rangle \beta$ defining the number of fluorescent photons detected during one bin width per molecule and equal to $g \epsilon Q P T / \pi \omega^2$ (Koppel, 1974). In an application to measure the binding of myosin fragments to actin, Borejdo (1979a) used 5-iodoacetamido-fluorescein (IAF) covalently bound to HMM or S-1, for which $\epsilon = 2.9 \times 10^{-16}$ cm^2, $Q = 80\%$, and with P fixed at 0.8×10^{14} photons per second, ω at 8 μm, and T at 10 msec, giving $\langle n \rangle \beta = 1.7$. The signal-to-noise ratio in the fluorescence correlation experiment depends, in addition, on $\langle n \rangle \beta$ on the total number of bins observed (M) and the characteristic time of the autocorrelation function Γ^{-1}. With these parameters assuming typical values of $M \sim 10^5$ and $\Gamma^{-1} = 10$ msec, the signal-to-noise ratio is about 60.

It may be opportune to mention briefly at this point a technically very similar, but conceptually diverse, method of measuring diffusion coefficients and/or reaction rates, that of fluorescence photobleaching recovery (FPR) (Axelrod et al., 1976; Koppel et al., 1976). Instead of relying on the random fluctuations in fluorescent signal, this technique follows the recovery of fluorescence after a brief exposure to an intense laser beam that imposes a local gradient in the concentration of the fluorescent molecules. The recovery occurs by replenishment of intact fluorophores in the bleached spot by lateral transport from the surroundings. The photobleaching technique has found widespread use in studying lateral transport of membrane proteins (e.g., Webb, 1976; Schlessinger et al., 1977).

3. Application to Muscle Proteins: Binding of S-1 and HMM to Actin

Borejdo (1979a) investigated binding of myosin fragments to actin in the presence of MgATP (Eq. 11); when only the myosin moiety was fluorescently labeled (with IAF) and actin was present in excess, he found that Eq. (12) simplifies to

$$G(\tau) = (g\epsilon QP)^2/\pi\omega^2[1 + K\overline{C}_A)/K\overline{C}_A)](1 + \tau/\tau_+)^{-1} \qquad (15)$$

where τ_+ is defined in Eq. (14a) and τ_M refers to the characteristic time of labeled myosin fragments. Thus the autocorrelation function due to S-1 or HMM diffusing in the presence of actin and MgATP has the same functional dependence as the simple diffusion (Eq. 10). The characteristic time τ_+ is now determined by the rate of free diffusion of myosin fragment as it is slowed down by its interaction with actin. The characteristic time τ_+ was measured at increasing actin concentrations; at sufficiently large excess of actin, it was found to be proportional to $\overline{C}_A$, as demanded by Eq. (14a). From the slope of the plot of τ_+ vs $\overline{C}_A$, the apparent association constant was determined. Figure 4(A and B) shows the autocorrelation functions of HMM diffusing in the presence of MgATP and increasing actin concentration and demonstrates that the diffusion is indeed slowed down when the actin concentration rises. The apparent affinity of binding of S-1 and HMM to actin was determined as 8.8×10^3 and 2.2×10^4 M^{-1}, respectively, close to the apparent binding constant for the formation of the ternary complex between actin, 5'-adenylyl imidodiphosphate [AMP-P(NH)P], and S-1 (Greene and Eisenberg, 1978). The small ratio of the binding constant of HMM to that of S-1 is in line with recent observations in several laboratories that in the absence of the nucleotide (Margossian and Lowey, 1976; Highsmith, 1978) and in its presence (Greene and Eisenberg, 1978) HMM binds only severalfold more strongly than S-1. This observation opens the possibility that the binding of the second HMM head to actin contributes little to the free energy of binding (but see Greene and Eisenberg, 1980).

The fluorescence fluctuation technique is rapid in comparison with conventional methods, such as equilibrium dialysis or analytical centrifuge, and has the further advantage that the reactants can be used in exceedingly small concentrations.

4. Possible Applications: Kinetics of Actomyosin ATPase

Fluorescence-based signals can be used as indicators of the enzymic state of the cross-bridge in the contracting muscle fiber. The fluorescence fluctuations analysis then can be applied to estimate the kinetics of dif-

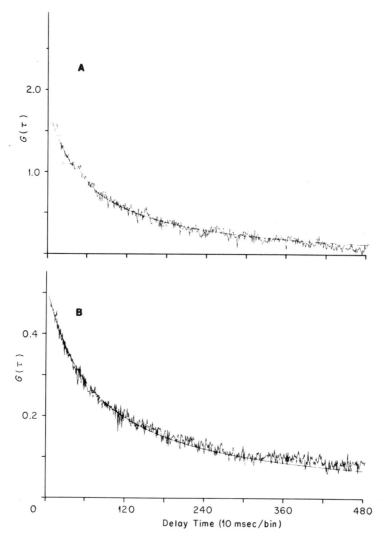

FIG. 4. Autocorrelation functions of the photomultiplier current fluctuations due to the diffusion of fluorescently labeled heavy meromyosin (HMM) in the presence of increasing concentrations of actin; 0.5 μM HMM in the presence of 0.1 M KCl, 2.5 mM MgATP, 10 mM Tris buffer, pH 7.6, and (A) 10 μM actin, (B) 20 μM actin. From Borejdo (1979a), with permission.

ferent steps in the overall kinetic cycle. Further, availability of the indicator of the cross-bridge enzymic chemistry would allow for experimental testing of those hypotheses of muscle contraction that imply that the cross-correlation functions of fluctuations in the indicators reflecting various enzymic and mechanical states of the cross-bridge are nonzero (Borejdo, 1979b) (cross-correlation function is a mathematical construction conceptually related to the autocorrelation function and defined as a time average of the product of one indicator with the time-delayed different indicator). The experimental demonstration of such cross-correlation functions would be particularly welcome support for this type of cycling cross-bridge models. The discussion of the indicators of the mechanical state of the cross-bridge is deferred to the next section. Here I point out some fluorescence-based signals that can conceivably be used as indicators of the enzymic state of the corss-bridge and may be used in conjunction with the mechanical indicators in constructing experimental cross-correlation functions.

As demonstrated by Elson and Magde (1974), fluorescence correlation spectroscopy can be of practical use in estimating the kinetics of a chemical reaction providing the reaction is associated with a large change in fluorescent quantum yield (or extinction coefficient) of the fluorophore. The complex of IAF-labeled HMM (or S-1) and actin has the same fluorescence as IAF–HMM or IAF–S-1 alone, and the fluctuation approach is incapable in this case of providing kinetic data for step 2 (Fig. 1). If an appropriate fluorophore were to be found, however, the fluctuation method could become a powerful tool in determining the kinetics of this important reaction. A first step in this direction has been made by Lin (1978), who attached dansyl aziridine to Cys-373 of F-actin and observed emission intensity changes when S-1 bound to that actin. The changes were large enough to be of practical use, but they did not clearly reverse on dissociation of acto-S-1 complex by ATP. In contrast, Porter and Weber (1979) found that binding of S-1 to F-actin caused reversible quenching of dansyl aziridine fluorescence at a wavelength shorter than 530 nm, and the reversible increase in fluorescence of actin bound dye N(iodoacetylamino)naphthylamine-5-sulfonic acid (1,5 IAEDANS, Hudson and Weber, 1973) above 445 nm. Similarly, the fluorescence intensity of 1,N-enthenoadenosine diphosphate incorporated into F-actin significantly increases upon binding of HMM, but there are confinding claims as to whether the excess fluorescence is proportional to the amount of HMM bound (Ando and Asai, 1976; 1979; Miki et al., 1976). Another approach potentially useful in investigating binding may be the energy transfer method in which fluorescence increases upon binding (e.g., of actin to myosin) owing to the excitation of the acceptor dye by proximal donor molecule (Takashi, 1979). Yet another possible approach is to use nonfluorescent probes: when F-actin combines with S-1, HMM, or myosin, there occur increments in, for example, turbidity (White and Taylor, 1976) or flow birefringence (Tawada, 1969). Although the changes are small, either of these parameters could, in principle, be used as an indicator of fluctuations (see Section II,E,1 for discussion of solution turbidity as indicator of fluctuations).

An indicator that has already been used with spectacular success in working out partial reactions of S-1 ATPase is the intrinsic fluorescence of S-1 tryptophan first identified by Werber *et al.* (1972); for reviews, see Taylor, 1973; Trentham *et al.*, 1976). The tryptophan fluorescence of S-1 is enhanced between 5% and 15% depending on specific nucleotide occupancy and the effect can be amplified by the use of different nucleotides. For example, upon binding of thioITP or thioIDP to myosin there is a large decrease in protein fluorescence. This quenching is easier to detect than the increase in protein fluorescence that occurs on ATP binding. Another example is offered by 4',4'-bisanilinonaphthalene-8-sulfonate (bis-ANS) (Rosen and Weber, 1969), which is bound reversibly to the ATPase site and can be displaced therefrom by ATP (Takashi *et al.*, 1977). Since, in analogy to ANS, only bound bis-ANS fluoresces, the kinetics of binding of ATP can be followed more easily, and the interpretation then becomes identical to that given by Magde *et al.* (1974) for the case of binding of ethidium bromide to DNA. However, it must be pointed out that when applied to muscle fibers both Trp and bis-ANS fluorescence methods may suffer from the unspecific effects; for example, Trp is known to be present in actin and bis-ANS binds to it.

Morales and Borejdo (1978) have pointed out that in detecting fluctuations, an alternative to the intrinsic (or protein-bound sensor) fluorescence could be the signal that arises in the nucleotide itself—and which changes as a result of binding to the ATPase sites (steps 4 and 5, Fig. 1). Trentham *et al.* (1976) reviewed chromophoric and fluorescent nucleotides and the systems in which they have been used; to this review the reader is referred for comprehensive details. Suffice it to say here that, in the case of myosin ATPase, formycin triphosphate is particularly suitable because of its favorable spectral changes upon binding and because it is capable of supporting contraction of glycerinated fibers (Bagshaw *et al.*, 1972). The hydrolysis of a fluorescent ATP analog, β-naphthyl triphospate, has been shown to lead to a change in fluorescence intensity (Kagawa *et al.*, 1974). However, this analog did not induce superprecipitation of actomyosin solution (Fujisaki and Asai, 1978) and therefore most likely will be ineffective in inducing contraction of muscle fibers. Neither of the above sensors has so far been used in fluctuation spectroscopy.

It should be pointed out that whenever the changes in the fluorescence mentioned above are small, it will be difficult to revolve the kinetic term from Eq. (12). Magde *et al.* (1974) have succeeded because in the case of binding of ethidium bromide to DNA the fluorescence changes a great deal.

Another class of fluorescent signals with potential application in fluctuation analysis is that associated with NADH fluorescence in a linked assay system. An example is a pyruvate kinase–lactate dehydrogenase system that can be adapted to either steady state (Imamura *et al.*, 1966) or transient kinetic (Trentham *et al.*, 1972) studies of ADP release into the medium (step 3, Fig. 1). Another example is a linked assay system using glyceraldehyde-3-phosphate dehydrogenase and 3-phosphoglycerate kinase following inorganic phosphate release. For fluctuation analysis, as for the transient kinetic case, it is necessary that the linked system utilize or produce NADH rapidly compared with the steady state of ADP formation. Trentham *et al.* (1972) have established conditions under which this requirement is met. Linked assay techniques may prove to be particularly important in the kinetic study of muscle fibers. The steady-state rate of ADP release from contracting muscle fibers has been already measured by this technique by Pybus and Tregear (1975), who followed the rate of disappearance of NADH absorption (rather than fluorescence), and by Loxdale (1976), who adapted the technique for the continuous monitoring of muscle ATPase activity with the simultaneous recording of muscle tension. Recently, Takashi and Putnam (1979) used the pyruvate kinase–lactate dehydrogenase system to demonstrate the feasibility of continuous monitoring of the steady-state ATPase of isometrically contracting single muscle fibers.

C. POLARIZED FLUORESCENCE FROM MUSCLE FIBERS

1. Static Polarization of Fluorescence

We have seen that the total fluorescence issuing from protein, the protein-bound fluorophore or from the substrate molecule can be conveniently used as an indicator of occupation number fluctuations and that the analysis of such fluctuations can provide information about translational diffusion or kinetics of chemical reactions or both. For studying the rotational molecular motions in solution or such processes as the rotational reorientations of myosin cross-bridges as envisaged by the cross-bridge theory (Fig. 1), polarization of fluorescence techniques that are sensitive to such motions are conveniently used. However, for a meaningful application, it is imperative first to show that the polarized fluorescence issuing from muscle fibers is indeed an indication of the occupation number of cross-bridges with a given orientation in space. Myosin cross-bridges in muscle form an integral part of a complex cellular machinery, and without conclusive evidence it is not at all obvious that the polarization of fluorescence issuing from a muscle fiber has anything to do with myosin cross-bridges. Endeavors to show the correlation between the fluorescent field around the fiber and cross-bridge orientation began with the work of Aronson and Morales (1969), who utilized the polarization of tryptophan fluorescence from glycerinated rabbit muscle to show that its value changes reversibly in step with the physiological state of muscle. The "perpendicular" polarization function defined as

$$P_\perp = (I_{\perp\perp} - I_{\perp\parallel}/(I_{\perp\perp} + I_{\perp\parallel})$$

turned out to be particularly sensitive. Here $I_{\perp\perp}$ denotes fluorescent light intensity when both exciting and fluorescent light are polarized in the direction perpendicular to the long axis of muscle fiber and $I_{\perp\parallel}$ is the fluorescent intensity when the exciting light is perpendicular, and the emitted light parallel, to the axis. Dos Remedios et al. (1972a) measured $P_\perp$ in rigor, relaxed and contracting single muscle fibers with a significantly improved optical arrangement. These authors found $P_\perp$ to be insensitive to sarcomere length in relaxed muscle fibers and proportional to sarcomere length in rigor fibers; on the basis of these observations they conclude that the polarization of tryptophan fluorescence was indeed sensitive to the orientation of the myosin subfragment 1 in the fiber. In an elegant application of this finding, Dos Remedios et al. (1972b) perfused single fibers of rabbit psoas with appropriate analogs of ATP to force the cross-bridges into succession of states presumably corresponding to different molecular species during the contractile cycle, and identified analogs that simulate different individual states in the cycle of cross-bridge activity.

The disadvantage of using tryptophan as a source of fluorescence lies in the fact that myosin cross-bridges are not the only structures that contribute to the fluorescent signal; actin alone contributes around 40% of myofibrillar tryptophan. While other structures may well be static, the fluorescence is detected on top of a significant background. Moreover, tryptophan is neither particularly good, nor a simple fluorophore. It has therefore been advantageous to observe fluorescence from the extrinsic probe attached to the S-1 moiety of myosin (Nihei et al., 1974). A probe suited to act as an extrinsic marker must meet certain criteria:

1. It has to be covalently and rigidly bound, otherwise one would observe rotations of the dye itself rather than those of the molecules of interest.
2. It has to be specifically bound to myosin cross-bridges.
3. It should have high Q and ϵ for easy detection.
4. It should be resistant to photodegradation to prevent the illuminating light beam from reducing the fluorescent light intensity below the level acceptable for detection.

5. It should have simple transition moment structure if the fluorescent field is to be interpretable.

6. It should leave the muscle fiber functionally intact; i.e., ideally, the mechanical and enzymic properties of labeled muscle fiber should be no different from that of an unlabeled fiber.

The dye (1,5-IAEDANS) meets some of these criteria fairly well. It has been established by the time-resolved fluorescence polarization decay technique (see below) that 1,5-IAEDANS does not move relative to S-1 even on the nanosecond time scale (Mendelson *et al.*, 1973). Ways have been found to introduce the dye into skinned single fibers of rabbit psoas muscle in such a way that myosin heavy chains are predominantly labeled (Borejdo and Putnam, 1977). Although 1,5-IAEDANS is not a particularly good dye ($Q = 0.27$, $\epsilon = 1 \times 10^{-17}$ cm^2) and it bleaches rather easily (Hudson and Weber, 1973), it is usable in static polarization of fluorescence experiments where the illuminating light flux can be kept low. Finally, it has reasonably simple dipole structure (Hudson and Weber, 1973) and it does not affect the rigor tension of muscle fibers or their Ca^{2+} sensitivity (Borejdo and Putnam, 1977). [However, in solution it has been found to reduce the actin activation of HMM and to decrease the velocity of the rate-limiting binding step (Mulhern and Eisenberg, 1978).] Borejdo and Putnam (1977) have measured polarization of fluorescence from single skinned glycerinated fibers labeled with 1,5-IAEDANS, fiber "ghosts" irrigated with fluorescent HMM, and labeled myofibrillar bundles. They have confirmed the observation of in-step variation of the polarized fluorescence $P_\perp$ with the functional state of muscle fiber, and of independence of $P_\perp$ on sarcomere length during relaxation. An attempt was made to compare the experimental results with the prediction of a simple model that assumed the cross-bridges to form an assembly of helically arranged fluorophores and thus related the embedded directions of the absorption and emission dipoles with the intensity of the fluorescent field around the fiber (cf. also Tregear and Mendelson, 1975). When the fiber was forced into the rigor state, Borejdo and Putnam found the results to be in good agreement with the model, and were able to estimate the attitudinal angle θ of the long axis of the S-1 with respect to actin axis as 40°. The rigor angle falls close to the inclination of 45° estimated by Reedy *et al.* (1965) from electron micrographs of rigor insect muscle, while no agreement could be obtained in the relaxed state (presumably because an assembly of helically arranged fluorophores does not constitute under such circumstances an adequate model). In conclusion, static measurements suggest that polarization of fluorescence of extrinsically attached dye is indeed an indicator of cross-bridge attitude.

2. Fluctuations in Polarized Fluorescence from Single Muscle Fibers

Having attested to the authenticity of polarized fluorescence as a measure of an attitudinal angle of cross-bridges, Borejdo and Putnam (1979) and Borejdo, Putnam, and Morales (1979) detected and analyzed fluctuations in $P_\perp$ issuing from resting, rigor, and active single muscle fibers labeled with different dyes. They compared the suitability of 1,5-IAEDANS, 5-IAF, and iodacetamidotetramethylrhodamine (IATR) for fluctuation studies: the former was found to be unacceptable because of its extreme susceptibility to photodegradation (the quantum yield for photobleaching, q, was greater than 10^{-4} even under modest levels of illumination at 365 nm). IAF and IATR, on the other hand, were found to be better suited to this type of experiment. They combine intense fluorescence of fluorescine and rhodamine fluorophores, respectively, with the specific reactivity of the iodoacetyl functional group toward thiols: single muscle fibers incubated under appropriate conditions (relaxed state, at 0°C, for 15 minutes) with either fluorophore showed predominant heavy-chain labeling as ascertained by polyacrylamide gel electrophoresis. Both fluorophores showed reasonably high resistance to photobleaching. When illuminated with 1.2×10^{12} photons per second, the quantum yield for photobleaching was 1.2×10^{-5} and 8×10^{-6} for IAF and IATR, respectively. Finally, labeling with the dyes did not functionally affect muscle fibers as judged by their ability to develop isometric tension and by their Ca^{2+} sensitivity.

For detection of polarized fluorescence fluctuations, Borejdo and Putnam (1979) and Borejdo et al. (1979) used a modified version of the apparatus described earlier (Fig. 3). A Wollaston prism was incorporated above the barrier filter to split the fluorescent light into two orthogonally polarized beams diverging by 20°. Each beam was then incident on a photomultiplier tube followed by the same pulse-shaping electronics as shown in Fig. 3. The data were acquired and analyzed as previously described except that the computer evaluated the fluorescence ratio $R_\perp$, defined as $R_\perp = I_{\perp\perp}/I_{\perp\parallel}$, and the polarization of fluorescence $P_\perp$ for each time interval T (bin), and constructed autocorrelation functions for both. The performance of this apparatus was characterized by the parameter $\langle n \rangle \beta$ described in Section II,B,2, i.e., the number of fluorescent photons detected per molecule (cross-bridge) per time T. In a typical experiment using IAF, 5-msec sampling intervals and small light flux (1.2×10^{12} photons per second), $\langle n \rangle \beta = 0.6 \times 10^{-2}$. With 8.19×10^4 bins usually collected, Borejdo and Putnam (1979) obtained S/N ratios of about 4.

Figure 5 shows the autocorrelation function of fluctuations in the polar-

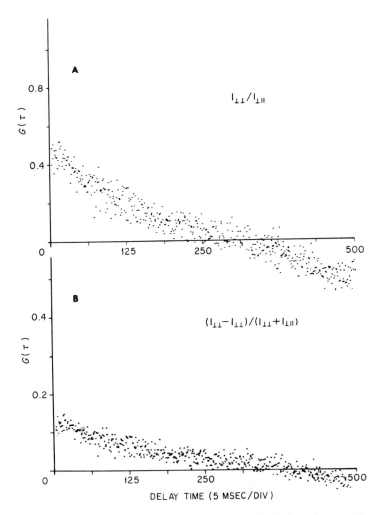

FIG. 5. The autocorrelation functions of fluctuations in (A) the intensity ratio $R_\perp$ and (B) polarized fluorescence $P_\perp$ from contracting single fiber of rabbit psoas muscle.

ization ratio $R_\perp$ and polarization of fluorescence $P_\perp$ for active single muscle fibers whose myosin cross-bridges have been labeled with IAF. In contrast with rigor or resting fibers whose autocorrelation functions were flat (not shown), active muscle gave rise to nonzero correlation functions with the characteristic time of the order of 500 msec (468 ± 99 msec, $n = 5$). Because the rational quantities such as R and P are independent of the absolute number of fluorophores present at any time in the laser beam and are sensitive only to the occupancy of different attitudinal states of the cross-bridge, Borejdo *et al.* (1979) concluded that during muscle contraction, but not at rest or rigor, the cross-bridge moieties of single muscle fibers appear to be fluctuating in rotational attitude. From the amplitude of fluctuations the number of independent fluorophores (labeled cross-bridges) contributing to the varying signal was estimated at 2.3×10^6, in good agreement with the value calculated from the rate of photon arrival at the photomultiplier. Inevitably, a number of pitfalls are possible in a complex experiment of this kind. Among those considered by the authors were number fluctuations (i.e., fluctuations in the number, not in the occupation number of given rotational attitude) of the cross-bridges in the illuminated volume, and associated with the gross motion of the fiber, fluctuations in birefringence due to periodic structural changes in thick filaments and the effects associated with the bleaching of the fluorophores.

Formal relationship between the experimental autocorrelation functions and the kinetic parameters of Fig. 1 has not yet been established, and so it is premature to attempt to assign specific values to any of the transitions on the basis of the fluctuation data. Nevertheless, the result that emerged from these studies was that most likely only slow cross-bridge reorientations are present. Even though for technical reasons sampling time T was 5 msec and rotational reorientations occurring at few hundred hertz rate would not be completely resolved (cf. Fig. 2), at least an indication of such processes should be observable. Absence of such more rapid motions argues for the idea that under truly isometric conditions cross-bridges are quasi-stationary (Eisenberg and Hill, 1978). This contrasts with the situation prevailing when the fibers are perturbed (Huxley and Simmons, 1971), when the presence of rapid reorientations is deduced. It is perhaps no accident that the steady-state ATPase of single rabbit psoas muscle fiber assessed under isometric conditions is as low as 1.6 to 1.9 Hz (Takashi and Putnam, 1979).

3. Polarized Fluorescence Fluctuations vs. Time-Resolved Anisotropy Decay

An alternative fluorescence-based method for following rotational motions of molecules is the time-resolved fluorescence anisotropy decay (TRFAD) technique (Weber, 1953), and a comparison with the fluctuation approach deserves a comment. For *in vitro* work the TRFAD technique has been preferred. In this technique the orientation of fluorophore at the time of absorption of the exciting photon is compared with the orientation at a later time of emission of the fluorescent photon associated with the same excitation event. The amount of depolarization of light that occurs during a single fluorescent lifetime is related to the rotational diffusion coefficient. The method works well for the cases when the rates of fluorescence decay and of the rotational depolarization are comparable. An application of this technique to muscle proteins in solution addressed such questions as the segmental flexibility of HMM, wherein it was found that there is considerable flexibility localized near the (S-1)–(S-2) connecting joint (Mendelson *et al.*, 1973), and the influence of Ca^{2+} on the hindrance of the rotary mobility of myosin heads assembled in thick filaments, where no effect was found (Mendelson and Cheung, 1976). Capitalizing on the dramatic difference in rotational mobility of S-1 and actin, the affinity of S-1 (Highsmith *et al.*, 1976) and of HMM (Highsmith, 1978) to actin was measured. The interaction of actin and the nucleotide binding sites on S-1 was also followed (Highsmith, 1976).

However, when the molecule of interest rotates so slowly that during the fluorescent lifetime the amount of depolarization is very small, as is most likely the case with the rotational motion of cross-bridges during muscle contraction, the method does not provide a useful measurement of the rotational diffusion.

When following rotatory motions of dichroic chromophores, either intrinsic (retinal) or extrinsic (eosin isothiocyanate), this problem may be overcome by analyzing relaxation of dichroism induced by polarized bleaching light pulse (Cone, 1972; Cherry and Schneider, 1976). In the future it may also be possible to record the relaxation of polarized fluorescence following the polarized bleaching pulse. In the meantime one can take full advantage of the fact that such limitation does not apply to the fluorescence correlation method. This is because the calculation of the autocorrelation function involves correlations of the fluorescence excited by a photon at one orientation of the molecule with the fluorescence excited by a different photon at a time sufficiently later so that the molecule had a chance to alter orientation to a greater degree. Consequently, the correlation method is capable of revealing rotational motions even when the fluorescent lifetime is very short compared to the characteristic time of rotation. Ehrenberg and Rigler (1974) and Aragon and Pecora (1975) have explicitly demonstrated that the autocorrelation function contains terms that relax independently of the fluorescence decay time.

In practice the fluorescence orientation correlations are easier to obtain for slow rotations because (as discussed in Section II,B,2) the efficient evaluation of the correlation function requires that one detect one, or more, fluorescent photons per molecule per characteristic time. The polarized fluorescence fluctuations technique seems therefore to be particularly well suited for the study of the kinetics of muscle cross-bridges.

D. Muscle Tension

1. Theoretical Investigations

The scheme illustrated in Fig. 1 associates the tension-generating step with the transition of the cross-bridge from perpendicular to angled attitude corresponding to rigor configuration. Each time this power stroke is executed a mechanical impulse is delivered to actin filaments, the size, duration, and frequency of which is determined by the kinetic coefficients of the scheme (Oplatka, 1972). The total contractile force developed by the muscle is a superposition of such impulses. In this sense the contractile force is an indirect indicator of cross-bridge kinetics. An immediate consequence of this picture is that the contractile force should fluctuate about its average value and that there should be corresponding fluctuations in sarcomere length. Jackson and Oplatka (1974) investigated the amplitude of the intersarcomere distance and z-line position fluctuations in a theoretical study of a model muscle subjected to mechanochemical, restoring, damping, and inertial forces. They explicitly solved the equation for a simple case where both damping and inertial effects were neglected, and arrived at the conclusion that the rms amplitude of fluctuations in the distance between any pair of sarcomeres is minimal at the center of the muscle, whereas the amplitude of fluctuation in the position of the z-line is predictably minimal near the fixed ends. Both fluctuations increased in amplitude with increasing muscle length. Hill (1975) considered both amplitude and time behavior of fluctuations in force in an idealized muscle consisting of one-half sarcomere in direct contact with the force-detecting instrument. The force was developed by the simplest "self-consistent" cycling two-state mechanism (Hill, 1974; Hill and Chen, 1974; Chen and Hill, 1974; Hill et al., 1975) with one unattached state in which the cross-bridge exerts no force, and one attached state in which the cross-bridge exerts force $F(x)$ along the direction of filaments. In a model of this kind F and the rate constants governing transitions between two states are functions of the familiar axial distance x defining the position of the base of the cross-bridge relative to the position of the current site of attachment chosen so that $F(0) = 0$ (Huxley, 1957). If the position-dependent rate constants for attachment are f and g' and for detachment g and f', then the power spectrum and mean square of force fluctuations are (Hill, 1975)

$$G(\omega) = \frac{4N}{d} \int_{-d/2}^{d/2} \frac{F^2(g + f')(f + g')\,dx}{S(S^2 + \omega^2)} \tag{16}$$

$$\sigma^2 = \frac{N}{d} \int_{-d/2}^{d/2} \frac{F^2(g + f')(f + g')\,dx}{S^2} \tag{17}$$

where $S = f + g + f' + g'$, N is the total number of cross-bridges in a half-sarcomere, and d is the repeating distance of actin binding sites $(= 360 \text{ Å})$.

A more recent attempt to estimate the magnitude of expected force fluctuation was that of Carlson (1975a), who proposed a mechanical model for coupling of structural elements in a single sarcomere and for coupling of one sarcomere to another. The rms magnitude of force fluctuations estimated on the basis of this model was 3×10^{-4} dyne per sarcomere, and the mean force per sarcomere was 4×10^{-2} dyne. The large value of the relative rms fluctuation of 0.75% was due to the fact that fluctuations of a single sarcomere were considered. Fujime and Yoshino (1978) have investigated both amplitude and time dependence of force and sarcomere position fluctuations for an elastic model similar to that of Carlson. In their formulation the x dependence of forces and rate constants was not taken into account, and the resulting power spectra were single Lorentzians, in contrast to complete expression given by Eq. (16). Brokaw (1976) was the first to use Hill's formalism applied to a simple self-consistent two-state model of a single half-sarcomere and to develop a stochastic computational method to study the properties of cross-bridges during contraction. The computed rms amplitude of fluctuations in muscle force was (for the most realistic parameters of the model) 1.5×10^{-9} dyne per cross-bridge, and the relative rms fluctuation was 0.97%. Brokaw also simulated the time evolution of the steady-state force during isometric contraction, shortening and stretching as well as force transients following rapid changes in length. With the view of obtaining realistic estimate of the relative amplitude of tension fluctuations to be expected in real muscles, Borejdo and Morales (1977) used Brokaw's Monte Carlo approach to simulate Hill's two-state model consisting of up to 20 half-sarcomeres in series, acting against a series elastic component. The relative rms fluctuation was found to depend inversely on the number of cross-bridges included in the model and to depend weakly on the total number of sarcomeres. Their extrapolated values to the case of a muscle comprising of 400 sarcomeres and 10^6 cross-bridges yielded rms relative fluctuation in force to be between 0.01 and 0.06%; Borejdo and Morales (1977) computed the power spectra of force fluctuations and found them in good agreement with the experimentally determined spectra (see below).

For a more complete investigation of the stochastic behavior of muscle it is necessary to use more realistic, multistate models (Eisenberg and Hill, 1978). In a series of theoretical papers Chen (1975a,b, 1977, 1978a,b) has presented a general formalism for the calculation of the power spectra of fluctuations in the concentration of intermediates in a system undergoing coupled elementary chemical reactions, which is applicable to such models (for review, see Chen, 1978d). An interesting observation made by Chen (1975a) is that steady-state systems may under certain circumstances exhibit "peaking"; i.e., their power spectra may show a local maximum at a frequency other than zero. Such a situation cannot arise in an equilibrium system (Chen, 1978a,b), a fact that can be used to distinguish between equilibrium and nonequilibrium systems (Chen, 1975a,b, 1978c).

Borejdo (1979b) used a computational method to calculate the steady-state statistical behavior of a large population of cross-bridges distributed among different states in a multistate kinetic scheme such as the one shown in Fig. 1. The autocorrelation functions of fluctuations in the concentration of cross-bridges in all intermediate states was computed. Muscle tension was related to the population of the two attached force-generating states. The force developed by the cross-bridge at any specific value of the axial displacement x was computed from the pair of free energy curves that had associated four pairs of x-dependent rate constants consistent with them. The autocorrelation functions of force fluctuations were found to depend only on the single pair of rate constants defining transitions between the attached states. Thus a practical way of estimating these specific rate constants from the experimental autocorrelation functions of force fluctuations was presented.

2. Experimental Realization

Several research groups have attempted to observe directly sarcomere length fluctuations by employing laser diffraction techniques. Larson et al. (1968) and Goldspink et al. (1970) have reported sarcomere length fluctuations of the order of 1% during the steady-state isometric contraction of frog sartorius and chick latissimus dorsi whole muscle. In controversy with these results, Cleworth and Edman (1969, 1972) and Kawai and Kuntz (1973) have failed to observe any such fluctuations in the isometrically contracting single fibers of the semitendinosus muscle of frog, and they claimed that the results of Davies and his collaborators did not represent the behavior of a functionally active single fiber. Nevertheless, it is likely that the fluctuations in sarcomere length may be present, but are too small to be observed by the light-diffraction technique. The spatial resolution achieved in the above experiments ranged between 6 and 30 Å (between 0.03 and 0.15% of sarcomere length). Moreover, the macroscopic dimensions of the laser beam (~ 1 mm) must have caused averaging of possible local length fluctuations. For this reason Borejdo and Morales (1977) continued the search for fluctuations in the steady-state tension rather than in sarcomere length. They recorded the steady-state tension developed by stimulated single muscle fibers by a sensitive electrooptical transducer capable of resolving the expected fluctuations in magnitude and frequency (Borejdo and Schweitzer, 1977). They then applied fluctuation analysis to define the underlying frequency components through the power spectra and amplitude of fluctuations. During rest or in rigor they found no fluctuations in tension, but in contraction it was possible to demonstrate their presence and to estimate amplitude at about 0.003% of the mean muscle force. Figure 6 shows the representative power spectra of contracting and rigor muscle and documents the presence of slow fluctuations in active preparations. The dominant frequency components underlying the tension signal were usually contained in the range of 0–2 Hz. Borejdo and Morales (1977) attempted to isolate and exclude the possibility of artifactual origin of tension fluctuations due to the mechanical motions of the fiber and concluded that the observed fluctuations authentically reflect the mechanical impulses delivered by myosin cross-bridges. Because the high tension sensitivity of Borejdo and Morales' apparatus was secured at the expense of frequency response, no information about possible high frequency fluctuations was obtained. Here it may be noted that the coincidence of time scales of polarized fluorescence and tension fluctuations is suggestive of the absence of high-frequency tension signal.

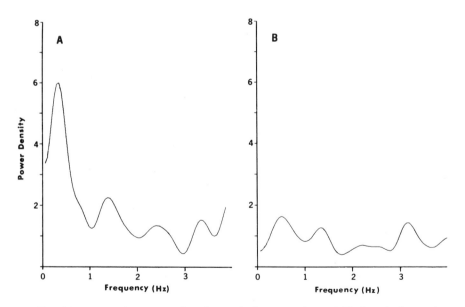

FIG. 6. Power density spectra of (A) isometrically contracting and (B) rigor single muscle fibers. The relative root mean square amplitude of fluctuations in (A) is estimated at about 0.003% of steady-state tension. After Borejdo and Morales (1977), with permission.

E. OTHER INDICATORS

In principle, any indicator that follows the mechanical, enzymic, or
dynamic behavior of cross-bridges—whether in the fiber or in
solution—can be used in fluctuation spectroscopy. In practice, for technical reasons neither of the following indicators of occupation number
fluctuations has been applied to study the contractile phenomena. I therefore limit myself to a brief discussion of the underlying principles and possible applications to muscle contractility. The indicators to be discussed
include light scattering, electrical conductance, and the ionic current
flowing across excitable membranes.

1. Light Scattering

Scattering of light arises from the variations in the refractive index of
the medium. In conventional quasi-elastic light scattering experiments
(QELS) one observes the interference pattern produced by the large collection of scattering molecules illuminated by the coherent laser beam.
The fluctuations in the intensity of the interference speckles contain information about the diffusion coefficient of the scattering units: the characteristic time of fluctuations in the intensity of the speckles is of the order
of magnitude of time required for a molecule to diffuse one-half of the
wavelength of light. The fluctuations in intensity produced by an occa-
sional molecule entering or leaving the volume defined by the laser beam
(occupation number fluctuations) are insignificant in usual experimental
configuration in this type of experiment. In addition, they occur on a
much larger time scale: the characteristic time is of the order of magnitude
of time necessary for the molecule to diffuse across the laser beam diameter (cf. Section II,B,1). Because the conventional QELS technique is
usually considered a separate discipline. I shall discuss it together with
its applications to muscle contractility in the following section. Here I
touch on light scattering as an indicator of occupation number fluctuations.

The occupation number fluctuations can be detected in a QELS-type
experiment if the number of molecules in the laser beam is sufficiently reduced; under these conditions the relative rms number fluctuations increase sufficiently (cf. Eq. (1)] to reveal themselves as modulations of the
interference fluctuations. Schaeffer and Berne (1972) and Schaeffer and
Pusey (1972) have analyzed the statistical properties of the scattered light
when both interference and number fluctuations are present. In practice it
is easier to suppress the contribution of interference fluctuations al-
together. This can be done, for example, by the use of large-aperture detection optics to collect simultaneously many interference zones (coher-

ent areas) and so to average their fluctuations, or by working with an incoherent light source (cf. Reich and Kam, 1979). The utility of the method, for which Magde (1977) appropriately suggests the name turbidity correlation analysis (TCA), has been demonstrated experimentally by Schaeffer (1973) in his study of the motion of bacteria. Its application to investigate the kinetics of contractile reactions will be limited to those cases in which the chemical reaction results in a change of the refractive index of the participants or influences the molecular mobility. An example of the former approach is binding of HMM or S-1 to actin, which is known to involve a change in solution turbidity (Tawada, 1969; Fraser *et al.*, 1975; White and Taylor, 1976).

A related technique, in which the absorbance of molecules serves as an indicator of occupation number has been discussed by Magde (1977). In spite of the fact that absorbance is not usually considered to be sufficiently sensitive to monitor a small number of molecules, Magde has shown that large relative fluctuations can be expected if certain conditions (intermediate optical densities, small size of illuminating beam) are met.

2. Electrical Conductance of Ionic Solutions

The specific resistivity is another practical indicator of fluctuations. The resistivity depends on the number and size of charged particles in the system under study; the relaxation of the spontaneous fluctuations in the number of charged ions resulting from a chemical reaction will be reflected in the autocorrelation function of resistivity fluctuations. Elson and Webb (1975), Magde (1977), and Feher (1978) have reviewed the subject; it is sufficient to remark here that in a pioneering study Feher (1970) and Feher and Weissman (1973) have made this approach practical. By passing a constant current through a small capillary tube they converted resistance into voltage fluctuations and measured them to determine the kinetic parameters for the dissociation of a model solution ($BeSO_4$ at equilibrium). They were gratified by a complete agreement with the results of classical perturbation experiments.

An application to muscle proteins covers any interactions that involve charged species. Binding of ATP or its analogs to myosin (Morales and Botts, 1953), hydrolysis of ATP and associated release of P_i (Trentham *et al.*, 1976), and binding of divalent metal cations to G-actin (Oosawa and Kasai, 1971) are good examples. Similarly, conformational changes in the myosin molecules during hydrolysis may be accompanied by a change in the number of bound ions leading to fluctuations in the resistivity of the muscle fiber. Finally, the measurements of the longitudinal impedance of muscle fibers and its fluctuations may be important in revealing the electrical properties of sarcoplasmic reticulum (Mobley *et al.*, 1974, 1975).

3. Current and Voltage Fluctuations in Excitable Membranes

The current and voltage fluctuations in membranes carry the distinction of being the first occupation number fluctuations to be explored experimentally. The fluctuations arise because the permeability of the membrane to the specific ions is affected either by the electric field across the membrane or by suitable neurotransmitters. The permeability changes are in turn due to opening and closing of ionic channels in the membrane. Spectral analysis supplies information about single channel conductance and about the mean "on" state of a channel.

It is beyond the scope of this article to review the vast experimental data on fluctuations from excitable biological membranes. The formal description of different types of membrane noise has been reviewed by Stevens (1972) and Varveen and DeFelice (1974). The work of Hagins (1965) and Varveen and Derksen (1965) on noise analysis from squid retina and frog nodes of Ranvier deserve special mention as being the first investigations of noise in biological systems. Transmitter-induced conductance fluctuations have been extensively studied by Katz and Miledi (1970, 1972) and Anderson and Stevens (1973). Hill and Chen (1972) were the first to compute theoretically the power density spectra of fluctuations in the steady-state K^+ current.

Being limited to membrane-associated phenomena, current and voltage fluctuations can offer only an indirect insight into the kinetics of the contractile process, for example through analogy with the kinetics of the active transport carrier molecules (Segal, 1972).

III. Quasi-Elastic Light Scattering

The dynamic light scattering, or quasi-elastic light scattering (QELS), technique is also based on detection of spontaneous thermodynamic fluctuations. In contrast to the situation reviewed in Section II,A, the scattered light intensity fluctuations do not arise because of occupation number fluctuations; rather they are a result of modulation of the interference of coherent light scattered from the molecules in solution. To form a qualitative picture of the situation prevailing in laser light scattering experiments and to define the distinction between number and interference fluctuations, consider what happens when a large number of scattering objects are placed in the coherent laser beam. The only restriction placed upon the objects is that they have to scatter photons; i.e., their refractive index must be different from that of the surrounding solvent. A collection of objects of this kind will give rise to a diffraction pattern resulting from the interference of light scattered from all objects and consisting of discrete "speckles" of light, each inversely related to the dimensions of scattering objects. The contribution of each object to the scattered field enters through the phase of the light scattered by it, which in turn is a function of its position. When the objects move, the phase of scattered light changes randomly in time as the objects diffuse from point to point, and, consequently, the intensity of the "speckles" fluctuates. Thus the fluctuations arise not because the number of particles in a defined volume varies, but because the phase of the wave scattered by each particle changes randomly as it diffuses through the volume. For this reason, and because it historically evolved earlier and independently, laser light scattering is usually divorced from number fluctuations; I shall retain this distinction and devote this section exclusively to QELS. Reviews are periodically published on the subject, recent ones including articles by Pecora (1972), Cummins (1974), Carlson (1975b), and Schurr (1977). More extensive treatment can be found in books by Cummins and Pike (1974), Berne and Pecora (1974), and Chu (1974). I shall therefore limit myself to an elementary description of the principles underlying QELS and cover more comprehensively the application of the technique to the contractile system. The applications are classified into four broad categories depending on the process that contributes to fluctuations: free diffusion, changes in molecular conformation, chemical reaction, and a complex combination of processes contributing to the fluctuations in whole muscles.

A. Free Diffusion of Muscle Proteins

1. Basic Concepts

A particularly convenient treatment of the principal equations of QELS for freely diffusing particles was given by Clark *et al.* (1970). Consider a plane wave illuminating solution of particles. This field will induce in each scattering particle a radiating dipole moment; the total electric field at the photodector will be the sum of the fields radiated by the particles:

$$E(t) = \sum_{j=1}^{N} E_j(t) = \sum_{j=1}^{N} E_0 \exp[i\phi_j(t) - i\omega_0 t] \tag{18}$$

where E_0 is the position-independent amplitude of the scattered electromagnetic field, ω_0 is the angular frequency of the illuminating wave, and $\phi_j(t)$ is the phase factor of the jth particle. The phase factor defined as $\phi_j(t) = (\mathbf{k}_0 - \mathbf{k}_s) \cdot \mathbf{r}_j(t)$ characterizes the position of the particle. It is important to note that the phase of the scattering particle changes only when it moves in the direction of vector $\mathbf{K} = \mathbf{k}_0 - \mathbf{k}_s$; motion normal to K does not alter the phase. The magnitude of $\mathbf{K}$ is a function of the scattering angle θ, the wavelength of light λ, and the refractive index of solution n, $|K| = (4\pi n/\lambda)\sin \theta/2$. In attempting to describe the temporal variation of the electric field (or scattered light intensity $I \sim |E(t)|^2$) we again give up trying to predict its detailed time evolution. We revert to the statistical description of the phenomenon and construct the autocorrelation function of the fluctuations. The autocorrelation function in this case describes the relaxation of the spontaneous intensity fluctuation back to the average value, and, in the simplest case, it is obviously related to the diffusive properties of the scatterers. Thus for identical, ideal, infinitely dilute optically isotropic spheres the autocorrelation function of intensity fluctuation assumes the form

$$G(\tau) = 1 + \exp(-\tau/\tau_c); \; \tau_c = \tfrac{1}{2}DK^2 \qquad (19)$$

where D is the translational diffusion coefficient of the scatterers. To grasp the meaning of Eq. (19), imagine that Fig. 2 now describes fluctuations in the scattered light intensity, and suppose that at a given time t the superposition of phases of the scattered waves is such that the intensity is at the maximum. This superposition will change to a new, uncorrelated superposition after the lapse of sufficient time τ_c so that the phase of each particle changes by $\sim \pi$. But as we remarked above, in order to change phase by π, the particle must move (along the direction of $\mathbf{K}$) a distance π/K. On the other hand, for a particle executing a three-dimensional random walk, the root mean square distance traveled in time τ_c is equal to $6D\tau_c$ (cf., e.g., Chandrasekhar, 1954). If this distance is to be equal to π/K, then $\tau_c = \frac{1}{6}\, \pi^2)1/DK^2$, which roughly agrees with the result given in Eq. (19). In summary, the characteristic time of intensity fluctuations is, in this simple case, at each angle inversely related to the translational diffusion coefficient of the scatterers. In practice, D is determined more accurately from the slope of the plot of $\Gamma = 1/\tau_c$ vs K^2.

The alternative (frequency domain) representation of simple diffusion is obtained by applying the Fourier transform to Eq. (19) [cf. Eq. (8)]. The resulting power density spectrum is of the "Lorentzian" shape [i.e., it decays with frequency as $\Gamma/((2\pi\nu)^2 + \Gamma^2)$], where $\Gamma = 2DK^2$, is the bandwidth of the Lorentzian (and the decay rate of the autocorrelation function).

2. Application to Muscle Proteins

The accuracy and speed with which the determination of the translational diffusion coefficient is achieved by QELS was exploited in the study of myosin and its fragments. Herbert and Carlson (1971) obtained power spectra of light scattered from solutions of skeletal muscle myosin at high ionic strength. They confirmed the original observation of Godfrey and Harrington (1970) that myosin under these conditions exists in equilibrium between monomeric and dimeric forms. They have adapted their QELS apparatus for absolute scattered intensity measurements and obtained, from Zimm plots, the molecular weight and radius of gyration of monomeric myosin and the equilibrium constant for the monomer–dimer reaction. They were then able to resolve the experimental power spectra into two components corresponding to myosin monomer and dimer and to estimate the corresponding diffusion coefficients ($D^0_{mon} = 1.25 \times 10^{-7}$; $D^0_{dim} = 0.84 \times 10^{-7}$ cm^2 per second). By assuming an appropriate shape for the molecules (prolate ellipsoids of revolution) they calculated from Perrin's equations the long axes as 1481 ± 130 Å and 2121 ± 260 Å for monomer and dimer, respectively.

Carlson and Fraser (1974) measured autocorrelation functions of diffusing actin, and later Fraser et al. (1975) extended this study to the diffusion of HMM and S-1. Figure 7 illustrates the representative correlation functions obtained at the scattering angle of 90°. The slowly decaying, nonexponential function for actin is consistent with a large, slowly diffusing molecule, which at the same time rotates and flexes. Its diffusion coefficient was estimated by Carlson and Fraser (1974) at 0.10×10^{-7} cm^2 per second. From the rapidly decaying HMM and S-1 functions, the respective diffusion coefficients were estimated at 1×10^{-7} and 6×10^{-7} cm^2 per second. Hochberg et al. (1977) also obtained slowly relaxing, nonexponential decay curves for actin and estimated a value of the diffusion coefficient close to the one reported by Fraser et al. Freely diffusing HMM gave rise to single exponential decays and the diffusion coefficient smaller than that reported by Fraser et al. and equal to 3.2×10 cm^2 per second, in close agreement with the value measured by Asai (1974) and Borejdo (1979a). Hochberg et al. (1977) observed that in the presence of 5 mM MgCl$_2$ the autocorrelation functions of HMM were no longer single exponentials and that the best fit gave decay times that were much longer than that of HMM alone. Upon adding ATP the effect disappeared. These observations were ascribed to ATP-reversible aggregation of HMM by Mg^{2+}.

The accuracy with which the QELS method measures the translational diffusion coefficient warrants an attempt to compute the dimensions of ellipsoid of revolution hydrodynamically equivalent to S-1 (Borejdo, 1979a). For the ellipsoids of semi-axes a and b and axial ratio $q = b/a$, Perrin's expressions give the angle averaged translational frictional coefficient f_T as a function of q and length of semi-axis a. They also relate the rotational frictional coefficient f_R to the same quantities. The mean f_T estimated from Fig. 7 for S-1 is 0.7×10^{-7} gm per second, and $f_R = 0.365 \times$

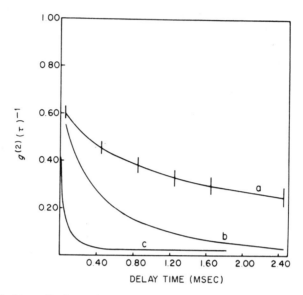

FIG. 7. Typical intensity fluctuation autocorrelation functions of actin, 1 mg/ml (curve a); HMM, 2 mg/ml (curve b); and S-1, 2 mg/ml (curve c). Actin preparations, in contrast to both HMM and S-1, give variable results, hence the average trace is shown together with the error bars; 3 mM MgATP, 2 mM P$_1$, 3 mM imidazole, 0.1 M KCl, 3 mM imidazole buffer, pH 7.0, at 0.5°C. From Fraser *et al.* (1975), with permission.

10^{-19} gm cm per second from time-resolved polarized fluorescence decay experiments (Mendelson *et al.*, 1973). To be consistent with both translational and rotational data, S-1 must be a prolate ellipsoid of revolution with the short semi-axis $a \simeq 36$ Å and axial ratio close to 3. A similar conclusion was reached on the basis of X-ray scattering experiments by Kretzschmar *et al.* (1978); Yang and Wu (1977), however, interpreted their viscosity data so as to suggest that S-1 is an oblate ellipsoid with $q = 6$.

B. Conformational Fluctuations of F-Actin

In addition to diffusive motions, fluctuations in the scattered light intensity may arise because of the change in conformation of the large scattering object. Of particular importance in physical chemistry is the segmental diffusion of the elements of flexible random coils and the flexural vibrations of rodlike macromolecules. Pecora (1965, 1968a,b) has developed theoretical expressions for the autocorrelation functions of the light scattered by such macromolecules. The results of these theoretical investigations predict that in many situations of practical interest the intensity autocorrelation function should be proportional to the sum of exponential terms of the type

$$G(\tau) \sim 1 + [P_0^2 \exp(-2DK^2\tau) + 2P_0 \sum_{j=1} P_j \exp(-2DK^2\tau - \tau/\tau_j)]$$

(20)

where P_j (the form factor) and τ_j (the jth relaxation time) define the jth mode of internal motion. P_j is a function of scattering vector $\mathbf{K}$, molecular size, and shape, and it describes the relative importance of the jth mode of internal motion.

The practical implication of Eq. (20) is that at the limit $K \to 0$ (small scattering angles) the contribution of the translational diffusion term vanishes and only the sum of exponentials defining the contributions of the internal modes of motion remains. If the P_j terms do not vanish as $K \to 0$, then the plot of the inverse of the observed characteristic time vs K^2 should yield, as an intercept, the inverse of the average value of the dominant internal modes (τ_F). This was the basic premise beneath the series of experiments by Fujime and his co-workers undertaken to ascertain whether freely diffusing actin polymers are flexible. The experimental approach of Fujime *et al.* was to fit the observed photocurrent spectrum to a single Lorentzian to determine the effective half-width $\Gamma = 1/\tau_c$. Under all experimental conditions, it was found that Γ depended on K^2 as $\Gamma = 2DK^2 + 1/\tau_F$. Thus, according to Eq. (20), actin was supposedly flexible, τ_F being the average relaxation time of the internal modes of motion. Fujime (1970) further claimed that τ_F is to a good approximation equal to the first-order relaxation time of the Harris–Hearst polymer model. Fujime and Ishiwata (1971) measured Γ for actin interacting with other muscle proteins: HMM, S-1, and tropomyosin. They found that binding of HMM to actin progressively decreased Γ, left D mysteriously unchanged, and therefore increased τ_F (i.e., made actin more flexible). This effect reached a maximum at the molar ratio of HMM to actin of 1:6. Binding of S-1 made no difference to the relaxation times of actin, whereas the addition of tropomyosin made it stiffer, as expected. Ishiwata and Fujime (1972) investigated by the same technique the effect of calcium on the flexibility of reconstituted thin filaments, namely the F-actin–tropomyosin–troponin complex (Weber and Murray, 1973). Physiological Ca^{2+} ion concentrations were found to influence the flexibility of the complex: below 1 μM, little flexibility was observed, whereas above 1 μM the filament behaved as though troponin were absent. These results (reviewed by Oosawa *et al.*, 1973) assign to the flexibility of actin a physiological role not only in the regulation of muscle contraction, but also during the force generation process.

The experimental results of Fujime and his collaborators have been challenged by Carlson and Fraser (1974); the lively controversy that developed has intrigued many muscle researchers and deserves brief comment here. Carlson and Fraser (1974) studied F-actin and its complexes with myosin fragments using a digital autocorrelator to measure $G(\tau)$. They found, in conflict with Fujime, that the correlation functions were not single exponentials (and hence the power spectra could not be fitted by a single Lorentzian curve), that the bandwidth Γ was not proportional to K^2, and that the plot of Γ vs K^2 did not intercept the ordinate at a nonzero value of Γ. In addition, there was a substantial difference in the rates of relaxation, those of Fujime being at all angles severalfold smaller. As suggested by Schurr (1977), the resolution of the controversy may lie in the fact that Carlson and Fraser (1974) used the correlation technique that emphasizes the short-time behavior of the relaxation process. This would correctly describe the free translation and deformation of F-actin. Indeed, for sufficiently large and flexible macromolecule, the relationship between Γ and K^2 can be computed rigorously by the application of the Rouse–Zimm model of a flexible polymer (Lin and Schurr, 1978), and such calculation shows that the $D - K^2$ relation as observed by Carlson and Fraser (1974) is what would be expected. Fujime and his co-workers, on the other hand, in fitting a single Lorentzian to their experimental power spectra, may have overlooked the fast relaxation processes that appear as a high-frequency tail of the Lorentzian curve. If so, then the relaxation times of Fujime, while still reflecting some internal relaxation time of F-actin, are not simply related to the first-order relaxation mode of the Harris–Hearst polymer model.

The controversy has been recently put to rest by Maeda and Fujime (1977), who reinvestigated the dynamic light scattering from F-actin solutions using the digital autocorrelator (rather than the spectrum analyzer). In concurrence with Carlson and Fraser's results, they, too, reported that the autocorrelation functions showed highly nonexponential decays, that $\Gamma - K^2$ plots were nonlinear and intersected the Γ axis at $K^2 = 0$. Similar conclusions have been reached by Hochberg et al. (1977), who utilized low actin concentrations (0.1 mg/ml) so that molecular, and not gel, properties were evident.

Recently, Newman and Carlson (1980) have provided clear evidence for the flexibility of native scallop adductor thin filaments by comparing correlation functions obtained at varying temperatures and ionic strengths. They report rms amplitude of fluctuations of the order of several hundred angströms. There thus appear to be a congengus that actin filaments do execute conformational fluctuations. In retrospect, it is indeed difficult to believe that a molecule with the axial ratio of at least 1:200, such as actin, is not flexible. Even a cylindrical steel wire with the bending modulus $\epsilon = 1.6 \times 10^{-20}$ N/cm^2 and Young's modulus of 2.2×10^8 N/cm^2 and the dimensions such as those of actin will execute lateral conformational fluctuations of the order of tens of angstroms. From the comparison of the end-to-end distance (R) and contour length (L) of electron microscopic images of F-actin, it is possible to estimate the bending modulus of a molecule. Oosawa (1977) has reported the value of ϵ estimated by this direct method as being 100 times smaller than that of steel, and consequently conformational fluctuations several hundred angstroms in amplitude would be *a priori* expected.

As mentioned above, even though the flexibility parameter extensively used by Fujime and his collaborators in the earlier work is not obviously related to any particular mode of intramolecular motion, it does indirectly reflect on the actin flexibility. The results obtained using their method, in particular promotion of flexibility of F-actin by HMM (Fujime and Ishiwata, 1971; Fujime et al., 1972), regulatory action of Ca^{2+} on the flexibility of reconstituted thin filaments (Ishiwata and Fujime, 1972), and the decrease of flexibility of actin decorated with HMM by the addition of β-actinin (Maeda et al., 1974), are all legitimate observations.

The flexural rigidity of thin filaments was also measured *in vivo*, where the interpretation of the results is much simpler (Umazume and Fujime, 1975; Yanagida and Oosawa, 1978). When skinned fibers of the semitendinosus muscle of frog were stretched and electric field was applied along the fiber axis, the intensity of all observable lines increased. The analysis of the decay process when the field was turned off gave the flexural rigidity of actin as 2 to 3×10^{-17} dyn cm^2 (Umazume and Fujime, 1975). Fujime and Yoshino (1978) extended the theoretical treatment of the effect in terms of the interaction between the electric dipoles of thin filaments and the applied field and established experimentally that the flexural rigidity of thin filaments strongly depended on the concentrations of free Ca^{2+} ions in the myofibrillar space (Yoshino et al., 1978). These effects have been reviewed by Fujime et al. (1979).

C. ACTIN–MYOSIN INTERACTIONS

A chemical reaction can also, in principle, lead to the fluctuations in the intensity of scattered light, and QELS, like occupation number fluctuations, can be used to follow chemical kinetics. Because ultimately it is the polarizability of the solute that scatters light, there must be a change in polarizability associated with a chemical transformation for it to be detectable by light scattering. The theoretical treatment of light scattering from chemically reactive systems has covered a variety of reactions

(Berne and Pecora, 1974). The important point that emerged from these theories is that, when the chemical relaxation time is appreciably faster than the characteristic time for diffusion, the intensity fluctuations in the scattered field contain a fast component independent of scattering angle.

Dynamic light scattering autocorrelation functions from complex enzymic systems in steady state are formidable to interpret theoretically; nevertheless, useful information can be extracted from QELS applied to such a system when combined with other, parallel measurements. Thus Fraser et al. (1975) combined QELS with viscosity and turbidity measurements to determine the extent of binding of HMM and S-1 to actin under conditions of maximally activated ATPase activity. They corroborated of an earlier claim by Eisenberg and his collaborators, based on ultracentrifuge, enzymic activity and kinetic measurements (Eisenberg et al., 1972; Eisenberg and Kielley, 1972; Chock et al., 1976) that under such conditions acto-HMM and acto-S-1 are markedly dissociated. In the experiments of Fraser et al. (1975) less than 10% of HMM, and even smaller fractions of S-1, were bound to actin.

In a later study, Hochberg et al. (1977) attempted to visualize the changes in the dynamic behavior of actomyosin systems associated with mechanochemical interactions. Prompted by observations of Oplatka et al. (1974) and Borejdo and Oplatka (1976) asserting that the interactions between molecularly dispersed myosin fragments HMM and S-1 with actin in the presence of MgATP are capable of inducing mechanochemical response, they measured the autocorrelation functions of light scattered from dilute acto-HMM solutions under conditions of suppressed and activated ATPase activity. Hochberg et al. (1977) did not detect the presence of an angle-independent component of the autocorrelation function indicative of the reaction relaxation time. The active complex gave substantially shorter characteristic time of the autocorrelation at higher angles. Because, in the control experiments with enzymically inactivated HMM and with cross-linked F-actin no such changes were observed, the authors interpreted these results in terms of the flexibility changes of acto-HMM induced by active mechanochemical coupling. Neither Fraser et al. (1975) nor Hochberg et al. (1977) have made an attempt to interpret their results in terms of the formal theory relating the autocorrelation function of scattered intensity fluctuations to the kinetic constants of a coupled chemical reaction.

The distinguishing feature of the contributing effects of chemical reaction to the scattered light intensity—the independence of the scattered field on angle—was also absent from Herbert and Carlson's (1971) early studies of the myosin monomer–dimer equilibrium.

D. Intensity Fluctuations from Active Muscle

Application of QELS to study of the kinetics of contracting muscle fibers carries considerable promise because it is a nondestructive, rapid, dynamic investigative tool. This approach was pioneered by Carlson and his co-workers (Carlson *et al.*, 1972; Bonner and Carlson, 1975; Carlson, 1975a), who studied the fluctuations in the intensity of the light scattered by resting, rigor, and isometrically contracting frog sartorius muscle and by bundles of fibers dissected from frog semitendinosus. The principal finding that emerged from this work was that the physiological state of muscle is reflected in the scattered light autocorrelation function. As expected, rigor muscle gave flat autocorrelation functions, a result consistent with the notion that no mechanical activity exists in such preparations and confirmed later by occupation number fluctuations experiments (cf. Borejdo and Morales, 1977). Somewhat surprisingly, relaxed fibers showed nonflat autocorrelation functions, which may possibly be explained in terms of the bound diffusion model of Carlson and Fraser (1974), which presumes the scattering elements (to be identified below) to execute constrained random axial displacements about equilibrium positions even during relaxation. Contracting muscles gave rise to autocorrelation functions that depended on the time of data collection with respect to the beginning of stimulation. During the plateau of isometric tetanus, i.e., under the conditions where no gross movements of muscle occur, the autocorrelation functions showed large amplitudes and decay times of the order of 1 msec (at room temperature). On the basis of this information, Carlson (1975a) attempted an identification of the structural elements of the myofibril responsible for the phase-shifted light scattering. His analysis reveals that myosin cross-bridges cannot be the elements in question: if all the other structures are presumed stationary during contraction, the total mass of the cross-bridge is simply too insignificant to give the large decay amplitudes observed. Further, there is little doubt that the cross-bridges are constrained to execute cyclic motions over a distance not exceeding 10 nm (Ford *et al.*, 1977); in other words, their translational diffusive motion (if any) is severely restricted—a fact further contributing to the decrease in autocorrelation function amplitude. Inescapably, Carlson (1975a) concluded that the elements responsible for fluctuations were larger structures, such as thin and thick filaments or whole I and A bands. These structures have been shown by Bonner and Carlson (1975) to maintain (exclusively) axial velocities of the order of 20 μm/second, close to the maximal velocities of shortening of sarcomeres in isometrically contracting bundles of tree frog semitendinosus muscle (Borejdo and Mason,

1976). In addition to the fluctuations in the scattered intensity contributed by axial movements, there are fluctuations resulting from variations in the polarizability of the scattering elements. Their presence was revealed by Bonner and Carlson (1975), who observed scattering in the plane perpendicular to the fiber axis. In this configuration, the axial motions of the scattering elements were in the direction perpendicular to the scattering vector K and hence did not contribute to the scattered intensity fluctuations. The familiar $\Gamma - K^2$ plots gave a straight horizontal line suggesting that the scattering elements did not execute motions perpendicular to the fiber axis. The observed fluctuations under those conditions were attributed to fluctuations in the polarizability of the scattering elements, due presumably to changes in the polarizability of the thick or thin filaments. The characteristic time of these fluctuations was approximately 1 msec. The results provided convincing evidence for the presence of large-scale fluctuations in the gross structural elements of sarcomeres, or of the sarcomeres themselves. Such fluctuations can only be caused by forces that fluctuate during contraction, as discussed in Section II,D,1, and which have been shown explicitly to be present in contracting fibers (Borejdo and Morales, 1977).

IV. Prospects for the Future

In developing the argument in favor of the application of fluctuation spectroscopy to contractility, I naturally emphasized the positive aspects of the technique. In fairness, the often formidable technical and conceptual difficulties associated with various aspects of fluctuation analysis must also be considered. In the following I underline these difficulties and suggest ways to overcome them in the hope of stimulating more widespread applications of the techniques. To begin with the fluorescence technique, the most serious systematic interference is the photolytic degradation of the fluorophore. Apart from the gradual loss of the signal and uncertainty in the instantaneous fluorophore concentration, photobleaching may cause local differences in the concentration of the fluorophore between illuminated and neighboring regions and hence lead to spurious convection and hydrodynamic fluctuations. The susceptibility to photodegradation can be quantitatively assessed by computing the ratio of number of photons absorbed to the number destroyed per unit time, which is expressed by the ratio $B = gQ/q$ (Magde et al., 1974). For iodoacetamidotetramethyl rhodamine, which has so far proved most resistant to photodegradation, and with the detection geometry employed in the polarization of fluorescence fluctuations experiments, $B = 8000$, a relatively high number. Nevertheless, further improvement would be welcome. This is because, in polarized fluorescence experiments summarized in Section II,C,2, the number of fluorescent photons detected per labeled cross-bridge per bin width, which to a decisive extent determines signal-to-noise ratio, was significantly less than 1. This in turn implies (Magde *et al.*, 1974) that by increasing laser power one can achieve larger S/N ratios, a critical requirement for polarized fluorescence fluctuations work. Without a photostable fluorophore, however, any further increase in the illuminating light flux is impossible. It is hoped that laser dye technology will eventually produce a "perfect" dye according to the criteria mentioned in Section II,C,1, and it appears that the first step may have already been taken by the development of the fluorinated coumarin dyes (Schimitschek *et al.*, 1974). The synthesis of such dyes in the form of iodoacetimido derivatives, and determining whether it qualifies *in vivo* on muscle fibers according to these criteria mentioned earlier may well be the next step in the application of fluorescence fluctuation spectroscopy to contractility.

A number of technical problems, of less formidable magnitude and associated with data collection and processing, remain. Geometrical collection efficiency of the spectrometer is disappointingly low because of the need for compromise between the requirement for high numerical aperture of the objective and the diametrically opposite requirement for the meaningful interpretation of polarization of fluorescence functions. Axelrod (1979) has proposed a numerical correction to allow for the use of high numerical apertures in polarization measurements. In data processing a welcome development is the construction of a high correlation efficiency, large memory capacity, real time digital correlator now under construction in our laboratory. It will solve lingering problems associated with the tradeoff between correlation efficiency and maximum length of data collection now plaguing some installations.

The considerable success with which the fluorescence photobleaching recovery (FPR) experiments have met in the study of the translational diffusion makes it likely that FPR will also be used in the future to study the rotational motions of the cross-bridges.

When relying on muscle force as an indicator of fluctuations, the photodegradation problems are, for better or for worse, replaced by those associated with the poor frequency response of the mechanical transducer such as the one used by Borejdo and Morales (1977). In a simple transducer of the type where the displacement of the flexible beam can be measured with an accuracy of a few angstroms, high ("seismographic") sensitivity is obtained by making the arm highly compliant, thus limiting its characteristic vibration frequency. More sophisticated transducer designs, such as those based on optical heterodyne spectroscopy (Dragsten *et al.*, 1974; Kwaaitaal, 1974; Nokes *et al.*, 1978), fiber optic sensing of beam displacement (Thorson and White, 1975; Powell, 1974), linear variable differential transformer (Primak, 1974), and differential capacitance measurements (Dratler, 1977), combine extreme (subangstrom) sensitivity with kilohertz frequency response and should find application in this kind of study.

Focusing on QELS technique, the most serious objection to applying it to muscle, or even simple two-component acto-HMM solution, is its nonspecificity. To the sampling laser beam, most objects appear much the same: there is little variation of refractive index in biological materials. The interpretation of the experimental autocorrelation functions is then uncertain because one does not know which component contributes to the scattering. For the same reason, dust and other contaminating particles can thwart a QELS experiment. It appears that the most promising future application of QELS will be a detailed investigation of the motions of large scattering elements in single muscle fibers, where complicating effects of interfiber coupling and shear are eliminated.

Finally, a few words about experimental material. For reasonably resolved autocorrelation functions, the data collection time has to be at least several minutes. This is particularly true of occupation number fluctuations, where relative fluctuations are much smaller than in QELS and hence a longer time is necessary for accumulation of statistically significant data. Live fibers will not sustain steady-state tension for more than a few seconds, even at low temperature. Glycerinated fibers, until recently, were not significantly better. The development of an improved glycerinating procedure where the fibers are never allowed to enter into the rigor state (Kawai, 1978; Borejdo and Putnam, 1979) allows for the contractile tension to be steadily developed for up to 30 minutes. Such fibers, in addition, seldom break upon stimulation, are readily demembranated, and maintain their regular sarcomere (and hence diffraction) pattern during contraction.

V.   Concluding Remarks

In overview, it is apparent that, although progress has been made recently in the application of fluctuation techniques to the field of muscle contractility, many aspects of the topic are still in their infancy. There is little doubt that the application of fluctuation techniques will proliferate in the study of contractility in spite of the fact that considerable progress is being made simultaneously in improving the perturbation methods (Pecht and Rigler, 1977). The inherent attractiveness of the fluctuation approach, wherein one can extract kinetic information during the steady-state contraction of the physiologically intact muscle fiber is too overwhelming to permit defeat by experimental difficulties. In Sections II and III, I have reviewed these applications that directly bear on the problems in contractility, whether already accomplished or being a likely prospect for the future. I have attempted to show, by identifying the relevant references, the relationship between amplitudes of fluctuations and the number of various species within observational volume as well as the relationship between the autocorrelation functions and the thermodyna￢ic or rate parameters. The discussion of experimental realization of number fluctuations centered around different indicators that translate the number variations into measurable signals. Because the principles underlying detection of fluctuations in different indicators of cross-bridge activity are similar, the description of experimental realization was confined to the most extensively utilized probe—fluorescence of molecules. I have attempted to emphasize differences between number fluctuations and the scattered light intensity fluctuations.

With this perspective, it is relevant to ask the question: How much closer has the application of the fluctuation spectroscopy brought us toward answering the fundamental questions posed at the beginning? Has it been proved that the cross-bridges interact cyclically with actin filaments in a sequence of steps indicated in Fig. 1? I think the answer to this question is, partially, yes. The method has provided evidence for rotational motions of cross-bridges pointing to slow motions taking place under truly isometric conditions; future work, especially the application of polarized fluorescence fluctuations to single muscle fibers should be able to tell us whether fast motions exist as well, and whether the kinetic parameters revealed by the correlation functions change in optimally working muscle. The answer to the second question: Is there evidence for the coupling between enzymic and mechanical cycles of the cross-bridges? has to await further work. The measurement of cross-correlation functions between the indicators of enzymic and mechanical activity, as suggested above, is the only decisive experimental technique capable of providing the answer.

ACKNOWLEDGMENTS

I would like to thank Drs. Y-der Cheu, E. Elson, T. L. Hill, Z. Kam, M. F. Morales, A. Muhlrad, A. Oplatka, J. Schlessinger, and M. Werber for valuable comments on the manuscript, Drs. F. Carlson, S. Fujime, and A. Weber for providing papers prior to publication, and to Mrs. S. Gibraltar for expert typing and editorial assistance. The author is an Established Investigator of the American Heart Association. Research was supported by grants USPHS-HL-16683, NSF 22698, and American Heart Association Grant CI.

REFERENCES

Anderson, C. R., and Stevens, C. F. (1973). *J. Physiol.* (*London*) **235**, 655–692.
Ando, T., and Asai, H. (1976). *J. Biochem.* (*Tokyo*) **79**, 1043–1047.
Ando, T., and Asai, H. (1979). *J. Mol. Biol.* **129**, 265–277.
Aragon, S., and Pecora, R. (1975). *Biopolymers* **14**, 119–137.
Aronson, J. F., and Morales, M. F. (1969). *Biochemistry* **8**, 4517–4522.
Asai, H. (1974). *J. Phys. Soc. Jpn.* **36**, 1114–1120.
Axelrod, D. (1979). *Biophys. J.* (in press).
Axelrod, D., Koppel, D. E., Schlessinger, J., Elson, E. L., and Webb, W. W. (1976). *Biophys. J.* **16**, 1055–1069.
Bagshaw, C. R., Eccleston, J. F., Trentham, D. R., Yates, D. W., and Goody, R. S. (1972). *Cold Spring Harbor Symp. Quant. Biol.* **37**, 127–135.
Berne, B. J., and Pecora, R. (1974). "Dynamic Light Scattering." Wiley (Interscience), New York.
Bonner, R. F., and Carlson, F. D. (1975). *J. Gen. Physiol.* **65**, 555–581.
Borejdo, J. (1979a). *Biopolymers* **18**, 2807–2820.
Borejdo, J. (1979b). *Biophys.J.* **29**, 49–63.
Borejdo, J., and Mason, P. (1976). *J. Mechanochem. Cell Motil.* **3**, 151–161.
Borejdo, J., and Morales, M. F. (1977). *Biophys. J.* **20**, 315–334.
Borejdo, J., and Oplatka, A. (1976). *Biochim. Biophys. Acta* **440**, 241–258.
Borejdo, J., and Putnam, S. (1977). *Biochim. Biophys. Acta* **459**, 578–595.
Borejdo, J., and Putnam, S. (1979). *Biophys. J.* **25**, 19a.
Borejdo, J., and Schweitzer, A. (1977). *J. Mechanochem. Cell Motil.* **4**, 189–204.
Borejdo, J., Putnam, S., and Morales, M. F. (1979). *Proc. Natl. Acad. Sci. U.S.A.* **76**, 6346–6350.
Brokaw, C. J. (1976). *Biophys. J.* **16**, 1013–1027.
Cain, D. F., and Davies, R. E. (1962). *Biochem. Biophys. Res. Commun.* **8**, 361–366.
Carlson, F. D. (1975a). *Biophys. J.* **15**, 633–649.
Carlson, F. D. (1975b). *Annu. Rev. Biophys. Bioeng.* **4**, 243–264.
Carlson, F. D., and Fraser, A. B. (1974). *J. Mol. Biol.* **89**, 273–281.
Carlson, F. D., Bonner, R., and Fraser, A. (1972). *Cold Spring Harbor Symp. Quant. Biol.* **37**, 389–396.
Chandrasekhar, S. (1954). *In* "Noise and Stochastic Processes" (N. Wax, ed.), p. 55. Dover, New York.
Chen, Y. (1975a). *Proc. Natl. Acad. Sci. U.S.A.* **72**, 3807–3811.
Chen, Y. (1975b). *J. Theor. Biol.* **55**, 229–243.
Chen, Y. (1977). *J. Theor. Biol.* **65**, 357–367.
Chen, Y. (1978a). *J. Chem. Phys.* **68**, 1871–1875.
Chen, Y. (1978b). *Adv. Chem. Phys.* **37**, 67–97.
Chen, Y. (1978c). *Biophys. J.* **21**, 279–285.
Chen, Y. (1978d). *Adv. Chem. Phys.* **37**, 67–97.
Chen, Y., and Hill, T. L. (1973). *Biophys. J.* **13**, 1276–1295.
Chen, Y., and Hill, T. L. (1974). *Proc. Natl. Acad. Sci. U.S.A.* **71**, 1982–1986.
Cherry, R. J., and Schneider, G. (1976). *Biochemistry* **15**, 3657–3661.
Chock, S. P., Chock, P. B., and Eisenberg, E. (1976). *Biochemistry* **15**, 3244–3253.
Chu, B. (1974). "Laser Light Scattering." Academic Press, New York.
Civan, M. M., and Podolsky, R. J. (1966). *J. Physiol.* (*London*) **184**, 511–534.
Clark, N. A., Lunacek, J. H., and Benedek, G. B. (1970). *Am. J. Phys.* **38**, 575–585.
Cleworth, D. R., and Edman, K. A. P. (1969). *Science* **163**, 296.
Cleworth, D. R., and Edman, K. A. P. (1972). *J. Physiol.* (*London*) **227**, 1–17.

Cone, R. A. (1972). *Nature (London)*, *New Biol.* **236**, 39–43.
Cummins, H. Z. (1974). *In* "Photon Correlation and Light Beating Spectroscopy" (H. Z. Cummins and E. R. Pike, eds.), pp. 285–330. Plenum, New York.
Cummins, H. Z., and Pike, E. R., eds. (1974). "Photon Correlation and Light Beating Spectroscopy." Plenum, New York.
Debye, P. (1947). *J. Phys. Colloid Chem.* **51**, 18–32.
Dos Remedios, C. G., Millikan, R. G. C., and Morales, M. F. (1972a). *J. Gen. Physiol.* **59**, 103–120.
Dos Remedios, C. G., Yount, R. G., and Morales, M. F. (1972b). *Proc. Natl. Acad. Sci. U.S.A.* **69**, 2542–2546.
Dragsten, P. R., Webb, W. W., Paton, J. A., and Capranica, R. R. (1974). *Science* **185**, 55–57.
Dratler, J. (1977). *Rev. Sci. Instrum.* **48**, 327–335.
Ehrenberg, M., and Rigler, R. (1974). *Chem. Phys.* **4**, 390–401.
Ehrenberg, M., and Rigler, R. (1976). *Quart. Rev. Biophys.* **9**, 69–81.
Eigen, M., and DeMaeyer, L. (1963). *In* "Techniques of Organic Chemistry" (A. Weissberger, ed.), Vol. 3, pp. 895–1054. Wiley (Interscience), New York.
Eisenberg, E., and Hill, T. L. (1978). *Prog. Biophys. Mol. Biol.* **33**, 55–82.
Eisenberg, E., and Kielley, W. W. (1972). *Cold Spring Harbor Symp. Quant. Biol.* **37**, 145–152.
Eisenberg, E., Dobkin, L., and Kielley, W. W. (1972). *Biochemistry* **11**, 4657–4660.
Elson, E. L., and Magde, D. (1974). *Biopolymers* **13**, 1–27.
Elson, E. L., and Webb, W. W. (1975). *Annu. Rev. Biophys. Bioeng.* **4**, 311–334.
Feher, G. (1970). *Biophys. J.* **10**, 118a.
Feher, G. (1978). *Trends Biochem. Sci.* **3**, N111–N113.
Feher, G., and Weissman, M. (1973). *Proc. Natl. Acad. Sci. U.S.A.* **70**, 870–875.
Ford, L. E., Huxley, A. F., and Simmons, R. M. (1977). *J. Physiol. (London)* **269**, 441–515.
Fraser, A. B., Eisenberg, E., Kielley, W. W., and Carlson, F. D. (1975). *Biochemistry* **14**, 2207–2214.
Fujime, S. (1970). *J. Phys. Soc. Jpn.* **29**, 751–759.
Fujime, S., and Ishiwata, S. (1971). *J. Mol. Biol.* **62**, 251–265.
Fujime, S., and Yoshino, S. (1978). *Biophys. Chem.* **8**, 305–315.
Fujime, S., Ishiwata, S., and Maeda, T. (1972). *Biochim. Biophys. Acta* **283**, 351–363.
Fujime, S. Yoshino, S., and Umazume, Y. (1979). *In* "Current Problems of Sliding Filament Model and Muscle Mechanics" (H. Sugi, ed.). Tokyo Univ. Press, Tokyo.
Fujisaki, H., and Asai, H. (1978). *J. Biochem. (Tokyo)* **83**, 403–407.
Godfrey, J. E., and Harrington, W. F. (1970). *Biochemistry* **9**, 886–893.
Goldspink, G., Larson, R. E., and Davies, R. E. (1970). *Experientia* **26**, 16–18.
Greene, L., and Eisenberg, E. (1978). *Proc. Natl. Acad. Sci. U.S.A.* **75**, 54–58.
Greene, L., and Eisenberg, E. (1980). *J. Biol. Chem.*, **255**, 549–554.
Hagins, W. A. (1965). *Cold Spring Harbor Symp. Quant. Biol.* **30**, 403–418.
Halpern, W., and Alpert, N. R. (1971). *J. Appl. Physiol.* **31**, 913–925.
Hanson, J., and Huxley, H. E. (1954). *Nature (London)* **173**, 973–977.
Herbert, T. J., and Carlson, F. D. (1971). *Biopolymers* **10**, 2231–2252.
Highsmith, S. (1976). *J. Biol. Chem.* **251**, 6170–6172.
Highsmith, S. (1978). *Biochemistry* **17**, 22–26.
Highsmith, S., Mendelson, R. A., and Morales, M. F. (1976). *Proc. Natl. Acad. Sci. U.S.A.* **73**, 133–137.
Highsmith, S., Kretzschmar, M., O'Konski, C. T., and Morales, M. F. (1977). *Proc. Natl. Acad. Sci. U.S.A.* **74**, 4986–4990.
Hill, T. L. (1968). *Proc. Natl. Acad. Sci. U.S.A.* **61**, 98–105.

Hill, T. L. (1974). *Prog. Biophys. Mol. Biol.* **28**, 267–340.
Hill, T. L. (1975). *Prog. Biophys. Mol. Biol.* **29**, 105–159.
Hill, T. L. (1977). "Free Energy Transduction in Biology." Academic Press, New York.
Hill, T. L., and Chen, Y. (1972). *Biophys. J.* **12**, 948–959.
Hill, T. L., and Chen, Y. (1974). *Proc. Natl. Acad. Sci. U.S.A.* **71**, 2478–2481.
Hill, T. L., Eisenberg, E., Chen, Y., and Podolsky, R. J. (1975). *Biophys. J.* **15**, 335–372.
Hochberg, A., Low, W., Tirosh, R., Borejdo, J., and Oplatka, A. (1977). *Biochim. Biophys. Acta* **460**, 308–317.
Hudson, E. N., and Weber, G. (1973). *Biochemistry* **12**, 4154–4161.
Huxley, A. F. (1957). *Prog. Biophys. Biophys. Chem.* **7**, 255–318.
Huxley, A. F., and Niedergerke, R. (1954). *Nature (London)* **173**, 971–973.
Huxley, A. F., and Simmons, R. M. (1971). *Nature (London)* **233**, 533–538.
Huxley, H. E. (1979). *In* "Molecular Bases of Force Development in Muscle" (N. B. Ingels, ed.), pp. 1–13. Palo Alto Med. Res. Found., Palo Alto, California.
Imamura, K., Tada, M., and Tonomura, Y. (1966). *J. Biochem. (Tokyo)* **59**, 280–289.
Ishiwata, S., and Fujime, S. (1972). *J. Mol. Biol.* **68**, 511–522.
Jackson, J. L., and Oplatka, A. (1974). *Biorheology* **11**, 315–322.
Johnson, K. A., and Taylor, E. W. (1978). *Biochemistry* **17**, 3432–3442.
Kagawa, H., Kuwajima, T., and Asai, H. (1974). *Biochim. Biophys. Acta* **338**, 496–504.
Katz, B., and Miledi, R. (1970). *Nature (London)* **226**, 962–963.
Katz, B., and Miledi, R. (1972). *J. Physiol. (London)* 224, 665–699.
Kawai, M. (1978). *Biophys. J.* **22**, 97–103.
Kawai, M., and Kuntz, I. D. (1973). *Biophys. J.* **13**, 857–876.
Kawai, M., Brandt, P., and Orentlicher, M. (1977). *Biophys. J.* **18**, 161–172.
Koppel, D. E. (1974). *Phys. Rev. A* **10**, 1938–1945.
Koppel, D. E., Axelrod, D., Schlessinger, J., Elson, E. L., and Webb, W. W. (1976). *Biophys. J.* **16**, 1315–1329.
Kretzschmar, K. M., Mendelson, R., and Morales, M. F. (1978). *Biochemistry* **17**, 2314–2318.
Kushmerick, M. J. (1977). *Curr. Top. Bioeng.* **6**, 1–37.
Kwaaitaal, T. (1974). *Rev. Sci. Instrum.* **45**, 39–41.
Larson, R. E., Kushmerick, M. J., Haynes, D. H., and Davies, R. E. (1968). *Biophys. J.* **8**, MA4.
Lee, Y. W. (1960). "Statistical Theory of Communication." Wiley, New York.
Lin, S.-C., and Schurr, J. M. (1978). *Biopolymers* **17**, 425–461.
Lin, T. C. (1978). *Arch. Biochem. Biophys.* **185**, 285–299.
Loxdale, H. D. (1976). *J. Physiol. (London)* **260**, 4–5.
Lymn, R. W., and Taylor, E. W. (1971). *Biochemistry* **10**, 4617–4624.
Maeda, T., and Fujime, S. (1977). *J. Phys. Soc. Jpn.* **42**, 1983–1991.
Maeda, T., Ishiwata, S., and Fujime, S. (1974). *Biochim. Biophys. Acta* **336**, 445–452.
Magde, D. (1977). *In* "Chemical Relaxation in Molecular Biology" (I. Pecht and R. Rigler, eds.), Vol. 24, pp. 43–83. Springer-Verlag, Berlin and New York.
Magde, D., Elson, E. L., and Webb, W. W. (1974). *Biopolymers* **13**, 29–61.
Magde, D., Webb, W. W., and Elson, E. L. (1978). *Biopolymers* **17**, 361–376.
Margossian, S. W., and Lowey, S. (1976). *Fed. Proc., Fed. Am. Soc. Exp. Biol.* **35**, 1580.
Matsubara, I., Yagi, N., and Endoh, M. (1979). *Nature (London)* **278**, 474–476.
Mendelson, R. A., and Cheung, P. (1976). *Science* **194**, 190–192.
Mendelson, R. A., Morales, M. F., and Botts, J. (1973). *Biochemistry* **12**, 2250–2255.
Miki, M., Kouyama, T., and Mihashi, K. (1976). *FEBS Lett.* **66**, 98–101.
Mobley, B. A., Leung, J., and Eisenberg, R. S. (1974). *J. Gen. Physiol.* **63**, 625–637.

Mobley, B. A., Leung, J., and Eisenberg, R. S. (1975). *J. Gen. Physiol.* **65,** 97–113.

Morales, M. F. (1975). *J. Supramol. Struct.* **3,** 105–111.

Morales, M. F., and Borejdo, J. (1978). *Horiz. Biochem. Biophys.* **5,** 99–118.

Morales, M. F., and Botts, J. (1953). *Discuss. Faraday Soc.* **13,** 425–441.

Mulhern, S., and Eisenberg, E. (1978). *Biochemistry* **17,** 4419–4425.

Newman, J., and Carlson, F. D. (1980). *Biophys. J.* **29,** 37–47.

Nihei, T., Mendelson, R. A., and Botts, J. (1974). *Proc. Natl. Acad. Sci. U.S.A.* **71,** 274–277.

Nokes, M. A., Hill, B. C., and Barelli, A. E. (1978). *Rev. Sci. Instrum.* **49,** 722–728.

Oosawa, F. (1977). *Biorheology* **14,** 11–19.

Oosawa, F., and Kasai, M. (1971). *In* "Subunits in Biological Systems" (S. N. Timasheff and G. D. Fasman, eds.), pp. 261–322. Dekker, New York.

Oosawa, F., Fujime, S., Ishiwata, S., and Mihashi, K. (1973). *Cold Spring Harbor Symp. Quant. Biol.* **37,** 277–285.

Oplatka, A. (1972). *J. Theor. Biol.* **34,** 379–403.

Oplatka, A., Gadasi, H., and Borejdo, J. (1974). *Biochem. Biophys. Res. Commun.* **58,** 905–912.

Pecht, I., and Rigler, R., eds. (1977). "Chemical Relaxation in Molecular Biology," Vol. 24. Springer-Verlag, Berlin and New York.

Pecora, R. (1965). *J. Chem. Phys.* **43,** 1562–1564.

Pecora, R. (1968a). *J. Chem. Phys.* **48,** 4126–4128.

Pecora, R. (1968b). *J. Chem. Phys.* **49,** 1036–1043.

Pecora, R. (1972). *Annu. Rev. Biophys. Bioeng.* **1,** 257–276.

Podolsky, R. J. (1960). *Nature (London)* **188,** 666–668.

Podolsky, R. J., St. Onge, R., Yu, L., and Lymn, R. W. (1976). *Proc. Natl. Acad. Sci. U.S.A.* **73,** 813–817.

Porter, M., and Weber, A. (1979). *FEBS Lett.* **105,** 259–262.

Powell, J. A. (1974). *Rev. Sci. Instrum.* **45,** 302–303.

Primak, W. (1974). *Rev. Sci. Instrum.* **45,** 1550–1553.

Pybus, J., and Tregear, R. T. (1975). *J. Physiol. (London)* **247,** 71–89.

Rabiner, L. R., and Gold, B. (1975). "Theory and Applications of Digital Signal Processing." Prentice-Hall, Englewood Cliffs, New Jersey.

Reedy, M. K., Holmes, K. C., and Tregear, R. T. (1965). *Nature (London)* **207,** 1276–1280.

Reich, S., and Kam, Z. (1979). *Opt. Commun.* **30,** 293–298.

Reif, F. (1965). "Fundamentals of Statistical and Thermal Physics." McGraw-Hill, New York.

Rosen, C. G., and Weber, G. (1969). *Biochemistry* **8,** 3915–3920.

Schaeffer, D. W. (1973). *Science* **180,** 1293–1295.

Schaeffer, D. W., and Berne, B. J. (1972). *Phys. Rev. Lett.* **29,** 475.

Schaeffer, D. W., and Pusey, P. N. (1972). *Phys. Rev. Lett.* **29,** 843–845.

Schimitschek, E. J., Trias, J. A., Hammond, P. R., and Atkins, R. L. (1974). *Opt. Commun.* **11,** 352–355.

Schlessinger, J., Axelrod, D., Koppel, D. E., Webb, W. W., and Elson, E. L. (1977). *Science* **195,** 307–309.

Schurr, J. M. (1977). *Crit. Rev. Biochem.* **4,** 371–432.

Segal, J. R. (1972). *Biophys. J.* **12,** 1371–1390.

Sleep, J., and Taylor, E. W. (1976). *Biochemistry* **15,** 5813–5817.

Stevens, C. F. (1972). *Biophys. J.* **12,** 1028–1047.

Stevens, C. F. (1975). *Fed. Proc., Fed. Am. Soc. Exp. Biol.* **34,** 1364–1369.

Takashi, R. (1979). *Biochemistry* **18,** 5164–5169.

Takashi, R., and Putnam, S. (1979). *Anal. Biochem.* **92**, 375–382.

Takashi, R., Tonomura, Y., and Morales, M. F. (1977). *Proc. Natl. Acad. Sci. U.S.A.* **74**, 2334–2338.

Tawada, K. (1969). *Biochim. Biophys. Acta* **172**, 311–318.

Taylor, E. W. (1973). *Curr. Top. Bioenerg.* **5**, 201–231.

Taylor, E. W. (1979). *CRC Critical Rev. Biochem.* **6**, 103–164.

Thorson, J., and White, D. C. S. (1975). *IEEE Trans. Biomed. Eng.* **22**, 293–299.

Tregear, R. T., and Mendelson, R. A. (1975). *Biophys. J.* **15**, 455–467.

Trentham, D. R., Bardsley, R. G., Eccleston, J. F., and Weeds, A. G. (1972). *Biochem. J.* **126**, 635–644.

Trentham, D. R., Eccleston, J. F., and Bagshaw, C. R. (1976). *Q. Rev. Biophys.* **9**, 217–281.

Umazume, Y., and Fujime, S. (1975). *Biophys. J.* **15**, 163–180.

Varveen, A. A., and DeFelice, L. J. (1974). *Prog. Biophys. Mol. Biol.* **28**, 189–265.

Varveen, A. A., and Derksen, H. E. (1965). *Kybernetik* **2**, 152–160.

Webb, W. W. (1976). *Q. Rev. Biophys.* **9**, 49–68.

Weber, A., and Murray, J. M. (1973). *Physiol. Rev.* **53**, 612–673.

Weber, G. (1953). *Adv. Protein Chem.* **8**, 415–459.

Weissman, M., Schindler, H., and Feher, G. (1976). *Proc. Natl. Acad. Sci. U.S.A.* **73**, 2776–2780.

Werber, M. M., Szent-Györgyi, A. G., and Fasman, G. D. (1972). *Biochemistry* **11**, 2872–2882.

White, D. C. S., and Thorson, J. (1973). *Prog. Biophys. Mol. Biol.* **27**, 175–255.

White, H. D., and Taylor, E. W. (1976). *Biochemistry* **15**, 5818–5826.

Yagi, N., Ito, M. H., Nakajima, H., Izumi, T., and Matsubara, I. (1977). *Science* **197**, 685–687.

Yanagida, T., and Oosawa, F. (1978). *J. Mol Biol.* **126**, 507–524.

Yang, J. T., and Wu, C. (1977). *Biochemistry* **16**, 5785–5789.

Yoshino, S., Umazume, Y., Natori, R., Fujime, S., and Chiba, S. (1978). *Biophys. Chem.* **8**, 317–326.

Respiration-Linked H+ Translocation in Mitochondria: Stoichiometry and Mechanism

MÅRTEN WIKSTRÖM AND KLAAS KRAB

Department of Medical Chemistry
University of Helsinki
Helsinki, Finland

I. Introduction and Scope

The subject of this review is presently highly controversial. This has not made it easy to compile a picture that would not add to the confusion. After careful consideration it was felt that we should take a clear position instead of reviewing "from above" all the available data and suggestions on the subject. Care has been taken, however, to substantiate our position in detail, especially in cases where it is not shared by others. In doing this, we put special focus on aspects that may underlie the present differences, hoping thereby to help resolve them. Nevertheless, it should be pointed out, particularly to students of this subject, that although our chosen approach may appear tendentious in some sections, this is because we feel that, by intentionally sharpening the dialogue and contrasting the different views against one another, the controversies may be settled sooner. For a more complete picture of the present subject, excellent earlier and more recent review articles are recommended (Azzone and Massari, 1973; Azzone *et al.*, 1977; Boyer *et al.*, 1977; Greville, 1969; Mitchell, 1976a; Papa, 1976; Skulachev, 1971), as well as several symposium volumes (Azzone *et al.*, 1978a; Dutton *et al.*, 1978a; Ingledew and Moore, 1979; Mukohata and Packer, 1979).

It is largely accepted today that the conservation of redox energy in respiration and photosynthetic (see Hauska and Trebst, 1977; Crofts *et al.*, 1975) electron transport takes place by a process in which the net translocation of hydrogen ions across an energy-transducing biomembrane plays an essential part. This conceptual development can be largely ascribed to the theoretical and experimental breakthrough of Mitchell's chemiosmotic theory of oxidative and photosynthetic phosphorylation (Mitchell, 1961, 1966, 1968, 1976a; Greville, 1969). We must not, however, be deceived by the success of this concept to regard the problem of biological energy conservation as solved. While we may accept the general idea that a current of protons makes an energetic connection between oxidoreduction and ATP synthesis, the following fundamental questions still remain largely unresolved:

1. How is the protonic potential $(\Delta\bar{\mu}_{H^+})$[1] generated by the redox reactions?
2. How is this potential utilized by the ATP synthase?

---

[1] *Abbreviations and Symbols:* C side, C phase, outer (cytoplasmic) side or phase of the mitochondrial inner membrane; E_h, Oxidoreduction potential relative to the standard hydrogen electrode; E_m, midpoint or half-reduction redox potential; ΔE_h, difference in redox potential, redox potential span; FCCP, carbonylcyanide p-trifluoromethoxyphenylhydrazone (classical uncoupling agent); HOQNO, 2-n-Heptyl-4-hydroxyquinoline-N-oxide (respiratory

3. Is the "protonic connection" between oxidoreductions and ATP synthesis made purely osmotically (Mitchell, 1968, 1977a)? Could it be made in a more localized fashion through the membrane proper or its interphases (Williams, 1973, 1974, 1975; Kell, 1979), by direct interactions between redox proteins and ATP synthase (Boyer, 1965, 1974; Chance, 1972; Ernster, 1977; Slater, 1972a), or perhaps by both localized and delocalized routes in parallel (see, e.g., Padan and Rottenberg, 1973; Rottenberg et al., 1967)?

It is interesting that all these questions are asked at the level of *molecular mechanism,* and we note that the problem of oxidative phosphorylation (and photosynthetic phosphorylation) is not solved at that level.

In this chapter we are concerned only with the first question above, which represents the most fundamental event in energy conservation by respiratory and photosynthetic organisms. Because of limited space and the traditions of this laboratory, we will discuss only mitochondrial H⁺ translocation. For reviews on the photosynthetic and bacterial systems, the reader is referred to the articles by Crofts and Wood (1977), Dutton et al. (1978b), Hauska and Trebst (1977), Witt (1978), and Harold (1977), respectively. The likelihood may be emphasized, however, that redox-linked proton translocation may occur by similar molecular principles, whether respiratory or photosynthetic in origin.

Concluding this introductory section, it cannot be too strongly stressed that the molecular mechanisms of redox-linked proton translocation must be most intimately related to the mechanisms of biological electron and hydrogen transfer. It is strongly believed that neither process can be fully understood without understanding of the other.

In the sections to follow we will briefly discuss the major proposed molecular mechanisms of proton translocation. Then follows an assessment of the experimental approaches and results on mitochondrial proton

---

chain inhibitor); H⁺/P$_i$ symport, transport process leading to coupled uptake of H⁺ and H$_2$PO$_4^-$, i.e., net uptake of H$_3$PO$_4$; J_0, rate of redox reaction; rate of respiration; L_o, coupling constant relating J_0 to its driving force (ΔG), M side, M phase, inner (matrix) side of the inner mitochondrial membrane; n_0, stoichiometric numbering relating proton translocation of electron flow; pH$_0$, pH of extramitochondrial space; outside pH; S, oxidized substrate of the respiratory chain; SH$_2$, reduced, hydrogenated substrate of the respiratory chain; ΔG, Gibbs free energy difference (products minus reactants); ΔG_{0x}, Gibbs free energy difference for a redox reaction; ΔG_p, Gibbs free energy difference for ADP phosphorylation (phosphate potential); Δp, proton motive force (see also $\Delta\bar{\mu}_{H^+}$); ΔpH, transmembrane (outside minus inside) pH difference; $\Delta\bar{\mu}_{H^+}$, transmembrane (outside *minus* inside) difference in electrochemical proton potential; electrochemical proton gradient; proton motive force; $\Delta\psi$, transmembrane (outside *minus* inside) difference in electrostatic potential; membrane potential; μ, electrochemical potential.

translocation and its stoichiometry, as linked to oxidoreduction in different segments of the respiratory chain. After a brief review of proton translocation in submitochondrial particles and in purified respiratory chain segments that have been "reconstituted" into liposomes, we conclude by discussing some molecular and topological aspects of proton translocation linked to the function of the cytochrome aa_3 and bc_1 complexes. In this connection we have intentionally left out the NADH–ubiquinone reductase segment, which at present seems to be less studied than the "cytochrome chain" and for which the stoichiometry of H^+ translocation seems to be the least certain (Section VII,C). However, for proposals of the H^+-translocating function of this complex, see De Vault (1976), Garland *et al.* (1972), Ohnishi (1973, 1975), Ragan (1976), Singer and Gutman (1971).

II. H^+ Translocation: Principles and Definitions

A. THE REDOX LOOP

In connection with and intimately linked to the proposal of the chemiosmotic theory, Mitchell also proposed the redox or o/r loop principle of redox-linked proton translocation (Mitchell, 1961, 1966, 1968, 1972, 1976a). Although this proposal is not an obligatory part of the more general theory (see Mitchell, 1976a), it has been strongly associated with it, primarily as a result of vigorous support of it (Mitchell, 1979; Mitchell and Moyle, 1979a,b).

The essence of the redox loop is that the redox centers of the respiratory chain (i.e., hemes, nonheme iron, FAD, FMN, copper, and ubiquinone) are *themselves so organized* with respect to the membrane's electroosmotic barrier (not necessarily the membrane proper as it is seen in the electron microscope) that (*a*) hydrogen transfer alternates with electron transfer; and (*b*) H and e^- transfer reactions are vectorially oriented *across the electroosmotic barrier* [see also concepts of group translocation and ligand conduction (Mitchell, 1977b, 1979)].

With these premises, protonations and deprotonations take place on opposite sides of the barrier (membrane), so that flow of reducing equivalents across a loop yields net translocation of H^+ with generation of both an electrical ($\Delta\psi$) and a chemical (ΔpH) gradient, which together constitute the electrochemical proton gradient ($\Delta\bar{\mu}_{H^+}$), or the proton motive force (Δp), analogous to the situation in a fuel cell.

An important experimentally testable feature of the redox loop is that it catalyzes net translocation of not more than 1 H^+ per redox equivalent transferred across it. Thus the number of redox loops in the respiratory chain should coincide with the number of H^+ ions translocated per transferred electron. This is precisely where the large experimental controversies lie at present: Are the stoichiometries of proton translocation compatible with the redox loop model, or are they not?

At this point it may be stressed that in a redox loop the proton is translocated by electroneutral "symport" with the electron (as translocation of hydrogen), whereas the charge is translocated in a *separate molecular event* by electron translocation in the opposite direction. Thus the proton–electron symport in a redox loop is typically the resultant of *direct linkage* between the two particles as in classical reduced hydrogen carriers, such as ubiquinol (Mitchell, 1977a). Mitchell has stressed repeatedly the logical and strategic superiority (see, e.g., Mitchell, 1979) of the direct redox loop type of coupling between oxidoreduction and proton translocation, over the alternative concept of less direct coupling, such as in a redox-linked proton pump (see Section II,B). However, the number of known "classical" hydrogen carriers is limited in the respiratory chain. It may even be discussed to what extent electron–proton coupling is necessarily much different in hydrogen carriers, such as ubiquinone or flavin, than it may be in the cytochromes of A and B type, which show pH-dependent midpoint redox potentials (Straub and Colpa-Boonstra, 1962; Artzatbanov *et al.*, 1978; Urban and Klingenberg, 1969; Van Gelder *et al.*, 1977; Wilson *et al.*, 1972a,b). Both in ubiquinol and in reduced FAD or FMN, the electrons are delocalized and spend only part of the time around the atom to which the proton is bound. With this we wish to point out that the distinction between direct and indirect coupling (Mitchell, 1977a) of proton translocation to electron transfer is not sharp but continuous. Therefore, redox centers formally of the electron transfer type (e.g., hemes) may be linked to proton translocation just as "naturally" as the hydrogen carriers, although the proton does not bind to ferrous iron. The proton, however, may yet be closely linked to the electron, for instance by binding to an axial ligand of the heme iron or to other groups in the vicinity provided by the apoprotein (Wikström and Krab, 1978a). It seems to us that a strict division of proton–electron coupling into direct and indirect categories is a rather artificial classification of linked phenomena that may occur on a continuous scale of particle distances, only one extreme of which is exemplified by the notion of direct coupling.

A more distinct feature of the redox loop is the direction of the redox reaction itself *across* the membrane. As pointed out by Mitchell (1977a), the distances traversed in this way by the reducing equivalents need not be as long as the thickness of the phospholipid bilayer (as they are usually drawn schematically), but may be minimal owing to proton channel or well structures in the respiratory chain complexes. In any case, and in contrast to general belief, such transmembranous electron translocation has not been unequivocally demonstrated in any single case for the mitochondrial respiratory chain (see Section VIII,A and Wikström and Krab, 1979a).

In the concept of group translocation advanced by Mitchell (see, e.g., Mitchell, 1977b, 1979), it is emphasized that the spatially specific transfer of a chemical group from donor to acceptor moiety on an enzyme's surface (a process that must be intrinsically vectorial with respect to the frame of the enzyme molecule), may be specifically directed across a biomembrane to yield automatic coupling between metabolism and transport. This would be achieved only by organization of the enzyme molecule in and through the membrane in such a way that the ligand conduction path is directed transmembranously. Clearly, this is the more general principle of which the redox loop concept is the best-known example. However, from the recent studies of electron transport, catalyzed by cytochrome oxidase (Section VIII,A) or the cytochrome bc_1 complex (Section VIII,B), it may be concluded that transmembranous electron (group) translocation finds little experimental support as the basis of redox-linked proton transport in mitochondria. It may be, for instance, that the group translocation idea, as applied to electron transport, is too simplified in the sense that it regards electron transfer centers merely as an array of electron conductors. Much less consideration is given to functions known to be linked to biological electron transport, such as protolysis and geometric adjustments of the redox centers and their apoproteins (conformational changes).

It may be relevant to point out in this connection that electron conduction across phospholipid membranes does not seem to require complicated structures, such as the cytochrome oxidase and cytochrome bc_1 complexes, but may be demonstrated in very simple artificial systems, as elegantly shown by Hinkle (1973).

B. THE PROTON PUMP

The simplest case of a redox-linked proton pump is so defined that, although the transfer of reducing equivalents may proceed in a direction that is indifferent with respect to the electroosmotic barrier of the membrane (but yet, of course, vectorially), this reaction is linked, or geared, through what may be rather loosely called conformational interactions in the redox protein complex, to translocation of H^+ across the membrane. Here we may distinguish between so-called Bohr-type coupling or linkage (see Chance et al., 1970; Papa, 1976; Wyman, 1948, 1968), which implies long-range (interpolypeptide) distances between centers of redox and H^+ transfer, and a more direct type of coupling taking cytochrome c as model, where the H^+ transfer center is in the immediate vicinity of the redox center (Wikström and Krab, 1978a, 1979a). Again (cf. preceding section), and now perhaps more easily, it is realized that a whole range of coupling distances are possible, and it may indeed by advisable as a research strategy (see Mitchell 1976b, 1979) to consider first the possibilities of short-range coupling, as these may be easier to tackle experimentally. It seems clear, however, from the recent research on the cytochrome oxidase segment of the repsiratory chain (Wikström and Krab, 1979a; see also Sections VII,A and VIII,A), that there is sufficient experimental basis for seriously considering a proton pump type of mechanism of H^+ translocation in the respiratory chain, and that simple electron translocation cannot explain the function of this enzyme.

From the foregoing it is obvious that the proton pump type of linked function is fundamentally different from that of the redox loop. The structural (or conformational) aspects are in the foreground simply owing to the necessity of "gearing" the redox reaction to H^+ translocation (and not merely H^+ association or release), and because this mechanism requires H^+-conducting channels in the redox proteins (Läuger, 1979; Wikström and Krab, 1979a). The possible chemistry of such channels has been recently discussed (Williams, 1975; Nagle and Morowitz, 1978). Instead of some "directional freedom" of the redox reaction proper as compared to the case in a redox loop, the electron transfer reactions themselves become particularly important owing to their obligatory coupling to H^+ translocation. This is now not merely a matter of positioning the redox centers with respect to the electroosmotic barrier, but puts interesting demands on the molecular linkage between the electron transfer and H^+ translocation (Wikström and Krab, 1979a).

C. Definitions

To prevent misunderstanding, it may be useful stringently to define the terms and symbols that we shall use to describe the different phenomena associated with respiration-linked translocation of protons.

Phenomenologically, we can distinguish between uptake of protons, translocation of electrical charges, and release of protons. We will use the symbols defined in Table I, together with specification of the segment of the respiratory chain in question, in describing experiments on proton translocation. The proton-translocating segments between NADH and ubiquinone, between ubiquinone (or succinate) and cytochrome c, and between cytochrome c and oxygen, are sometimes also referred to as coupling sites 1,2, and 3, respectively. As specified in Table I, we use the

TABLE I

OPERATIONAL TERMS AND SYMBOLS FOR RESPIRATION-LINKED PROTON
TRANSLOCATION[a]

	Per e^-	Per O (or $2e^-$)	Direction when linked to forward e^- transport
Proton uptake	$\overrightarrow{H}^+/e^-$	$\overrightarrow{H}^+/O$	From M side
Proton release	$\overleftarrow{H}^+/e^-$	$\overleftarrow{H}^+/O$	To C side
Transfer of (positive) electrical charge	$\overleftarrow{q}^+/O$	$\overleftarrow{q}^+/O$	From M side to C side

[a] The respiratory chain segment for which the symbol is used must be specified.

natural orientation of the mitochondrial membrane as reference for direction, whether mitochondria, submitochondrial particles (in which the orientation of the membrane, and of transport, is inverted, the M side being outside), or reconstituted systems are discussed. We have adopted the convention that proton release occurs from right to left (e.g., $\overleftarrow{H}^+$) and proton uptake from left to right (e.g., $\overrightarrow{H}^+$), and that the translocation of electrical charge occurs as translocation of positive charge from right to left (i.e., $\overleftarrow{q}^+$). In some cases we use symbols such as H^+/e^- or H^+/O without specification of direction. This refers to truly translocated protons including uptake, charge translocation, and release. We strongly discourage the use of terms such as $H^+/site$ or $H^+/\sim$ (which refer to the average value of $\overleftarrow{H}^+/2e^-$ per classical coupling site of oxidative phosphorylation), since these quotients are different for the different "sites," as we shall see later. In this article these notations will be used only when considered necessary for clarity.

III. Translocation of Protons and Electrical Charge: Experimental Standpoints

In this section we review the present standpoints on the stoichiometry of mitochondrial proton translocation separately for the different segments of the respiratory chain. We cite the earlier literature only when there appears to be particular reason to do so. Readers who wish to acquaint themselves with the earlier work in detail are recommended to consult the comprehensive review by Papa (1976).

A. A NOTE ON EARLY WORK

Part of the confusion on the stoichiometry of mitochondrial proton and charge translocation may be the result of the convention to report rounded-up data on the average number of H^+ or q^+ translocated "per site." Here the implicit assumption has been made that this number is meaningful owing to identical stoichiometries for the individual coupling sites. According to recent findings (Brand *et al.*, 1978; Wikström and Krab, 1978a, 1979a), this assumption is likely to be incorrect.

With reference to earlier work, it is often concluded that the charge translocation stoichiometry of mitochondrial respiration has been demonstrated to be $4q^+$ "per site." This conclusion is often (see, e.g., Pozzan *et al.*, 1979) made on the basis of work by Cockrell *et al.* (1966), Rossi *et al.* (1967), Rossi and Azzone (1969), and Azzone and Massari (1971). However, a careful inspection of these papers does not yield such a firm conclusion. Thus Cockrell *et al.* found a "K^+/site" quotient of about 3 with NADH-linked substrates, Rossi and Azzone found a "K^+/site" quotient of 2.8 with succinate as substrate if the actual rate of oxygen consumption was taken as the basis for the calculation, and this ratio increased to 4.1 if only the *increase* in oxygen consumption was taken into account upon addition of valinomycin. It is very doubtful whether that convention is correct (see Section III,B,3). Rossi *et al.* (1967) reported that the ratio of H^+ to K^+ transport was near unity when care was taken to prevent accumulation of substrate. This finding neither supports, nor does it contradict, a "K^+/site" quotient of 4. However, from their Fig. 6 (Rossi *et al.*, 1967) it can be seen that they observed a "K^+/site" ratio of about 3. In the only remaining paper by Azzone and Massari (1971) the "K^+/site" ratio was reported to be 3.6 when calculated on the total rate of oxygen consumption. This report disagrees with the earlier findings (Cockrell *et al.*, 1966; Rossi *et al.*, 1967; Rossi and Azzone, 1969), in part from the same laboratory, and also it is not possible to scrutinize it in detail since no original experimental traces were presented and insufficient detail was given on calibration and kinetic response of the oxygen and potassium electrodes (cf. Wikström and Krab, 1979a and Section III,B,3).

Another older set of data often referred to in this connection concerns the stoichiometry of calcium accumulation, usually given as Ca/O quotients (calcium accumulated per oxygen consumed). It is generally stated that a stoichiometry of "2Ca/site" has been established, usually with reference to papers by Rossi and Lehninger (1964) and Chance (1965). However, Chance reported that the Ca/O ratio is between 2.5 and 3 for succinate respiration, and about 3.8 for glutamate respiration, corresponding to "calcium per site" quotients of 1.25–1.5 and 1.27, respectively (and to "charge per site" quotients of 2.5–3 and 2.5, respectively).

Rossi and Lehninger (1964) measured the calcium uptake quotient relating uptake of the cation to the "extra" uptake of oxygen elicited by addition of calcium. Again, it is highly questionable (cf. above for K^+ uptake) whether this is the correct procedure (Nicholls, 1977; see also Section III,B,3). Moreover, no oligomycin was present to prevent calcium uptake coupled to hydrolysis of endogenous ATP (see Brand and Lehninger, 1975), which may easily have enhanced the observed stoichiometry.

We conclude that the earlier evidence for an average "charge per site" stoichiometry of 4, measured either on the basis of K^+ or Ca^{2+} uptake, is highly dubious. These experiments seem to indicate, however, that there may be separation of more than 4 electrical charges per $2e^-$ flowing from succinate to oxygen, and of more than 6 charges per $2e^-$ for the span between NADH and oxygen. In our view these data therefore do give an indication that the stoichiometries proposed by Mitchell (see, e.g., Mitchell, 1976a), i.e., "$2q^+$/site," may be underestimated (cf. Azzone *et al.*, 1977).

B. The Span between Succinate (Ubiquinol) and Oxygen

1. Oxidant-Pulse Measurements

H^+ translocation linked to electron transfer through this respiratory chain segment was first measured by Mitchell and Moyle (1967a) using the O_2-pulse relaxation method (cf. Section V). They found a H^+/O stoichiometry very near 4, which was reported to be independent of pH_0 in the range 5.5–8.5 and of replacing the 150 mM KCl medium with 250 mM sucrose, or the K^+ with choline chloride (contrast below).

Mitchell and Moyle took particular care to exclude that symport of H^+ and inorganic phosphate may have caused an underestimation of the stoichiometry, but Brand *et al.* (1976a) nevertheless found that although they could reproduce the findings of Mitchell and Moyle under their conditions, the $\overleftarrow{H}^+/O$ quotient rose to near 6 by four kinds of manipulations, all of which would be expected to prevent H^+/P_i symport. Thus the stoichiometry was apparently enhanced with N-ethylmaleimide or mersalyl at concentrations where these sulfhydryl reagents block the phosphate carrier. Furthermore, a similar rise was observed after depletion of the mitochondria of their endogenous P_i, or at low temperatures, where the P_i carrier is expected to be more highly inhibited than electron transport and proton translocation. In both the latter cases, the $\overleftarrow{H}^+/O$ quotient near 6 was not enhanced any further by N-ethylmaleimide.

The simplest conclusion from these findings is that under the conditions of the O_2-pulse experiments, H^+/P_i symport must take place at a very fast rate early during the net H^+ ejection phase, so that the loss of H^+ ions in this manner back across the membrane remains uncorrected by the usual extrapolation of the decay of the H^+ ejection (Brand *et al.*, 1976a). In support of this conclusion, Wikström and Krab (1978b, 1979a) have shown that N-ethylmaleimide indeed abolishes a lag in net H^+ ejection, which occurs in a time domain 10–150 msec after addition of O_2. It is suggested that his very fast burst of H^+/P_i symporter activity is the result of the corresponding initially very fast burst of respiration (see Section V,A), leading to a rapid rise in intramitochondrial pH, which is the main determinant of ΔpH under these conditions, ΔpH being, in turn, the "motive force" for P_i translocation. In addition to these findings, Brand *et al.* (1976a) showed directly that in the absence of N-ethylmaleimide there is indeed a very fast uptake of P_i to an extent that is easily compatible with a considerable lowering of the observed $\overleftarrow{H}^+/O$ quotient. We find it unfortunate that, in spite of these very valuable observations by Brand *et al.*, the significance of these findings should continue to be explained away by postulating extra release of protons from the ubiquinol system (Mitchell and Moyle, 1979b) or preferential oxidation of NADPH through the proton-translocating transhydrogenase (Moyle and Mitchell, 1978b; Mitchell and Moyle, 1979b; Mitchell, 1979), as induced by N-ethylmaleimide (see below and Sections III,D and V,A).

   In contrast to their earlier findings (Mitchell and Moyle, 1967a), Mitchell and Moyle (1979b) have more recently also found $\overleftarrow{H}^+/O$ quotients higher than 4 in the span between succinate and oxygen, not only with N-ethylmaleimide but also at low pH_0 or in the presence of choline chloride. However, the observed quotient was not much higher than 5 under their conditions. The "extra" proton was ascribed to arise from some unidentified reaction in the ubiquinone–cytochrome b segment that would somehow be favored by N-ethylmaleimide, or by the other experimental conditions reported to enhance the stoichiometry in a nonadditive fashion. The authors unfortunately did not consider the simple explanation that the various perturbations found to enhance the $\overleftarrow{H}^+/O$ ratio may simply have resulted in less leakage of P_i out of the mitochondria, or in an inhibition of the H^+/P_i symporter.

   The explanation offered by Mitchell and Moyle (1979b) contrasts to their finding that the $\overleftarrow{H}^+/2e^-$ quotient was only 4 in the span between succinate and cytochrome c (using ferricyanide as electron acceptor in place of oxygen), while it may be expected to rise to 5 if the "extra" proton arose from activity of the ubiquinone–cytochrome b segment. This inconsistency was recognized, but explained to be due to a lower rate of electron transport with ferricyanide as acceptor than with oxygen. This explanation is interesting and may require some further discussion.

   In the O_2-pulse type of experiment, the concept of respiratory rate is intricate (see Section V,A). The rate of consumption of the small aliquot of oxygen added is not constant, but is characterized by three distinct phases of very different velocity. These phases are due to (a) extremely rapid oxidation of cytochrome $c + c_1$ and other terminal carriers; (b) rapid oxidation of ubiquinol and components of the bc_1 complex on the substrate side of the antimycin block; and finally (c) much slower oxidation of substrate. Only this latter rate is comparable to the steady-state rate generally observed in aerobic respiring mitochondria, whereas the former are much faster (Penniston, 1972; Chance et al., 1965; see also Section V,A).

The statement by Mitchell and Moyle (1979b) that ferricyanide reduction occurred at a rate only 25% of that with O_2 as acceptor is surprising, since ferricyanide reduction by mitochondria in the steady state and at high concentrations of ferricyanide is much faster than the rate of oxygen consumption (Lee et al., 1967). As shown by Estabrook (1961), the apparent K_m for ferricyanide in accepting electrons from endogenous cytochrome c is about 10–15 μM, which is comparable to the concentrations used in ferricyanide pulse experiments (see Mitchell and Moyle, 1967b). From the data presented by Lee et al. (1967), it may be calculated that the half-maximal rate of ferricyanide reduction by succinate in the steady state is about three-fourths of the steady-state rate of oxygen consumption. It is therefore likely that the finding by Mitchell and Moyle is based on *average* rates of ferricyanide reduction and oxygen consumption. Since in the oxidant-pulse type of experiments a very limited amount of oxidant is added in comparison with the amount of reduced respiratory carriers, a large proportion of the added oxygen is consumed by an extremely fast rate. This does not occur on pulsing with ferricyanide, which intervenes at the stage of cytochrome c, so that the average rate of ferricyanide reduction will consequently be much slower than the average rate of oxygen consumption that is observed (Mitchell and Moyle, 1979b). But since this is hardly due to slower electron transport in the ubiquinol–cytochrome b segment, it follows that the observed lower $\overleftarrow{H}^+/2e^-$ ratio with ferricyanide as acceptor cannot be explained on that basis. On the other hand, this result can be explained as a result of proton-pumping by cytochrome oxidase (Wikström and Krab, 1979a). The effect of HOQNO on the $\overleftarrow{H}^+/O$ quotient (Mitchell and Moyle, 1979b) is discussed separately in Section III,D.

2. Reductant-Pulse Measurements

Lawford and Garland (1973) pulsed aerobic rotenone-treated beef heart mitochondria with reduced quinones. From the extent of extramitochondrial acidification, they calculated a $\overleftarrow{H}^+/O$ value close to 4. However, this value was arrived at only after correction of the fast backflow of H^+ into the mitochondria (see later).

Papa et al. (1977) have reported similar experiments, but their observed $\overleftarrow{H}^+/O$ quotients varied between 2 and 10 depending on the pH of the suspending medium. The reason for this is unclear, and more work may be required to confirm and extend these findings.

Wikström and Krab (1978a) reported experiments in which initial rates of duroquinol oxidation, oxygen uptake, and H^+ extrusion were measured in well coupled rat liver mitochondria. $\overleftarrow{H}/O$ (or per quinone formed, measured spectrophotometrically) was observed to be just below 6 in agreement with the O_2-pulse experiments of Brand *et al.* (1976a) with succinate as substrate. The lower values found by Lawford and Garland (1973) may be due in part to H^+/P_i symport, which was not blocked in the experiments; in part to the fact that beef heart mitochondria are generally less well coupled than rat liver mitochondria; and perhaps to the high rates of electron transport. In the latter case rapid alkalinization of the matrix space results in unexpectedly high rates of backflow of H^+, which no longer follow the simple linear diffusion equations used by Lawford and Garland to correct their results (see Krab and Wikström, 1979).

A $\overleftarrow{H^+}/O$ quotient near 6 has also been observed using an inhibitor-stop method in which the steady-state rate of succinate oxidation is related to the initial rate of proton uptake after a sudden respiratory blockade (Wikström and Krab, 1978a).

3. High $\overleftarrow{H^+}/O$ and $\overleftarrow{q^+}/O$ Ratios

Lehninger and collaborators have claimed that even higher values than $6\overleftarrow{H^+}/O$ (up to $8\overleftarrow{H^+}/O$) are obtained for succinate respiration both with the O_2-pulse technique (Lehninger *et al.*, 1977) and in initial-rate determinations (Brand *et al.*, 1976b; Reynafarje *et al.*, 1976; Reynafarje and Lehninger, 1977, 1978; Vercesi *et al.*, 1978). It was suggested that the lower value of $6\overleftarrow{H^+}/O$ in O_2-pulse experiments is due to swelling of the mitochondria in the salt media, and that values near 8 are obtained in media composed of sucrose and KCl. In extensive experiments conducted in this laboratory, we have been unable to reproduce these findings, but find $\overleftarrow{H^+}/O$ quotients near 6.0 (in the presence of N-ethylmaleimide) in O_2-pulse experiments also in sucrose–KCl media. The high quotients obtained from initial-rate measurements are likely to be overestimated owing to kinetic limitations of the Clark oxygen electrode (see Wikström and Krab, 1979a, and below).

Measurements of the charge translocation stoichiometry is seemingly an independent method to determine the stoichiometry of proton translocation. However, to obtain the correct stoichiometry the ion uptake process must nevertheless be related to the rate or extent of corresponding electron transport. Thus, if the latter measurement is underestimated, too high stoichiometries will be obtained whether H^+ ejection or uptake of K^+ or Ca^{2+} is measured.

As concluded in Section III,A, it is highly questionable whether the early data on K^+ and Ca^{2+} transport may be taken as support for the notion of a $\bar{q}^+/O$ ratio of "4 per site." However, more recently the stoichiometry of calcium uptake has been reexamined by Lehninger and associates (Brand et al., 1976c; Reynafarje and Lehninger, 1977; Vercesi et al., 1978), and a stoichiometry of 4 Ca^{2+} per oxygen atom reduced has been reported for succinate oxidation. The measurements have been made either on the basis of the extents or the rates of calcium uptake and oxygen consumption, respectively. There are two very pertinent objections against the use of the former approach. First, superficial binding of calcium to the membrane was not considered, which leads to overestimation of the Ca/O quotient (Nicholls, 1977). The second objection is more serious and is also pertinent to several measurements of K^+ translocation stoichiometries (see Section III,A). The oxygen consumption on which the stoichiometry was based is the "extra" oxygen uptake upon addition of calcium (see, e.g., Brand et al., 1976c), not the total oxygen consumption during calcium accumulation. As pointed out by Nicholls (1977), the $\Delta\bar{\mu}_{H^+}$ decreases dramatically on addition of calcium to respiring mitochondria (owing to a fall in $\Delta\psi$) so that the rate of respiration prior to the addition of the cation (or of valinomycin in the presence of K^+), which is mainly due to H^+ leakage driven by the high $\Delta\bar{\mu}_{H^+}$ in state 4, cannot be considered to persist in the new steady state during cation accumulation. Hence, the cation accumulation must be related to the *total* oxygen consumption to yield the correct stoichiometry.[2] As shown by Nicholls (1977), the Ca/O quotient drops to between 2.5 and 3 when these factors are taken into account. It may also be calculated from the data of Vercesi et al. (1978, Fig. 1) that the Ca/O quotient drops from near 4 to between 2.5 and 3 if the quotient is calculated on the basis of total oxygen consumption rather than on the "extra" oxygen.

Ca/O quotients have also been determined on the basis of *rates* of calcium uptake and oxygen consumption (Reynafarje and Lehninger, 1977; Vercesi et al., 1978). However, these measurements, which have also yielded Ca/O quotients close to 4, are beset with the great difficulty that the initial rate of oxygen consumption must be measured with the membrane-covered Clark electrode, which is very prone to underestimate such rates (see Wikström and Krab, 1979a, and below). This suspicion is, in fact, substantiated by the conspicuously low rates reported for both rat liver and rat heart mitochondria in these studies during active calcium transport. Rate measurements in our laboratory have consistently yielded Ca/O quotients near 3 for succinate respiration in agreement with the measurements by Nicholls (1977) based on reaction extents.

---

[2] This does not apply to determinations of the ADP/O ratio, since $\Delta\bar{\mu}_{H^+}$ is not much lowered upon transition to state 3 (Mitchell and Moyle, 1969; Nicholls, 1974).

There are also more recent studies of the ratio of potassium uptake to electron transport (Reynafarje and Lehninger, 1978; Pozzan *et al.*, 1979) as measured from initial rates during succinate oxidation in mitochondria. Both groups report a K$^+$/O quotient very close to 8 under optimal conditions in comparable experiments. The nature of such experiments may best be evaluated by studying the data of Reynafarje and Lehninger (1978; Fig. 1), who showed original experimental recordings of K$^+$ uptake, H$^+$ ejection, and oxygen consumption. The inspection reveals that it was necessary to evaluate the rate of respiration from the initial 6–7-second period after addition of succinate. As shown directly by Wikström and Krab (1979a), this is, however, a gross overestimation of the kinetic capabilities of a Clark oxygen electrode. It is considered imperative that these studies be repeated with an oxygen electrode that is kinetically competent in comparison with the K$^+$ and H$^+$ electrodes. The electrode used recently by Sigel and Carafoli (1978) appears to fulfil these kinetic requirements, but has so far been used only in the evaluation of H$^+$ and K$^+$ transport stoichiometries in the cytochrome c–O$_2$ span (see Section III,D). It may be considered diagnostic, however, that the stoichiometries found by Sigel and Carafoli for this span are considerably lower than those reported by Lehninger *et al.* and Azzone *et al.* for the same span using the conventional O$_2$ electrode (Alexandre *et al.*, 1978; Pozzan *et al.*, 1979). (See Note Added in Proof.)

We conclude that the $\overleftarrow{H}^+$/O and $\overleftarrow{q}^+$/O stoichiometry is most likely to equal 6 for the span between succinate (or ubiquinol) and O$_2$.

C. THE SPAN BETWEEN SUCCINATE (OR UBIQUINOL) AND CYTOCHROME c

This span of the respiratory chain corresponds to the classical coupling site 2 and may be studied separately from the other sites by using ferricyanide as oxidant, accepting electrons from endogenous cytochrome c (see Lee *et al.*, 1967; Estabrook, 1961). This may either be done anaerobically by initiating the reaction with an anaerobic aliquot of ferricyanide (Mitchell and Moyle, 1967b), or aerobically after blockage of the cytochrome oxidase reaction with cyanide. Electron transfer may be measured by recording the reduction of ferricyanide spectrophotometrically, and H$^+$ or other cation movements may be measured either by ion-specific electrodes or spectrophotometrically using metallochromic or pH indicators.

It is interesting that the observed stoichiometries of both proton and charge translocation for this segment are in full agreement in all laboratories concerned. Thus electron transport is coupled to ejection of 2H$^+$ ions per transferred electron, while the $\overleftarrow{q}^+$/e$^-$ stoichiometry is unity (Mitchell and Moyle, 1967b; Lehninger *et al.*, 1979; Pozzan *et al.*, 1979; Papa *et al.*, 1977; Wikström and Krab, 1978a). The only exception to this rule is provided by the interesting findings of Papa and co-workers (Papa *et al.*, 1977) that the apparent $\overleftarrow{H}^+/e^-$ quotient is raised to values well above 2 as the external pH is raised above 8.5. However, this finding may require further experimental study before any firm conclusions can be reached.

It may be commented here that the observed $\overleftarrow{q}^+/e^-$ stoichiometry of 1 for this span disagrees with the proposal by Moyle and Mitchell (1977) that calcium is taken up effectively as the monovalent species Ca^+ (but see Saris and Åkerman article in this volume). If this were the case, the observed Ca/e^- quotient should be 1.0 for this span, contrary to the Ca/e^- quotient of 0.5 reported by Pozzan *et al.* (1979) and confirmed in this laboratory (M. K. F. Wikström, unpublished observations).

What may be the reasons for this general agreement upon the stoichiometry of proton translocation for "site 2", while considerable controversy exists for the segments that include cytochrome oxidase? We suggest that such reasons may include (*a*) the less extensive intramito-chondrial alkalinization per transferred electron across the "site 2" segment, decreasing the risk of H^+ backflow and H^+/P_i symport; and (*b*) , that the method of determining the rate of electron transport is much less vulnerable to kinetic and calibration artifacts as compared to the determination of oxygen consumption. It seems that the controversy for the span between ubiquinone and oxygen arises mainly from differences concerning the cytochrome oxidase reaction, as is indeed verified below.

D. THE SPAN BETWEEN CYTOCHROME c AND OXYGEN

We have recently comprehensively reviewed the evidence originated in this laboratory that cytochrome oxidase functions as a proton pump with a $\overleftarrow{H}^+/e^-$ stoichiometry of 1 and a $\overleftarrow{q}^+/e^-$ stoichiometry of 2 (Wikström and Krab, 1979a). Fully consistent evidence for this notion has been obtained not only with intact mitochondria, but also with submitochondrial particles (Wikström and Saari, 1977; Sorgato and Ferguson, 1978; Sorgato *et al.*, 1978) and with isolated and purified oxidase reconstituted into the membranes of artificial liposomes (Wikström and Saari, 1977; Krab and Wikström, 1978; Casey *et al.*, 1979; Sigel and Carafoli, 1979; see also Section VII,A).

However, two schools question the validity of these experiments and conclusions; both have studied the cytochrome oxidase reaction almost exclusively in intact mitochondria. First, Mitchell and Moyle (1978, 1979a; Moyle and Mitchell, 1978a,b) maintain that cytochrome oxidase merely translocates electrons so that the $\overleftarrow{H}^+/e^-$ stoichiometry is nil and the $\bar{q}^+/e^-$ stoichiometry is equal to unity, and that the observations reported from this and other laboratories are "explained by an unfortunate combination of experimental and interpretational difficulties" (Mitchell and Moyle, 1979b). This criticism has been dealt with in detail (see Wikström and Krab, 1978b,c, 1979a,b) and has been shown to be unfounded. However, many of the conclusions reached by Mitchell and Moyle have been supported more recently by Lorusso *et al* (1979), whose findings will be scrutinized below.

The other school comprises the group of Azzone *et al.* in Padua (see Azzone *et al.*, 1978b, 1979; Pozzan *et al.*, 1979) and the group of Lehninger *et al.* in Baltimore (see Alexandre *et al.*, 1978; Lehninger *et al.*, 1977, 1978, 1979), who, while they agree with the proposal of cytochrome oxidase as a proton pump, claim that the $\overleftarrow{H}^+/e^-$ stoichiometry is 2 and that the $\bar{q}^+/e^-$ stoichiometry is 3. We have recently discussed the data of Alexandre *et al.* (1978) in detail (see Wikström and Krab, 1979a), and found that their observed stoichiometries are likely to be overestimated because of underestimation of electron transport rates. Their suggestion (and cf. Pozzan *et al.*, 1979) that the lower stoichiometry observed by us would be due to low respiratory rates in our experiments is not valid. Direct controls under the conditions reported by these investigators have failed to support their conclusions (Wikström and Krab, 1979a). Moreover, it has been shown that the backflow of H⁺ into the mitochondria can be accounted for quantitatively, *particularly* at relatively low rates of electron transfer (and proton translocation) (Krab and Wikström, 1979). It is also significant that when special care is taken to record oxygen consumption with a fast-responding oxygen electrode, the $\overleftarrow{H}^+/e^-$ and $\bar{q}^+/e^-$ ratios are found to be near 1 and 2, respectively, even at fast respiratory rates (Sigel and Carafoli, 1978).

It is interesting that although Azzone and collaborators also claim the high stoichiometries for the cytochrome oxidase segment, they actually confirm our data on ferrocyanide respiration and disagree with those of Lehninger and associates. Thus Azzone *et al.* (1978b) found a $\overleftarrow{H}^+/e^-$ stoichiometry near 1 even at high respiratory rates (contrast Alexandre *et al.*, 1978), but observed the higher stoichiometries exclusively when proton ejection is initiated by addition of valinomycin in the presence of ferrocyanide, not vice versa. Unfortunately, it is difficult to evaluate these data because so far only one set of experimental traces has been published (Fig. 2 in Azzone *et al.* 1978b), in which large drifts in the pH traces make it difficult to ascertain whether true rates were measured. Furthermore, the corrections made to account for ferricyanide reduction are uncertain and may have underestimated the electron transport rate. No mention was made as to whether the pH traces were also corrected for such an activity. In the work by Pozzan *et al.* (1979) details were lacking on the calibration and repsonse time of the oxygen electrode at the low temperatures employed. (See Note Added in Proof.)

Lorusso et al. (1979) measured O_2 consumption, ferricyanide generation and H^+ extrusion or uptake in rat liver mitochondria respiring with ferrocyanide (cf. Wikström, 1977; Wikström and Saari, 1977; Wikström and Krab, 1978c; Krab and Wikström, 1979). Under conditions where H^+ ejection was observed, the authors also observed an apparently slow initial phase of ferricyanide generation, the rate of which fell short of the corresponding rate of oxygen consumption. The apparently slow phase was followed by a faster phase in which net ferricyanide formation seemed to occur at a rate comparable with oxygen consumption. In addition, it was reported (and cf. Moyle and Mitchell, 1978a) that under uncoupled conditions the rate of H^+ consumption fell often 20–30% short of the rate of electron transfer measured on the basis of oxygen consumption, but not when measured on the basis of ferricyanide generation (contrast Wikström and Krab, 1978c, 1979a).

If these data were correct they would give strong support to the proposal by Moyle and Mitchell (1978a) that the ferricyanide generated during ferrocyanide oxidation is, in part, re-reduced by hydrogenated mitochondrial reductants on the C side of the membrane, with associated release of H^+ ions. Hence an imbalance of rates of net ferricyanide generation and of proton uptake would be expected with respect to the rate of oxygen consumption, exactly as described by Lorusso et al. (1979).

However, by dividing the rate of observed H^+ ejection in the coupled state by the putative rate of reduction of the generated ferricyanide, values between 1.5 and 3.6 were obtained (Lorusso et al., 1979). Since reduction of ferricyanide by a hydrogen donor on the C side of the membrane can account only for release of $1H^+/e^-$, it was necessary to postulate that the re-reduction of ferricyanide is not only associated with scalar release of protons in this manner, but is also associated with proton translocation (presumably with a stoichiometry varying between 0.5 and 2.6 H^+/e^-) in the "site" 1 and 2 segments of the respiratory chain. This surprising postulate was made (and cf. Moyle and Mitchell, 1978a) notwithstanding the well known fact, which to our knowledge has not up to now been challenged, that rotenone and antimycin block energy transduction completely in these two respective segments of the chain. The ferrocyanide experiments are routinely performed in the presence of these two inhibitors in order to prevent artifacts of precisely the kind now proposed by Lorusso et al. (1979) and Moyle and Mitchell (1978a).

The observed lag in spectrophotometric traces at 420 minus 500 nm ascribed by Lorusso et al. to a lag in net ferricyanide generation and therefore to re-reduction of generated ferricyanide, has also been observed sometimes in this laboratory (M. K. F. Wikström, unpublished observations), but is not usually present (see Wikström, 1977; Papa *et al.*, 1978b). In careful experiments the observed $\widetilde{H}^+/e^-$ quotient is close to unity whether measured on the basis of the rate of ferricyanide generation (Wikström, 1977; Papa *et al.*, 1978b) or on the basis of the rate of oxygen consumption (Wikström and Krab, 1978c; Papa *et al.*, 1978c). This contrasts greatly with the results of Lorusso *et al.* (1979; see also Papa *et al.*, 1978b), in which discrepancies were encountered between rates of oxygen consumption and net ferricyanide generation. We have observed that the lag at 420 *minus* 500 nm, when present, is abolished by using other wavelength couples that are also sensitive to the production of ferricyanide. This phenomenon cannot be due, therefore, to a true lag in net ferricyanide formation as assumed by Lorusso *et al.*, but probably is due to a spectral change or shift in a cytochrome with contribution at 420 nm.

The rate of endogenous antimycin-insensitive oxygen uptake prior to addition of ferrocyanide appears to be very high under the conditions of Lorusso *et al.* (1979). It is at least twice as high, as compared to the rates routinely observed in this laboratory (cf. Moyle and Mitchell, 1978a). More important, however, it seems that the oxygen consumption data of Lorusso *et al.* have not been corrected for this endogenous respiration. This may, in part, account for the observed discrepancies between rates of oxygen and H+ consumption and ferricyanide generation under uncoupled conditions. Furthermore, the authors assume a value of 250 μM O_2 in air-saturated 150 mM KCl at 25°C, which is considerably higher than the values estimated by Chappell (1964) and Mitchell and Moyle (1967a).

Lorusso *et al.* (1979) required 200 pmol of antimycin per milligram of mitochondrial protein to block an apparent impairment of H+ translocation linked to ferrocyanide oxidation after preincubation of the mitochondria in the presence of valinomycin. As shown by Estabrook (1962; see also Slater, 1967a), complete blocking of the bc_1 complex requires only 40–70 pmol of this antibiotic. Therefore it seems possible that the observed decrease in the rate and extent of H+ ejection was due to a high intramitochondrial pH generated by endogenous respiration in the presence of valinomycin. This could be counteracted by the well known weak protonophoric activity of high concentrations of antimycin (see Slater, 1967a).

Papa *et al.* (1978a–c) have repeatedly claimed that H+ ejection linked to ferrocyanide oxidation by rat liver mitochondria cannot be due to cytochrome oxidase function, since the appearance of H+ ions in the C phase is counteracted by HOQNO, which is known to block the bc_1 complex. This view was reiterated by Lorusso *et al.* (1979), who concluded that at HOQNO concentrations sufficient to block net H+ ejection in this system, the increase in proton conductance of the membrane by this compound was insufficient to explain the blockage. This conclusion was reached after comparison of the protonophoric activity of HOQNO with that of the classical uncoupler FCCP, assayed as the rate of proton uptake into mitochondria treated with valinomycin in a medium of low potassium content. Under such conditions the measured H^+ uptake is driven exclusively by the electrical diffusion potential of K^+. However, under the conditions where HOQNO is observed to block net H^+ ejection driven by ferrocyanide oxidation, possible backflow of H^+ ions into the mitochondria will be driven nearly exclusively by the pH gradient (alkaline inside), since the membrane potential is effectively collapsed in these experiments by the presence of K^+ and valinomycin in the medium.

Between 5 and 10 nmol of HOQNO per milligram of mitochondrial protein are required to block net H^+ ejection linked to ferrocyanide oxidation (Lorusso et al., 1979). This should be compared to the requirement of only 0.17 nmol per milligram of protein for complete inhibition of the bc_1 complex (see Slater, 1967a). The concentration of HOQNO used by Papa et al. in the ferrocyanide experiments is, in fact, of the same order of magnitude or higher than the overall extent of H^+ ejection observed in the absence of HOQNO (see, e.g., Lorusso et al., 1979). It is therefore quite possible that the observed effect of these high concentrations of HOQNO is simply an HOQNO/H^+ "symport" driven by the pH gradient and analogous to the well known H^+/P_i symport, with accumulation of the antibiotic with H^+ on the inside of the membrane. Such an effect would be truly uncoupling only under conditions where $\Delta\psi$ is collapsed by some other mechanism (e.g., by valinomycin plus K^+ as in the ferrocyanide experiments), and would go entirely unnoticed in the determinations of protonophoric activity of HOQNO by Lorusso et al. (1979). This possibility, which appears much more likely than a putative inhibition of the bc_1 complex, can be tested directly by application of the acid–base pulse method described in detail by Mitchell and Moyle (1967d).[3] This type of "symport" effect of HOQNO may also account for the findings by Mitchell and Moyle (1979b) that this compound effectively diminishes the $\widetilde{H}^+$/O quotient during succinate oxidation by oxygen.

By titrations with HOQNO (Wikström, 1978) it can be shown that this compound has no effect whatsoever on the *initial rate* of H^+ extrusion linked to ferrocyanide oxidation by mitochondria, but that it merely accel-

---

[3] Using this method we have recently demonstrated unequivocally that HOQNO indeed causes a large increase in the proton permeability of the mitochondrial membrane at concentrations that correspond exactly to those at which this compound abolishes H^+ ejection linked to oxidation of ferrocyanide (Krab and Wikström, 1980).

erates the reuptake of H$^+$ as expected from an uncoupling effect. Azzone *et al.* (1978b) have also shown that HOQNO starts blocking net H$^+$ ejection only at concentrations that are uncoupling, as revealed from stimulation of the state 4 respiratory rate.

E. ENERGETICS AND STOICHIOMETRY OF H$^+$
    TRANSLOCATION IN THE CYTOCHROME CHAIN

The scheme shown in Fig. 1 summarizes our view of proton translocation linked to oxidation of succinate (or ubiquinol) by molecular oxygen, comprising both classical coupling sites 2 and 3 (see also Wikström and Krab, 1978a, 1979a). The figure also indicates the agreement between the proposed stoichiometries of proton translocation and the thermodynamic "balance" between spans of oxidoreduction potentials and the electrochemical proton gradient in state 4 mitochondria.

As pointed out previously, it is hard to visualize how the high stoichiometries suggested by the Baltimore and Padua groups (Sections III,A–D) would be compatible with these thermodynamic parameters. In fact, they would be compatible only if it is assumed that the proton translocation stoichiometry of the cytochrome oxidase reaction varies with $\Delta\bar{\mu}_{H^+}$ such that the high stoichiometries are realized at low values of $\Delta\bar{\mu}_{H^+}$, while the true mechanistic stoichiometry shifts to the lower values (Fig. 1) on the approach to state 4 and high electrochemical proton gradients. While such a control mechanism is not completely inconceivable, the only data available suggest that the stoichiometry of charge translocation at all coupling sites is constant over a wide range of values of the membrane potential (Brand *et al.*, 1978).

Furthermore, as demonstrated in this article, the controversies over the function of cytochrome oxidase do not seem to be due to different experimental conditions in different laboratories, but are more likely due to experimental and technical shortcomings in the determination of the stoichiometries. For this reason it seems premature at the present time seriously to consider a more complicated theory, such as one of intrinsically variable stoichiometries, until the problems at the experimental level are resolved.

The $\Delta\bar{\mu}_{H^+}$ value for state 4 mitochondria on which the data in Fig. 1 are based is of the order of 230 mV (Mitchell and Moyle, 1969; Nicholls, 1974; Nicholls and Bernson, 1977; see also Åkerman and Wikström, 1976). If the true value of the electrochemical proton gradient is much lower (Padan and Rottenberg, 1973; Van Dam *et al.*, 1977; Azzone *et al.*, 1978c), then it is obvious that higher proton translocation stoichiometries become possible on thermodynamic grounds. However, if a stoichi-

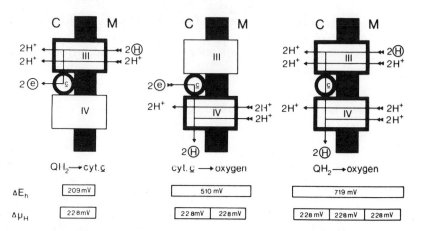

FIG. 1. Diagrammatic representation of proton translocation in the cytochrome chain. The respiratory chain complexes III and IV are depicted as rectangles plugged through the inner mitochondrial membrane (depicted black). C and M define the outside and the inside, respectively, of the membrane in each of the three diagrams (cytoplasmic side and matrix side). The circle designated by c represents cytochrome c, which is located on the C side of the membrane. The three diagrams represent (from left to right), ubiquinol–cytochrome c reductase, cytochrome c oxidase, and ubiquinol oxidation by O_2, respectively. Encircled letters H and e depict, with corresponding arrows, the transfer of hydrogen and electrons, respectively. The redox reactions are shown as two-equivalent reactions. Input of 2H at the upper right in the left and right diagrams represent hydrogen donation by ubiquinol (or by a hydrogenated substrate, such as succinate). Output of 2H at the bottom of the middle and right diagrams indicate the generation of H_2O from reduction of ½ O_2. Proton translocation is shown with arrows labeled 2H⁺. At the bottom of the figure the bars marked with ΔE_h and $\Delta \bar{\mu}_{H^+}$ give a quantitative comparison between the span of oxidoreduction potential traversed by the redox equivalents (data from Slater *et al.*, 1973) and the electrochemical proton gradient (data from Nicholls, 1974) in mitochondria respiring at state 4.

ometry of $3\overleftarrow{q}/e^-$ were realized for the cytochrome oxidase segment, which we consider very unlikely (Section III,D), the $\Delta \bar{\mu}_{H^+}$ in state 4 could not be higher than some 150–160 mV, which is the lower limit of all the published values.

Comparison of the proposed proton and charge stoichiometries for cytochrome oxidase with the state 4 values of ΔE_h and $\Delta \bar{\mu}_{H^+}$ (Fig. 1) would suggest that the overall cytochrome oxidase reaction operates near thermodynamic equilibrium with the proton motive force under such conditions. Apart from the fact that this would suggest a higher efficiency of energy conservation at cytochrome oxidase than previously anticipated (Erecińska *et al.*, 1974; Owen and Wilson, 1974; but see Slater *et al.*, 1973; Wikström and Saari, 1976), and less thermodynamic irreversibility of the terminal step of the respiratory chain, Fig. 1 also suggests that it should not be difficult, *for thermodynamic reasons,* to reverse the cytochrome oxidase reaction with generation of O_2 from water at high values of the electrochemical proton gradient. However, this contrasts to the large difficulties encountered in such attempts (Bienfait, 1975).

It is conceivable that the difficulties in demonstrating the full reversal of the cytochrome oxidase reaction experimentally stem from kinetic problems. One possibility comes from the observations that cytochrome oxidase appears to exist in both "active" and "inactive" states, activation occurring following electron transfer to oxygen (see, e.g., Antonini *et al.,* 1977). Another possibility, which may be related to the former, is the fact that in the fully oxidized state of aa_3 [which is generated in experiments on oxidase reversibility for thermodynamic reasons (see Bienfait, 1975)], the heme of cytochrome a_3 appears to be poorly accessible to ligands (see, e.g., Van Buuren, 1972). It may therefore be that the ferric heme a_3 has poor access to a reducing water molecule under such conditions, resulting in very low or insignificant rates of O_2 evolution. When more is known about the properties of "inactive" or "inaccessible" states of cytochrome oxidase, it may become possible to demonstrate reversibility under carefully selected experimental conditions. At the present time such conditions are not known.

F. The Span between NADH and Ubiquinone

$\overleftarrow{H}^+/2e^-$ and $\overleftarrow{q}^+/2e^-$ quotients ranging between 2 and 4 have been reported for this span of the respiratory chain (Lawford and Garland, 1972; Mitchell and Moyle, 1967b; Brand *et al.,* 1976a, 1978; Pozzan *et al.,* 1979).

While the lower ratios near 2 might be underestimates due to H^+/P_i symport (Brand *et al.,* 1976a), the highest ratios near 4 are also uncertain. The extrapolation procedure employed by Pozzan *et al.* (1979) causes uncertainties, and no mention was made in this work whether the reported quotients were based on the *increase* in rate of ferricyanide reduction on addition of calcium or on the total rate (cf. Section III,B,3). Furthermore, it was not discussed whether or not NADPH oxidation could have occurred to a significant extent under conditions where the pulsed oxidant is ferricyanide (cf. Section V,A), since, if it did occur, it would be expected to result in an enhancement of the stoichiometries above those inherent of "site 1" (Moyle and Mitchell, 1973; Rydström, 1977).

To these reviewers the stoichiometry characterizing proton translocation coupled to electron transfer across "site 1" is still an open question. Figure 2 compares the span of oxidoreduction potentials across "site 1" with the $\Delta\bar{\mu}_{H^+}$ in state 4 mitochondria (cf. Fig. 1). It is noted that with a

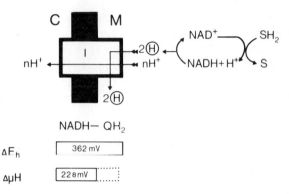

FIG. 2. Diagrammatic representation of proton translocation linked to NADH–ubiquinone reductase. The respiratory chain complex I is depicted as a rectangle spanning the inner mitochondrial membrane. For further explanation, see legend to Fig. 1.

stoichiometry of $2\overleftrightarrow{H}^+/2e^-$ and $2\overleftarrow{q}^+/2e^-$ a considerable amount of available energy would be lost as heat, while stoichiometric numbers of 4 seem incompatible a priori with the thermodynamic parameters (and cf. Section III,E). A stoichiometry of $3\overleftrightarrow{H}^+/2e^-$ and $3\overleftarrow{q}^+/2e^-$ would, on the other hand, fit snugly with these particular thermodynamic parameters. While such stoichiometries agree with the data on $\overleftarrow{H}^+/O$ quotients reported by Brand $et\ al.$ (1976a), the later studies by Brand $et\ al.$ (1978) on the $\overleftarrow{q}/e^-$ stoichiometries rather favor a value of $2\ \overleftrightarrow{H}^+/2e^-$.

IV. Stoichiometries from Thermodynamic and Related Steady-State Data

A. THERMODYNAMIC DATA

Independently from determinations with kinetic methods, it is in principle possible to evaluate the stoichiometric numbers of proton translocation through thermodynamic considerations. If we consider a redox-driven proton pump catalyzing the reaction

$$SH_2 + \tfrac{1}{2}O_2 + n_0H_{in}^+ \rightleftharpoons S + H_2O + n_0H_{out}^+ \qquad (1)$$

in which SH_2 and S are reduced and oxidized substrate and n_0 is the H^+/O, and assume equilibrium, then from setting

$$\Delta G = (\mu_S - \mu_{SH_2} - \tfrac{1}{2}\,\mu_{O_2}) + n_0(\mu_{H_{out}^+} - \mu_{H_{in}^+}) = \Delta G_{ox} + n_0\Delta\bar{\mu}_{H^+} \quad (2)$$

equal to zero, we obtain

$$H^+/O = n_0 = - (\Delta G_{ox}/\Delta \tilde{\mu}_{H^+}) \tag{3}$$

However, in general this equilibrium is not achieved, and we must resort to nonequilibrium (irreversible) thermodynamics (see Rottenberg, 1979).

An interesting approach has been used by Van Dam and associates (Van Dam and Westerhoff, 1977; Van Dam et al., 1978a,b). For situations not too far from equilibrium, where a *linear* relationship between the rate of the reaction of Eq. (1) and its driving force $-\Delta G$ may be postulated, Van Dam and Westerhoff (1977) derived Eq. (4).

$$J_0 = - L_0(\Delta G_{ox} + n_0 \Delta \tilde{\mu}_{H^+}) \tag{4}$$

An experimental verification of this relationship, in which L_0 is a positive constant, automatically yields n_0. The actual value of n_0 (i.e., the stoichiometry of proton translocation) obtained this way mainly depends on the precision of the determination of the thermodynamic parameters ΔG_{ox} and $\Delta \tilde{\mu}_{H^+}$. The main experimental problem in this use of Eq. (4) is the determination of the electrochemical proton gradient, $\Delta \tilde{\mu}_{H^+}$, which in practice necessitates the introduction of perturbants into the system, such as weak acids or bases (to determine ΔpH; see, e.g., Padan and Rottenberg, 1973; Nicholls, 1974), permeant ions [mostly K^+ or Rb^+ in the presence of the ionophore valinomycin; see Mitchell and Moyle (1969), Nicholls (1974), Padan and Rottenberg (1973)], or membrane potential probes (see, e.g., Åkerman and Wikström, 1976). All these methods share the difficulty that the chemical acitivty of an ionic species inside the mitochondrial matrix is hard to assess.

With this method, Van Dam and Westerhoff (1977) obtained H^+/O quotients above 9 (their reported values near 4.6 are for the H^+/e^- quotient, not for H^+/O due to the dimension of ΔG_{ox} used). This very high value probably derives from an underestimate of $\Delta \tilde{\mu}_{H^+}$, as already discussed by the same group in a different context (Van Dam et al., 1978a). The underestimate might thus be related to the possibility of a higher, more localized, $\Delta \tilde{\mu}_{H^+}$ than that measured between the bulk aqueous phases. However, a partial collapse of the gradient during separation of the mitochondria from the incubation mixture owing to anaerobiosis is another possibility (Nicholls, 1974).

Rottenberg (1979) has recently criticized the above approach on the basis that Van Dam et al. assumed completely coupled proton pumps, so that the only "leak" that may occur is the proton backflow driven by the $\Delta \tilde{\mu}_{H^+}$. Rottenberg prefers to leave open the possible existence of proton pumps that are incompletely coupled *at the molecular level*. Although this view is well understandable from a purely thermodynamic standpoint, we find it hard to visualize a proton translocator that thereby would be designed to lose energy as heat owing to incomplete coupling (Wikström and Krab, 1979a).[4] We prefer the simpler assumption a priori that coupling at the molecular level of the proton pump is complete with the likelihood of integer numbers for the true "intrinsic" stoichiometry (Wikström and Krab, 1978a, 1979a).

Rottenberg (1979) has rightly pointed out the importance of measuring "kinetic" stoichiometries of proton translocation at a $\Delta\tilde{\mu}_{H^+}$ of zero (so-called level flow conditions), so that there is no motive force for backflow of protons into the mitochondria during the measurement (see also Pozzan et al., 1979 and Section V,B). Rottenberg (1979) also presents some data gathered under "static head" conditions, where the net turnover of the output reaction, in this case proton translocation, is zero and its associated force ($\Delta\tilde{\mu}_{H^+}$) is maximal. In practice, this amounts to a comparison of $\Delta\tilde{\mu}_{H^+}$ and ΔG_{ox} values similar to that in Sections III,E and III,F. However, the stoichiometries arrived at by Rottenberg (1979) are higher than those on which Figs. 1 and 2 are based, owing to the much lower value of $\Delta\tilde{\mu}_{H^+}$ used by Rottenberg (180 mV; see also Section III,E).

Rottenberg and Gutman (1977) have compared the ΔG_{ox} and ΔG_p parameters of succinate-linked ATP-dependent reduction of NAD^+ in submitochondrial particles. Their results show that a minimum of 1.35 ATP molecules must be hydrolyzed per transfer of $2e^-$ from succinate to NAD^+. Therefore the $H^+/2e^-$ of "site 1" is unlikely to be equal to the H^+/ATP stoichiometry of the H^+-ATPase, as proposed by Mitchell (1966). The authors suggest that the $H^+/2e^-$ stoichiometry may be 4 (cf. Lehninger et al., 1979) and that the H^+/ATP stoichiometry is equal to 3 (see also Rottenberg, 1979). However, it seems to us that an intrinsic H^+/ATP stoichiometry of 2 for the ATPase [with an extra translocation of $1H^+/ATP$ due to ATP/ADP exchange and phosphate transport in whole mitochondria (see LaNoue et al., 1978; Klingenberg and Rottenberg, 1977)] has gained more experimental support (Nicholls, 1974; Brand and Lehninger, 1977; Brand, 1977; Nicholls and Bernson, 1977; Azzone et al.,

---

[4] To avoid misunderstanding we should emphasize that we do not imply complete coupling here between electron transport and proton translocation in the thermodynamic sense (i.e., $-\Delta G_0 = \Delta G_{H^+}$ is the Gibbs free energy change for proton translocation). In such an equilibrium condition there is obviously no driving force for the coupled reactions. However, the obvious requirement of $-\Delta G_0\ \Delta G_{H^+}$, which means that some energy is lost as heat, does not imply that there is "slipping" in the molecular machinery of the energy transducer due to lack of specificity in the electron and proton transfer reactions constituting the transducer elements (see Wikström and Krab, 1979a). Only this latter kind of "incomplete coupling" would lead to intrinsic H^+/e^- stoichiometries that differ from whole numbers. The extent of respiratory control in mitochondria suggests that the coupling is very nearly complete at this level (Wikström, 1980).

1978d; Thayer and Hinkle, 1973; but see also Sorgato *et al.*, 1978). Thus the results by Rottenberg and Gutman (1977) may also be consistent with a $H^+/2e^-$ ratio of 3 for "site 1," corresponding to a $\Delta G_p/\Delta G_{ox}$ ratio of 1.5 at equilibrium, and having certain other merits as discussed in Section III,F.

B. A STEADY-STATE RATE METHOD

Brand *et al.* (1978) have introduced an indirect method to determine (relative) charge translocation stoichiometries in the different segments of the respiratory chain. When it is assumed (e.g., in the presence of a small amount of uncoupling agent) that under specified experimental conditions (not too close to state 4) the backflow of H^+ across the mitochondrial membrane is linearly dependent only on the magnitude of $\Delta\tilde{\mu}_{H^+}$, and is exactly balanced in the steady state by generation of the proton gradient by redox-linked proton translocation, one can derive the steady-state expression

$$n_0 J_0 = K \, \Delta\tilde{\mu}_{H^+} \tag{5}$$

where K is a first-order rate constant of back-diffusion of protons, n_0 is the H^+/e^- stoichiometry, and J_0 is the rate of respiration.

Under conditions where the ΔpH component of the electrochemical proton gradient is minimized (see Brand *et al.*, 1978), Eq. (5) may be approximated by

$$n_0' J_0 = K \, \Delta\psi \tag{6}$$

where n_0' is now the stoichiometry of charge translocation, or $\overleftarrow{q}^+/e^-$. A comparison of plots of $\Delta\psi$ [measured conveniently by the safranine method (Åkerman and Wikström, 1976; Brand *et al.*, 1978)] versus J_0 with different substrates yields the *relative* $\overleftarrow{q}^+/e^-$ quotients of the different respiratory chain segments. With β-hydroxybutyrate, succinate, and TMPD plus ascorbate as substrates (corresponding to the coupling sites $1 + 2 + 3$, $2 + 3$, and 3, respectively), the relative stoichiometries were found to be $2:1.5:1$. Thus the $\overleftarrow{q}^+/e^-$ stoichiometry of "site 3" appears to be twice the stoichiometry of "site 2" according to these results, which is in excellent agreement with the proposal of Fig. 1 and the conclusions drawn in Sections III,A–E. On the other hand, these data do not support the contention (see, e.g., Mitchell, 1972) that the charge translocation stoichiometry is the same for "site 2" and "site 3", nor do they fit with a $\overleftarrow{q}^+/e^-$ quotient 1.33 times higher for succinate respiration as compared to respiration with TMPD + ascorbate, expected from the conclusions of the Baltimore and Padua groups (see Sections III,B,3, III,C, and

III,D). The data of Brand *et al.* (1978) were, in fact, quite significantly different from these two latter expectations.

V.   Special Aspects of the O_2-Pulse Technique

The O_2-pulse relaxation technique was introduced by Mitchell and Moyle (1967a) for determination of respiration-linked proton translocation and its stoichiometry. The technique itself and its inherent difficulties have been discussed to some extent previously (see, e.g., Greville, 1969; Mitchell and Moyle, 1967a,b; Papa, 1976). However, some particular aspects of this technique may have been less well recognized and have been brought into the foreground by the interpretation of recent experiments. We therefore discuss such aspects here in more detail, since they may be of importance for obtaining a correct picture of the potentialities and weaknesses of this technique.

Apart from the fast influx of protons in symport with P_i that tends to lower observed stoichiometries (Brand *et al.*, 1976a; Wikström and Krab, 1979a; see also Section III,B) with the O_2-pulse technique, the unusual kinetics of electron transfer in the respiratory chain when initiated by addition of O_2 to anaerobic mitochondria also puts certain restraints on the technique, as does the use of amounts of oxygen that are nearly stoichiometric with the amount of redox centers in the respiratory chain. These aspects will be discussed and related to the proposals (Mitchell and Moyle, 1979b) that observed $\bar{H}^+/O$ stoichiometries may be enhanced by action of nicotinamide nucleotide transhydrogenase under a set of different experimental conditions. This is an important point insofar as the proton-translocating property of the transhydrogenase (Moyle and Mitchell, 1973) has been proposed to be the reason for the higher stoichiometries of proton translocation observed by other workers (see Section III; see also Mitchell, 1979; Mitchell and Moyle, 1978, 1979b; Moyle and Mitchell, 1978a,b). The kinetics aspects of the O_2-pulse method will also be related to some difficulties in observing H^+ translocation linked to cytochrome oxidase (Moyle and Mitchell, 1978b; cf. Wikström and Krab, 1978b, 1979a).

A.   THE KINETICS OF OXYGEN REDUCTION
    AFTER A PULSE OF O_2

The oxygen pulse method is characterized by the addition of a very small amount of oxygen (usually about 1 nmol of O per milligram of protein: see Mitchell and Moyle, 1967b, 1979b) to a suspension of anaerobic mitochondria in the presence of a suitable substrate. The oxygen addition elicits a short burst of respiration which is linked to H$^+$ translocation, observed as an ejection of H$^+$ ions into the C phase with a sensitive pH electrode. After anaerobiosis, which usually occurs within 1 second, the H$^+$ ejection phase turns to reuptake of protons at a relatively slow rate, which is due to the low proton conductance of the inner mitochondrial membrane (see Mitchell and Moyle, 1967a). The $\overleftarrow{H}^+$/O stoichiometry is obtained by extrapolation of the decay phase to a point halfway between the O$_2$ addition and anaerobiosis, and by dividing the resulting amount of H$^+$ ejection by the amount of oxygen added (Mitchell and Moyle, 1967a).

Clearly, this method requires knowledge of the exact point of anaerobiosis. Usually, this has been calculated from the known state 3 rate of respiration with the substrate used but, as also pointed out by Papa (1976), the oxygen must be consumed at a much faster rate (cf. Penniston, 1972; Chance et al., 1965; Papa et al., 1975) under these conditions, which makes the extrapolation procedure liable to underestimation of the $\overleftarrow{H}^+$/O stoichiometry. However, this underestimate may not be serious, provided there are no fast phases of proton reuptake (see Papa, 1976; Wikström and Krab, 1979a; see also Sections III,B,1 and V,B), since the main part of the H$^+$ relaxation is much slower than the rate of H$^+$ ejection.

Rat liver mitochondria contain about 0.15 nmol of cytochrome aa_3 per milligram of protein, about the same amount of cytochrome c, about 0.075 nmol of cytochrome c_1, 0.075 nmol of Rieske's iron–sulfur protein, about 0.15 nmol of cytochromes b-562 and b-566, and about 2.5 nmol of ubiquinone per milligram of protein (see Slater, 1967b; Erecińska et al., 1976). Since anaerobic rat liver mitochondria show practically complete reduction of the cytochrome aa_3 complex and of cytochromes $c + c_1$ (including Rieske's high-potential iron–sulfur center; see Rieske, 1976), there are roughly 0.9 nmol of electron equivalents per milligram of protein in the terminal respiratory chain. In the presence of added substrates, and under the essentially deenergized conditions that precede a typical O$_2$ pulse, the b cytochromes and ubiquinone are reduced to an extent of at least 50%. We may therefore add a further 2.6 nmol of electron equivalents per milligram to yield a total of about 3.5 nmol of electron equivalents in the respiratory chain from ubiquinone to cytochrome aa_3. This should now be compared with the usual amount of 1 nmol of O per milligram of protein (i.e., 2 nmol of oxidizing equivalents) that is added in a typical O$_2$ pulse experiment.

As discussed in Section III,B,1, the O$_2$ pulse is followed by three kinetically very different phases of electron transport and oxygen consumption. The first phase comprises 0.9 nmol of e$^-$ per milligram of protein and has a half-time of about 5 msec (Chance et al., 1965; Papa, 1976; and see above). Thus nearly half of the added oxygen is consumed by this very fast velocity in a typical O_2-pulse experiment. The second phase corresponds mainly to oxidation of ubiquinol through the cytochrome chain, with $t_{1/2}$ of approximately 150 msec (Klingenberg and Kröger, 1967; Penniston, 1972) at a rate that is still considerably faster than the steady-state rate. This phase usually consumes the rest of the added oxygen (see above). It follows that the oxidation of components on the substrate side of ubiquinone occurs mainly after anaerobiosis. However, in the absence of added rotenone, and at somewhat higher oxygen concentrations, some NADH is also oxidized during the aerobic phase and may therefore contribute significantly to the $\overleftarrow{H}^+/O$ ratio (Mitchell and Moyle, 1967a–c). However, it is clear from the data presented by Mitchell and Moyle (1967c) that the aerobic phase comprises no significant reduction of the formed NAD^+ by hydrogenated substrates. Also, as demonstrated indirectly by Wikström and Krab (1979a) (see Fig. 2), the proton ejection phase of a normal O_2 pulse experiment in the presence of rotenone does not include significant oxidation of succinate. For these reasons it seems quite likely that the H^+ ejection phase in a typical O_2-pulse experiment comprises oxidation of ubiquinol and NADH, but that there is no significant oxidation of the reductants of these redox components until anaerobiosis and decay of the H^+ pulse.

This leads to the conclusion that it is really rather immaterial which substrate has been used to generate NADH from NAD^+ or, in the presence of rotenone, ubiquinol from ubiquinone, as long as these respiratory chain components are sufficiently reduced in the anaerobic phase prior to the next oxygen pulse. The presence of a substrate such as succinate or β-OH-butyrate will help to shorten the anaerobic preincubation times, and such a substrate may therefore be a useful constituent in this type of experiment.

This conclusion makes it highly uncertain whether there is significant oxidation of NADPH through the transhydrogenase in an O_2-pulse experiment. In fact, the data reported by Nicholls and Garland (1969), in which NADPH oxidation is shown to be very much slower than NADH oxidation, seem to exclude such a proposal.

For these reasons we cannot accept the explanation by Mitchell and Moyle (1979b; see also Mitchell, 1979) that various perturbations of rat liver mitochondria, including the addition of N-ethylmaleimide, would favor oxidation of NADPH and therefore enhance the observed $\overleftarrow{H}^+/O$ quotient. Thus, although N-ethylmaleimide certainly inhibits the activity of several dehydrogenases [including, incidentally, transhydrogenase (Earle et al., 1978)], but has little or no effect on oxidation of NADH or ubiquinol by the respiratory chain, this is not expected to have any effect whatsoever on the pathway of electron transport during the relevant H^+

extrusion phase on the basis of the conclusions drawn above. It seems much more plausible to concur with the conclusion of Brand *et al.* (1976a) that the enhancing effect of *N*-ethylmaleimide on the $\overleftarrow{H}^+/O$ quotients is due to the observed blockage of the H^+/P_i symporter (see also Section III,B,1).

B. KINETIC COMPATIBILITY OF K⁺ TRANSLOCATION IN O₂-PULSE EXPERIMENTS

It is interesting that many of the controversial aspects of the oxidant-pulse type of experiments seem specifically to concern those experiments where O_2 is the oxidant (for ferricyanide, see Section III,C). We would again ascribe this largely to the special kinetics of oxygen reduction discussed in the preceding section. Since a sizable fraction of the added oxygen is consumed very quickly, it may become doubtful whether the charge-compensating movement of K^+ in the presence of valinomycin is sufficiently rapid under all conditions to overcome the rapidly generating membrane potential. As shown by Wikström and Krab (1979a), this may become a problem with submitochondrial particles even at relatively high concentrations of K^+ (20 mM). It may therefore seem doubtful whether correct $\overleftarrow{H}^+/O$ quotients and K^+/O quotients are achieved in experiments (see Moyle and Mitchell, 1978b; Mitchell and Moyle, 1979b) with rat liver mitochondria, in which the extramitochondrial potassium concentration is well below 1 mM (see also Wikström and Krab, 1978b, 1979a,b). As shown by Azzone and Massari (1971), the K^+ uptake into mitochondria at saturating concentrations of valinomycin is limited by the extramitochondrial K^+ concentration at values below 1 mM even in the relatively slow steady-state type of experiments. Such a limit is therefore very probable, if not bound to occur in the very fast electron transfer following the O_2 pulse.

This contention was also directly supported by the finding (Wikström and Krab, 1978b) that the observed $\overleftarrow{H}^+/O$ ratio is enhanced considerably in O₂-pulse experiments with diaminodurene as substrate (cf. Moyle and Mitchell, 1978b), by performing the experiment in a KCl rather than in a sucrose medium. This increase in the extramitochondrial K^+ concentration also permitted a further enhancement of the proton translocation stoichiometry by *N*-ethylmaleimide, an enhancement that did not occur in the low K^+ medium (Moyle and Mitchell, 1978b), clearly due to the limit on net H^+ extrusion imposed by the membrane protential (see also Wikström and Krab, 1979a).

We conclude that the special type of kinetics of electron transfer and proton translocation in the O₂-pulse type of experiment puts stringent requirements on the exact conditions under which such experiments are performed. Unless these requirements are met, the technique may easily cause serious underestimation of the proton translocation stoichiometry.

VI. Proton Translocation in Submitochondrial Particles

The stoichiometry of proton uptake into submitochondrial particles has been studied far less than in intact mitochondria. Most of this work has recently been comprehensively covered by Papa (1976), and we have therefore refrained from repeating details here.

After the completion of the review by Papa, studies on submitochondrial particles have provided support for the notion of a proton-pumping function of cytochrome oxidase (Sorgato and Ferguson, 1978; Sorgato *et al.*, 1978; Wikström and Saari, 1977; Wikström, 1978). However, in single turnover experiments on cytochrome oxidase this function has so far not been demonstrable (Papa *et al.*, 1978a), but the difficulties encountered in the fast kinetics approach are formidable, as discussed recently in detail (Wikström and Krab, 1979a). This is mainly because the proton uptake into submitochondrial particles, linked to electron transfer from cytochrome c to oxygen, lags considerably behind the electron transfer events in single turnover experiments. Therefore, the results so far obtained by this method can hardly be taken to contradict the notion of a proton pump in cytochrome oxidase. The approach taken by Papa and collaborators (Papa *et al.*, 1978a) is, however, highly interesting, and further studies on the kinetics of the partial electron transfer reactions of cytochrome oxidase in relation to proton translocation are desirable.

It must always be kept in mind that with sonicated submitochondrial particles the risks of underestimating the $\vec{H}^+/O$ quotient are much higher than with intact mitochondria. This is due, first, to uncertainty with respect to the extent by which the membranes are truly inverted (see, e.g., Lötscher *et al.*, 1979), a matter that unfortunately is rarely controlled carefully.

Second, the small size of the particles combined with insufficient care to employ high intravesicular buffering power, leads to the very real danger that ΔpH builds up very rapidly and results in excessive proton leaks. Third, the intravesicular K^+ concentration is usually kept surprisingly low, which causes the risk (cf. Section V,B) that the rate of electrophoretic K^+ efflux catalyzed by valinomycin may not be sufficiently rapid to prevent significant generation of $\Delta\psi$ and hence significant leaks of protons (see, e.g., Wikström and Krab, 1979a).

For the above reasons it is necessary to view the $\vec{H}^+/O$ ratios of 6, 4, and 2 for the $NADH-O_2$, succinate$-O_2$, and cytochrome $c-O_2$ spans of the respiratory chain, respectively, with caution (Hinkle and Horstman, 1971; Papa *et al.*, 1975; Papa, 1976). In fact, earlier work by Papa *et al.* (1973, 1974a), both with the fast kinetic method and with a steady-state method, suggested that the stoichiometry of proton uptake is near $6H^+/O$ in the span between ubiquinol and oxygen, and it is not certain whether the extensive corrections made later (Papa *et al.*, 1975), which resulted in a quotient of 4, are entirely valid. A stoichiometry of $6\vec{H}^+/O$ in this span of the respiratory chain would agree with the view presented in Fig. 1, and also with the findings of Wikström and Saari (1977) that the $\vec{H}^+/O$ quotient is 4 for the span between cytochrome *c* and oxygen.

It seems to us that further experimental work on the submitochondrial system is necessary before any more definite conclusions can be drawn.

VII.   Proton Translocation in Reconstituted Systems

A.   Cytochrome *c* Oxidase

This respiratory chain complex has now been most extensively studied in reconstituted liposomes (see Wikström and Krab, 1979a). In contrast to the earlier conclusions by Hinkle and collaborators (Hinkle, 1973, 1974, 1978; Hinkle *et al.*, 1972), it has more recently been shown unequivocally that the transfer of one electron from cytochrome *c* to oxygen is linked to release of $1H^+$ on the outside of the membrane, and that this proton originates from the intravesicular space. There is also strong evidence that this proton translocation is electrogenic (Wikström and Saari, 1977; Krab and Wikström, 1978; Casey *et al.*, 1979; Sigel and Carafoli, 1979). This suggests (see Wikström, 1977) that $2H^+/e^-$ are taken up on the inside of the membrane, of which one proton is consumed in the formation of water, while the other is translocated to the outside and, furthermore, that the $\vec{q}^+/e^-$ stoichiometry is 2, not 1 as suggested by Mitchell (e.g., 1972; for a review, see Wikström and Krab, 1979a). The latter prediction was recently verified directly in reconstituted cytochrome oxidase vesicles by Sigel and Carafoli (1979), who measured the stoichiometry of potassium uptake in the presence of valinomycin and found a K^+/e^- ratio near 2.

We conclude that the proposal (Wikström, 1977; see also Wikström and Krab, 1979a) of cytochrome oxidase functioning as a proton pump with the indicated stoichiometries may be considered to be established for the reconstituted liposome system. It is significant that this function agrees quantitatively with our proposal in Fig. 1 and may therefore be taken to settle the controversy regarding the H^+/O stoichiometry of the cytochrome chain, which, as noted, was mainly the result of disagreement on the function of cytochrome oxidase. It must be stressed that the cytochrome oxidase liposomes contain only one highly purified protein, cytochrome c oxidase, leaving much less room for misjudgment of experimental results as compared to the much more complicated whole mitochondria or submitochondrial particles.

The conclusion that cytochrome oxidase is a redox-linked proton pump may have far-reaching consequences on the more general problem of primary energy conservation in biological membranes. By analogy, it would seem likely that proton translocation catalyzed by, at least, the cytochrome bc_1 complex (Sections III,C, VII,B, and VIII,B), would also occur by a proton pump type of mechanism, not by a redox loop, such as Mitchell's ubiquinone cycle (Mitchell, 1976b). A concrete proposal for an electron transfer and proton pump mechanism in this respiratory chain segment is therefore presented in Section VIII,B,3.

B. The Cytochrome bc_1 Complex

As shown by Leung and Hinkle (1975) and by Guerrieri and Nelson (1975), the oxidation of added quinols by added cytochrome c, catalyzed by isolated and purified cytochrome bc_1 complex reconstituted into liposomes, is linked to ejection of more than 1 H^+/e^- (nearly 2 $\overleftarrow{H}^+/e^-$) and uptake of 1 K^+/e^- in the presence of valinomycin. This agrees well with the stoichiometries observed for the ubiquinone–cytochrome c segment in intact mitochondria (Section III,C).

Although this result is incompatible with the earlier versions of Mitchell's redox loop model (see Papa, 1976), it is, in principle, compatible with the "proton motive ubiquinone cycle" proposed more recently (Mitchell, 1976b). There are some unexplained problems, however, such as the requirement of ubiquinone and of the iron–sulfur center S-3 of the smaller iron–protein (IP) subunit of succinate dehydrogenase, for a properly functioning "Q cycle" (see Trumpower and Katki, 1979). However, these components, particularly ubiquinone, may be present in sufficient quantities in isolated complex III (see Rieske, 1976; Hatefi, 1978).

C. The NADH–Ubiquinone Reductase Complex

Ragan and Hinkle (1975) first reported on H^+ translocation by complex I reconstituted into liposomes. The oxidation of added NADH by ubiquinone-1 was associated with proton uptake (see Papa, 1976 for discussion) with a stoichiometry greater than 0.7 H^+/e^- in addition to the proton uptake that is linked to reduction of quinone by NADH for trivial reasons. The experimental system was somewhat complicated by the presence of rotenone-insensitive redox activity, suggesting that the stoichiometry may be an underestimate. In view of the uncertainty of the true stoichiometry of this span of the respiratory chain in intact mitochondria (Section III,F), further studies on the reconstituted system are much desired. In such studies particular care should be taken to use a very well buffered intravesicular space, since this has proved to be essential for observation of correct proton translocation stoichiometries in cytochrome oxidase vesicles (Wikström and Saari, 1977; Krab and Wikström, 1978).

VIII.   Mechanistic Aspects of Proton Translocation in the Cytochrome Chain

A.   CYTOCHROME c OXIDASE (COMPLEX IV)

In the last 10 years or so the cytochrome oxidase reaction has represented the most typical model of an electron-translocating segment of a redox loop (see, e.g., Mitchell, 1966, 1972, 1976a,b; Mitchell and Moyle, 1967b, 1979a; Skulachev, 1971; Hinkle, 1973, 1974, 1978; Wikström, 1974). The experiments of Mitchell and Moyle (1967b) showing delayed uptake of H^+ from the C phase during ferrocyanide oxidation by rat liver mitochondria (but see Wikström, 1977; Wikström and Saari, 1977; Wikström and Krab, 1979a), and those of Papa *et al.* (1974b), showing H^+ uptake in submitochondrial particles linked to the cytochrome oxidase reaction, have nearly without exception been taken to establish the "factoid" (Mailer, 1979) that reduction of oxygen by cytochrome a_3 occurs near the M phase so that electron transfer from cytochrome c (located unequivocally on the C side of the membrane: see De Pierre and Ernster, 1977) to a_3 would necessarily be oriented *across* the membrane.

This concept was taken to be strongly supported by the finding of Hinkle and Mitchell (1970) that the redox potential of cytochrome a appeared to change relative to that of cytochrome c as a function purely of $\Delta\psi$ across the membrane in CO-inhibited rat liver mitochondria. Cytochrome a_3 showed an analogous though less quantitatively studied behavior in anaerobic mitochondria (Hinkle and Mitchell, 1970). These findings were interpreted to mean that the hemes of cytochromes a and a_3 are located toward the M side of the membrane, so that the electron equilibration between these hemes and the heme of cytochrome c (on the C side) would be directly influenced by the electric field.

It is essential to realize that H^+ uptake from the M phase in the cytochrome oxidase reaction does not constitute any evidence per se for locating the oxygen-reducing site (heme a_3) near the M side of the membrane. The H^+ ions may equally well be thought of as moving to the site of oxygen reduction (and water generation) through a H^+-conducting

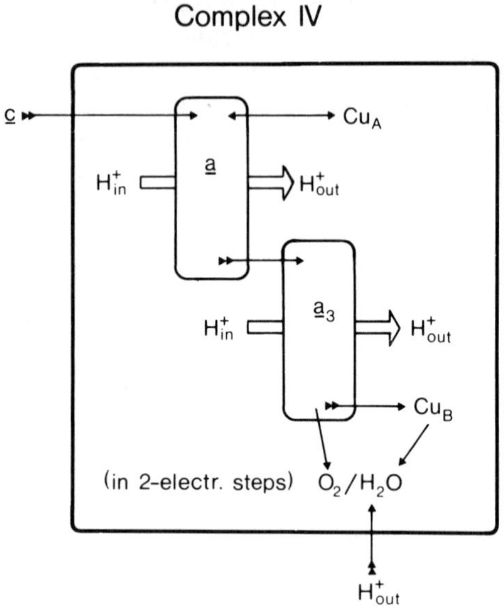

Complex IV

FIG. 3. Schematic representation of the energetics of electron transport in the cytochrome c–O_2 segment of the respiratory chain. The vertical dimension of the figure corresponds approximately to ΔE_h between cytochrome c (upper left) and the O_2/H_2O couple. Cytochromes a and a_3 (rectangles marked a and a_3) are depicted to "span" the difference in oxidoreduction potential between cytochrome c and O_2/H_2O and to conserve the released energy by functioning as redox-linked proton pumps of the type described in detail by Wikström and Krab (1979a). Cu_A and Cu_B represent low- and high-potential copper centers, respectively. Thin arrows indicate the transfer of electrons; wide arrows depict transmembraneous transfer of protons. It is assumed here that the H^+ released outside by the cytochrome a_3 pump is consumed in the formation of water. It may equally well be thought, however, that this proton is consumed prior to being released on the outside.

channel connecting the heme with the M phase (Hinkle, 1978; Wikström *et al.*, 1978), by analogy with the proton channel in the F_0 segment of the ATP synthase complex (see Kozlov and Skulachev, 1977; Hinkle and Horstman, 1971; Racker, 1972). In fact, at the extreme, the H^+ uptake could be the only transmembranous event of cytochrome oxidase catalysis if the hemes a and a_3 were situated near the C phase, into which the complex IV protrudes as far as nearly 50 Å (Henderson *et al.*, 1977; Blasie *et al.*, 1978; Chance *et al.*, 1977; Dockter *et al.*, 1977), and yet be fully consistent with the proton uptake data.

Also, the interpretation of the findings by Hinkle and Mitchell (1970) is not unique (see Wikström and Krab, 1979a). Thus the redox state of the copper atom that is very closely associated with the heme iron of cytochrome a_3 is unaffected by $\Delta\psi$ (or the mitochondrial energy state; see

Wilson *et al.*, 1975), while the redox state of heme a_3 is affected. Yet the copper is located within 5 Å from the heme iron (see Chance *et al.*, 1978). Clearly, a through-space effect of $\Delta\psi$ on vectorially oriented electron transfer reactions is very unlikely to be the correct explanation for the apparent effect of $\Delta\psi$ on cytochrome a_3 relative to cytochrome c.

The finding of a proton-pump function of cytochrome oxidase furnishes an alternative explanation of the findings by Hinkle and Mitchell (1970) also for the case of cytochrome a, since $\Delta\psi$ is expected to affect certain redox equilibria in a proton-pump mechanism without a requirement of vectorial electron translocation (see Wikström and Krab, 1979a).

We conclude that at present there exists no unequivocal evidence for electron translocation across the inner mitochondrial membrane as required by a redox type of arrangement of redox centers.

We have recently discussed in some detail how a proton pump such as that of cytochrome oxidase may function at the molecular level (Wikström and Krab, 1979a). Figure 3 is a highly schematic presentation of this function. In this scheme the proposed central role of cytochromes a and a_3 in energy transduction (proton translocation) has been emphasized. Such a role is mainly indicated by the pH dependence of their midpoint potentials and their sensitivity to "energization" of the mitochondrial membrane (Wikström and Krab, 1979a). This scheme further emphasizes the input of electrons of high energy (low redox potential, upper part of Fig. 3) and the output at low redox energy (high redox potential, lower part of Fig. 3). The drop in redox energy is shown to be "spanned" by cytochromes a and a_3, which are suggested to convert it into an electrochemical proton gradient by functioning as redox-linked proton pumps.

B.   Ubiquinone–Cytochrome c Reductase (Complex III)

The stoichiometry of H^+ ejection and charge translocation in this segment is firmly established (Sections III,C and VII,B). While these stoichiometries are in agreement with Mitchell's protonmotive Q cycle mechanism (Mitchell, 1976b), they do not contradict the possibility of other kinds of proton translocating mechanisms.

It was suggested by Wikström (1972b, 1973) that the b cytochromes of complex III may be intimately involved in energy transduction by means of redox-linked protolytic events, a property these cytochromes share with the cytochromes a and a_3 (Straub and Colpa-Boonstra, 1962; Urban and Klingenberg, 1969; Wilson *et al.*, 1972a). Papa *et al.* (1973, 1974a) subsequently proposed that cytochrome b-566 may function as the proton pump in this respiratory chain complex, but this proposal was later retracted (see Papa, 1976; Papa *et al.*, 1977, 1978a,b) in favor of the suggestion of an unidentified redox-linked proton pump situated "between" the b cytochromes and cytochrome c_1.

1. Revision of the Electron Transport Model of Wikström and Berden

In 1972 Wikström and Berden (1972) proposed a particular arrangement of electron transfer in the ubiquinone–cytochrome c_1 segment of the respiratory chain to account for the peculiar phenomenon of reduction of the b cytochromes upon oxidation of the c cytochromes (see also Slater, 1972b; Wikström, 1972a). The essence of this model is the split of electron transfer into two separate but tightly coupled pathways, afforded by separation of the redox potentials (E_h and E_m) of the $QH_2/QH\cdot$ and $QH\cdot/Q$ couples (Q = ubiquinone 10). This would lead to a corresponding separation in the redox energy of the two originally equipotential electrons of the QH_2/Q couple, so that one would gain energy (lower E_h) at the expense of the other (higher E_h). One particularly interesting mechanistic consequence of such a principle is that while a pair of electrons flow through such a system, the conservation of redox energy may now be restricted entirely to one of the two pathways (the one initiated at low E_h).

However, as predicted, the first attempt at such a model suffered from some inadequacies that have been revealed by later expeimentation. Nevertheless, it seems that the major principle of this model has survived so far, and that it may have stimulated interesting further developments such as the Q cycle and similar schemes (Mitchell, 1976b; Dutton et al., 1978b; Rich and Moore, 1976; Salerno et al., 1978).

Today, there are two quite obvious improvements that must be applied to the original model.

1. It seems likely that the stability constant of the ubisemiquinone is less than unity, even though the semiquinone must be stabilized by binding in order to perform the function envisaged in the model (see, e.g., Mitchell, 1976b). Hence, the $QH_2/QH\cdot$ couple is more likely to be of high potential (E_m), while the E_m of the $QH\cdot/Q$ couple should be correspondingly depressed below that of the two-equivalent QH_2/Q couple. It follows that the $QH_2/QH\cdot$ couple is the more likely reductant of cytochrome $c + c_1$ (via intermediates, see later), while the $QH\cdot/Q$ couple reduces the b cytochromes, and not vice versa as proposed originally.

Quite apart from the fact that this "transposition" of the two ubisemiquinone redox couples may be favored on theoretical grounds, it is also in good agreement with several epxerimental findings. Thus the redox kinetics of ubiquinone, b cytochromes, and cytochrome $c + c_1$ in O_2-pulse experiments in the presence of antimycin (Chance, 1974) agree very well with the "transpositioned" arrangement as demonstrated by computer simulations (D. De Vault and M. K. F. Wikström, unpublished observations), but do not agree with the model in its original form. The change is also consistent with the finding (Rich and Moore, 1976), supported by observations in this laboratory (M. K. F. Wikström, unpublished data), that cytochrome $c + c_1$ is rapidly reduced by a pulse of substrate in a reaction that is insensitive to antimycin, while substrate oxidation in the steady state is fully blocked by this antibiotic. Furthermore, the EPR studies of Konstantinov and Ruuge (1977) indicate that the QH·/Q couple is the reductant for the b cytochromes rather than the QH$_2$/QH· couple.

2. As demonstrated elegantly by Trumpower and collaborators (Trumpower and Katki, 1979; Trumpower and Edwards, 1979), the oxidation of QH$_2$ to QH· is likely to take place via Rieske's iron–sulfur protein, which is identical to the "oxidation factor" previously described by Nishibayashi-Yamashita *et al.* (1972), and which might also be identified with the British antilewisite (BAL)-sensitive "component X" described by Wikström and Berden (1972). The "oxidation factor" (i.e., Rieske's iron–sulfur protein) mediates electron transfer to cytochrome c_1 (see Trumpower and Katki, 1979).

After these revisions the Wikström–Berden scheme still suffers from two major inadequacies. First, it does not account for proton translocation; and second, there is considerable uncertainty in the revised scheme with respect to the antimycin-sensitive pathway of cytochrome b oxidation. In the following we will make an attempt to correct these inadequacies (Section VIII,B,3).

2. The Proton Motive Ubiquinone Cycle

The "Q cycle" was proposed by Mitchell (1976b) to account for the stoichiometry of proton and charge translocation (see Papa, 1976), and also to explain the anomalous behavior of the b cytochromes upon oxidation of cytochrome $c + c_1$. To account for the latter, the Q cycle was designed according to the principles outlined by Wikström and Berden (1972), but in addition, ubiquinone was postulated to function as the hydrogen-translocating limb of both redox loops 2 and 3, by functioning in a cycle. The Q cycle has more recently received much experimental support (see, e.g., Trumpower and Katki, 1979; Rich and Moore, 1976; Konstantinov and Ruuge, 1977; Grigolava and Konstantinov, 1977), also in the system of cyclic electron transport in chromatophores (Dutton *et al.*, 1978b; but see also Crofts *et al.*, 1977). However, the Q cycle also suffers from some difficulties (see Petty *et al.*, 1977, for the chromatophore system), the most significant of which for the mitochondrial system may be listed as follows.

1. The extensive work by Klingenberg and Kröger (see, e.g., 1967) on the role of ubiquinone in the respiratory chain seems to establish the "pool" function of this redox component, being an obligatory redox inter-

mediate (Kröger and Klingenberg, 1973) between the various dehydrogenases [which are present in much lower concentrations than the b and c cytochromes (Klingenberg, 1968)] and the cytochrome bc_1 complex (contrast Trumpower and Katki, 1979). While this pool function does not preclude special functions of bound ubiquinone species stoichiometric with certain components of the succinate–cytochrome c reductase system (see later), it is difficult to reconcile with the Q cycle, which seems to require a close cooperation between the iron–sulfur center S-3 of complex II (Ruzicka *et al.*, 1975; Ingledew *et al.*, 1976) and the postulated antimycin-sensitive reaction site of b-562 with ubiquinone (see Mitchell, 1976b; Trumpower and Katki, 1979). Similarly, it is also not easy to see how oxidation of durohydroquinol in mitochondria, or in reconstituted complex III vesicles (Section VII,B), would elicit normal proton translocation according to the Q cycle.

2. A more serious objection, though less recognized, is the fact that the Q cycle focuses on electron donation from the dehydrogenases as occurring from the M side of the membrane. This is in agreement with the location of succinate dehydrogenase (see De Pierre and Ernster, 1977) and appears necessary to account for the redox loop function of the cycle. However, oxidation of α-glycerophosphate by mitochondria is catalyzed by a corresponding dehydrogenase, which is located on the C side of the membrane (Klingenberg, 1970). Nevertheless, the oxidation of α-glycerophosphate is known to elicit "site 2" phosphorylation and to reduce ubiquinone (Ernster and Nordenbrand, 1967; Salach and Bednarz, 1973).

3. The finding by Case and Leigh (1976) that *both* the hemes of cytochromes b-566 and b-562 are very close to the C side of the membrane, as determined by dipolar interactions between aqueous paramagnetic ions and the heme centers, is clearly at variance with the Q cycle, as well as with the proposal (Mitchell, 1972; Wikström, 1972a; Papa, 1976) that the two b cytochromes would constitute a transmembranous electron-translocating limb of a redox loop.

3. The Proton-Pumping Cytochrome b Cycle

As indicated earlier (and see Wikström and Krab, 1979a), the proton pump function of cytochrome oxidase may suggest by analogy that the cytochrome bc_1 complex functions by a similar mechanism. Following this analogy, it appears that the b cytochromes may be the most likely candidates to be intimately involved in the proton translocation mechanism of such a pump (see Section VIII,B). It may therefore be interesting to consider how the ubiquinone–cytochrome c reductase system may be ar-

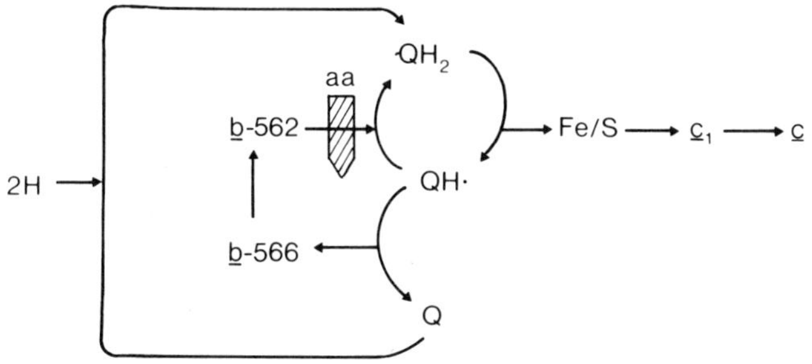

FIG. 4. Proposed scheme for electron transport in cytochrome bc_1 complex. Q, QH·, and QH₂ represent the quinone, semiquinone, and hydroquinone states, respectively, of a protein-bound species of ubiquinone. aa, antimycin; Fe/S, Rieske's iron–sulfur center; c_1 and c, cytochromes c_1 and c, respectively; b-562 and b-566 represent the corresponding b cytochromes (see Wikström, 1973); 2H depicts input of hydrogen from the bulk "pool" of ubiquinone-10. For further description, see text.

ranged to achieve such proton pumping and still be in accordance with the by now impressive amount of experimental evidence on electron transfer and proton translocation of this respiratory chain segment.

Our proposal for the arrangement of electron flow, which may be called the b cycle, is illustrated schematically in Fig. 4. This scheme is based on the Wikström–Berden model (Wikström and Berden, 1972), but with incorporation of the necessary amendments described in Section VIII,B,1. In addition to these amendments, it is suggested that the hemes of both b cytochromes lie near the C side of the membrane like the hemes of cytochromes c and c_1 and Rieske's nonheme iron center (see Case and Leigh, 1976; De Pierre and Ernster, 1977; Grigolava and Konstantinov, 1977; Trumpower and Edwards, 1979). This entire system of redox centers is suggested to operate in close association with a particular protein-bound species of ubiquinone, which may be present in stoichiometric amounts compared to the hemes and the nonheme iron protein (see Rieske, 1976; Hatefi, 1978). However, this function must be strictly controlled to establish a high- and a low-potential domain in the system. The two b cytochromes provide the pathway of electron transfer from the low-potential (QH·/Q) to the high-potential (QH₂/QH·, Fe/S, cytochrome c_1) domain and should therefore be intimately involved in energy transduction (see below). In other respects this system functions much like the Wikström–Berden model or the Q cycle, exhibiting, for instance, the seesaw phenomenon of reduction of cytochrome b upon oxidation of cytochrome c_1, as described in detail by Wikström and Berden (1972) and by Mitchell (1976b).

The *b* cytochromes are arranged in the sequence of their E_m values (see Dutton *et al.*, 1972), a sequence that also seems to be supported by kinetic studies (Chance, 1974; Papa *et al.*, 1972; and see Wikström, 1973). The *b* cytochromes are proposed to engage intimately in proton translocation (cf. cytochromes *a* and a_3 in Fig. 3) by being arranged as two elementary proton pumps of the type described by Wikström and Krab (1979a), each with a stoichiometry of $1H^+/e^-$. Figure 5 presents a more comprehensive scheme of the system, in which the thermodynamic aspects of electron flow and energy conservation are emphasized (cf. Fig. 3).

The "bound" Q and QH_2 of the complex III center are suggested to equilibrate with the bulk "free" ubiquinone pool, which is an obligatory electron transfer intermediate between the dehydrogenases and complex

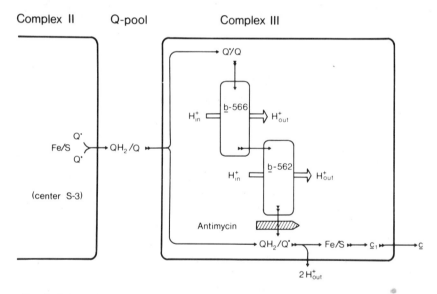

FIG. 5. Schematic representation of the energetics of electron transport in the succinate dehydrogenase–ubiquinone–cytochrome *c* segment of the respiratory chain. The vertical dimension of the figure corresponds to ΔE_h between cytochrome *c* and the (low-potential) semiquinone–quinone couple (here depicted as $Q\cdot/Q$). The redox potential of the center S-3 and of the ubiquinone pool is approximately halfway between the high- and low-potential domains of the cytochrome bc_1 complex during respiration (see text). Proton translocation occurs in intimate linkage with the *b* cytochromes, which are depicted to "span" the ΔE_h (cf. Fig. 3). The extra release of $2H^+$ per two electrons traversing the complex (bottom) is due to the trivial oxidation of ubiquinol by electron transfer centers. The figure is intended to depict the fate of two reducing equivalents donated by the ubiquinone pool, one of which takes the upper (low-potential) path through the $Q\cdot/Q$ couple and the *b* cytochromes, while the other takes the (high-potential) path via the $QH_2/Q\cdot$ couple to cytochrome *c* (cf. also Fig. 4). The former electron eventually also arrives to the high-potential $QH_2/Q\cdot$ couple in a final step, which may be blocked by antimycin (hatched arrow).

III (Kröger and Klingenberg, 1973). It should perhaps be pointed out in this connection that we would regard the Fe/S center S-3 of succinate reductase, with its two closely associated bound ubiquinone molecules (see Ingledew *et al.*, 1976; Salerno *et al.*, 1977), as a reductant of the ubiquinone pool (Fig. 5). This does not absolutely preclude the possibility of a more direct interaction with complex III under some conditions, but we do not feel that copurification of complex II and complex III proteins is a sufficient criterion for such interactions *in vivo* (contrast Trumpower and Katki, 1979). In fact, it seems that similar problems are also encountered in the "purified" complex IV (see, e.g., Penttilä *et al.*, 1979), which contains certain impurities that regularly copurify with the enzyme.

Although a more detailed analysis of the proposed "b cycle" is outside the scope of this article, we suggest that this model might provide an alternative, with only few modifications, also to the recent cyclic electron transfer and proton translocation models proposed for photosynthetic bacteria (Crofts *et al.*, 1977; Dutton *et al.*, 1978b; Mitchell, 1976b) and the plastoquinone–cytochrome *bf* system of chloroplasts (see Hauska and Trebst, 1977; Mitchell, 1976b).

IX. Epilogue

In the present article we have consciously endeavored to demonstrate that the acceptance of the more general postulate of chemiosmotic coupling in oxidative phosphorylation (and in photosynthetic phosphorylation), in which a current of protons generated by exergonic redox centers is utilized by the endergonic ATP synthase, does not necessitate acceptance of the postulated mechanism by which this current is generated in the chemiosmotic theory. We hope to have demonstrated that the latter postulate is, in fact, not tenable in the light of most recent research, at least not in primary energy conservation in mitochondria. Although it is regretted that this demonstration has required a very detailed scrutiny of experimental findings in some sections, with the consequence that some important findings have received far too little attention, we hope that our demonstration will help to stimulate further intensive research in the area of primary energy conservation in biological membranes. It seems to us that this most exciting area is still very far from being resolved and that it will engage a large number of investigators also in the years to come.

ACKNOWLEDGMENTS

Work conducted in this laboratory was supported by grants from the Sigrid Jusèlius Foundation and the Finnish Academy (Commission of Medical Sciences). K. K. acknowledges a long-term postdoctoral fellowship from the European Molecular Biology Organization (EMBO). We wish to extend particular thanks to the following colleagues, who have helped us with valuable comments and information on their work prior to publication: K. Åkerman, M. Brand, K. Van Dam, S. Ferguson, D. Kell, D. Nicholls, S. Papa, H. Rottenberg, J. Rydström, N.-E. Saris, E. Sigel, C. Sorgato, and B. Trumpower. We are also grateful to Ms. Hilkka Vuorenmaa and Ms. Marja Immonen for excellent technical assistance and help with preparation of the manuscript.

REFERENCES

Åkerman, K. E. O., and Wikström, M. K. F. (1976). *FEBS Lett.* **68,** 191–197.

Alexandre, A., Reynafarje, B., and Lehninger, A. L. (1978). *Proc. Natl. Acad. Sci. U.S.A.* **75,** 5296–5300.

Antonini, E., Brunori, M., Colossimo, A., Greenwood, C., and Wilson, M. T. (1977). *Proc. Natl. Acad. Sci. U.S.A.* **74,** 3128–3132.

Artzatbanov, V. Y., Konstantinov, A. A., and Skulachev, V. P. (1978). *FEBS Lett.* **87,** 180–185.

Azzone, G. F., and Massari, S. (1971). *Eur. J. Biochem.* **19,** 97–107.

Azzone, G. F., and Massari, S. (1973). *Biochim. Biophys. Acta* **301,** 195–226.

Azzone, G. F., Massari, S., and Pozzan, T. (1977). *Mol. Cell. Biochem.* **17,** 101–112.

Azzone, G. F., Avron, M., Metcalfe, J. C., Quagliariello, E., and Siliprandi, N., eds. (1978a). "The Proton and Calcium Pumps." Elsevier/North-Holland Biomed. Press, Amsterdam.

Azzone, G. F., Pozzan, T., Di Virgilio, F., and Miconi, V. (1978b). In "Frontiers of Biological Energetics" (P. L. Dutton, J. S. Leigh, and A Scarpa, eds.), pp. 375–383. Academic Press, New York.

Azzone, G. F., Pozzan, T., Massari, S., and Bragadin, M. (1978c). *Biochim. Biophys. Acta* **501,** 296–306.

Azzone, G. F., Pozzan, T., and Massari, S. (1978d). *Biochim. Biophys. Acta* **501,** 307–316.

Azzone, G. F., Pozzan, T., Di Virgilio, F., and Miconi, M. (1979). In "Cation Flux across Biomembranes" (Y. Mukohata and L. Packer, eds.), pp. 331–342. Academic Press, New York.

Bienfait, H. F. (1975). Ph.D. Thesis, University of Amsterdam.

Blasie, J. K., Erecińska, M., Samuels, S., and Leigh, J. S. (1978). *Biochim. Biophys. Acta* **501,** 33–52.

Boyer, P. D. (1965). In "Oxidases and Related Redox Systems" (T. E. King, H. S. Mason, and M. Morrison, eds.), pp. 994–1008. Wiley, New York.

Boyer, P. D. (1974). In "Dynamics of Energy-Transducing Membranes (L. Ernster, R. W. Estabrook, and E. C. Slater, eds.), BBA Library, Vol. 13, pp. 289–301. Elsevier, Amsterdam.

Boyer, P. D., Chance, B., Ernster, L., Mitchell, P., Racker, E., and Slater, E. C. (1977). *Annu. Rev. Biochem.* **46,** 955–1026.

Brand, M. D. (1977). *Biochem. Soc. Trans.* **5,** 1615–1620.

Brand, M. D., and Lehninger, A. L. (1975). *J. Biol. Chem.* **250,** 7958–7960.

Brand, M. D., and Lehninger, A. L. (1977). *Proc. Natl. Acad. Sci. U.S.A.* **74,** 1955–1959.

Brand, M. D., Reynafarje, B., and Lehninger, A. L. (1976a). *J. Biol. Chem.* **251,** 5670–5679.

Brand, M. D., Reynafarje, B., and Lehninger, A. L. (1976b). *Proc. Natl. Acad. Sci. U.S.A.* **73,** 437–441.

Brand, M. D., Chen, C.-H., and Lehninger, A. L. (1976c). *J. Biol. Chem.* **251**, 968–974.

Brand, M. D., Harper, W. G., Nicholls, D. G., and Ingledew, W. J. (1978). *FEBS Lett.* **95**, 125–129.

Capuano, F., Izzo, G., Altamura, N., and Papa, S. (1980). *FEBS Lett.* **111**, 249–254.

Case, G. D., and Leigh, J. S., Jr. (1976). *Biochem. J.* **160**, 769–783.

Casey, R. P., Chappell, J. B., and Azzi, A. (1979). *Biochem. J.* **182**, 149–156.

Change, B. (1965). *J. Biol. Chem.* **240**, 2729–2748.

Chance, B. (1972). *FEBS Lett.* **23**, 3–20.

Chance, B. (1974). *In* "Dynamics of Energy-Transducing Membranes" (L. Ernster, R. W. Estabrook, and E. C. Slater, eds.), B.B.A. Library, Vol. 13, pp. 553–578. Elsevier, Amsterdam.

Chance, B., Schoener, B., and De Vault, D. (1965). *In* "Oxidases and Related Redox Systems" (T. E. King, H. S. Mason, and M. Morrison, eds.), pp. 907–921. Wiley, New York. See especially discussion comment by Chance and Schindler, pp. 921–929.

Chance, B., Crofts, A. R., Nishimura, M., and Price, B. (1970). *Eur. J. Biochem.* **13**, 364–374.

Chance, B., Leigh, J. S., and Waring, A. (1977). *In* "Structure and Function of Energy-Transducing Membranes" (K. Van Dam and B. F. Van Gelder, eds.), pp. 1–10. Elsevier/North-Holland, Amsterdam.

Chance, B., Waring, A., and Saronio, C. (1978). *In* "Energy Conservation in Biological Membranes (G. Schäfer and M. Klingenberg, eds.), pp. 56–73. Springer-Verlag, Berlin.

Chappell, J. B. (1964). *Biochem. J.* **90**, 225–237.

Cockrell, R. S., Harris, E. J., and Pressman, B. (1966). *Biochemistry* **5**, 3219–3228.

Crofts, A. R., and Wood, P. M. (1978). *Curr. Top. Bioenerg.* **7**, 173–244.

Crofts, A. R., Crowther, D., Bowyer, J., and Tierney, G. V. (1977). *In* "Structure and Function of Energy-Transducing Membranes" (K. Van Dam and B. F. Van Gelder, eds.), pp. 139–155. Elsevier/North-Holland, Amsterdam.

De Pierre, J. W., and Ernster, L. (1977). *Annu. Rev. Biochem.* **46**, 201–262.

De Vault, D. (1976). *J. Theor. Biol.* **62**, 115–139.

Dockter, M. E., Steinemann, A., and Schatz, G. (1977). *In* "Structure and Function of Energy-Transducing Membranes" (K. Van Dam and B. F. Van Gelder, eds.), pp. 169–176. Elsevier/North-Holland, Amsterdam.

Dutton, P. L., Erecińska, M., Sato, N., Mukai, Y., Pring, M., and Wilson, D. F. (1972). *Biochim. Biophys. Acta* **267**, 15–24.

Dutton, P. L., Leigh, J. S., and Scarpa, A., eds. (1978a). "Frontiers of Biological Energetics," Vols. I and II. Academic Press, New York.

Dutton, P. L., Bashford, C. L., Van den Berg, W. H., Bonner, H. S., Chance, B., Jackson, J. B., Petty, K. M., Prince, R. C., Sorge, J. R., and Takamiya, K.-I. (1978b). *Proc. Int. Congr. Photosynthesis, 4th*, pp. 159–171.

Earle, S. R., O'Neal, S. G., and Fisher, R. R. (1978). *Biochemistry* **17**, 4683–4690.

Erecińska, M., Veech, R. L., and Wilson, D. F. (1974). *Arch. Biochem. Biophys.* **160**, 412–421.

Erecińska, M., Wilson, D. F., and Miyata, Y. (1976). *Arch. Biochem. Biophys.* **177**, 133–143.

Ernster, L. (1977). *In* "Bioenergetics of Membranes" (L. Packer, G. C. Papageorgiou, and A. Trebst, eds.), pp. 373–376. Elsevier/North-Holland, Amsterdam.

Ernster, L., and Nordenbrand, K. (1967). *Methods Enzymol.* **10**, 86–94.

Estabrook, R. W. (1961). *J. Biol. Chem.* **236**, 3051–3057.

Estabrook, R. W. (1962). *Biochim. Biophys. Acta* **60**, 236–248.

Garland, P. B., Clegg, R. A., Downie, J. A., Gray, T. A., Lawford, H. G., and Skyrme, J. (1972). *Fed. Eur. Biochem. Soc. Symp.* **28**, 105–117.

Greville, G. D. (1969). *Curr. Top. Bioenerg.* **3**, 1–72.

Grigolava, I. V., and Konstantinov, A. A. (1977). *FEBS Lett.* **78**, 36–40.

Guerrieri, F., and Nelson, B. D. (1975). *FEBS Lett.* **54**, 339–342.

Harold, F. M. (1977). *Curr. Top. Bioenerg.* **6**, 83–149.

Hatefi, Y. (1978). *Methods Enzymol.* **53**, 35–40.

Hauska, G., and Trebst, A. (1977). *Curr. Top. Bioenerg.* **6**, 151–220.

Henderson, R., Capaldi, R. A., and Leigh, J. S. (1977). *J. Mol. Biol.* **112**, 631–648.

Hinkle, P. C. (1973). *Fed. Proc., Fed. Am. Soc. Exp. Biol.* **32**, 1988–1992.

Hinkle, P. C. (1974). *Ann. N. Y. Acad. Sci.* **227**, 159–165.

Hinkle, P. C. (1978). *Fed. Eur. Biochem. Soc. Symp.* **45**, 79–83.

Hinkle, P. C., and Horstman, L. L. (1971). *J. Biol. Chem.* **246**, 6024–6028.

Hinkle, P. C., and Mitchell, P. (1970). *J. Bioenerg.* **1**, 45–60.

Hinkle, P. C., Kim, J. J., and Racker, E. (1972). *J. Biol. Chem.* **247**, 1338–1339.

Ingledew, W. J., and Moore, A. L., eds. (1979). *Biochem. Soc. Symp., Biochem. Soc. Trans.* **7** (in press).

Ingledew, W. J., Salerno, J. C., and Ohnishi, T. (1976). *Arch. Biochem. Biophys.* **177**, 176–184.

Kell, D. B. (1979). *Biochim. Biophys. Acta* **549**, 55–99.

Klingenberg, M. (1968). *In* "Biological Oxidations" (T. P. Singer, ed.), pp. 3–54. Wiley (Interscience), New York.

Klingenberg, M. (1970). *Eur. J. Biochem.* **13**, 247–252.

Klingenberg, M., and Kröger, A. (1967). *In* "Biochemistry of Mitochondria" (E. C. Slater, Z. Kaniuga, and L. Wojtczak, eds.), pp. 11–27. Academic Press, New York.

Klingenberg, M., and Rottenberg, H. (1977). *Eur. J. Biochem.* **73**, 125–130.

Konstantinov, A. A., and Ruuge, E. K. (1977). *FEBS Lett.* **81**, 137–141.

Kozlov, I. A., and Skulachev, V. P. (1977). *Biochim. Biophys. Acta* **463**, 29–89.

Krab, K., and Wikström, M. (1978). *Biochim. Biophys. Acta* **504**, 200–214.

Krab, K., and Wikström, M. (1979). *Biochim. Biophys. Acta* **548**, 1–15.

Krab, K., and Wikström, M. (1980). *Biochim. Biophys. J.* **186**, 637–639.

Kröger, A., and Klingenberg, M. (1973). *Eur. J. Biochem.* **34**, 358–368.

LaNoue, K., Mizani, S. M., and Klingenberg, M. (1978). *J. Biol. Chem.* **253**, 191–198.

Läuger, P. (1979). *Biochim. Biophys. Acta* **552**, 143–161.

Lawford, H. G., and Garland, P. B. (1972). *Biochem. J.* **130**, 1029–1044.

Lawford, H. G., and Garland, P. B. (1973). *Biochem. J.* **136**, 711–720.

Lee, C. P., Sottocasa, G. L., and Ernster, L. (1967). *Methods Enzymol.* **10**, 33–41.

Lehninger, A. L., Reynafarje, B., and Alexandre, A. (1977). *In* "Structure and Function of Energy-Transducing Membranes" (K. Van Dam and B. F. Van Gelder, eds.), pp. 95–106. Elsevier, Amsterdam.

Lehninger, A. L., Reynafarje, B., and Alexandre, A. (1978). *In* "Frontiers of Biological Energetics" (P. L. Dutton, J. S. Leigh, and A. Scarpa, eds.), pp. 384–393. Academic Press, New York.

Lehninger, A. L., Reynafarje, B., and Alexandre, A. (1979). *In* "Cation Flux across Biomembranes" (Y. Mukohata and L. Packer, eds.), pp. 343–354. Academic Press, New York.

Leung, K. H., and Hinkle, P. C. (1975). *J. Biol. Chem.* **250**, 8467–8471.

Lorusso, M., Capuano, F., Boffoli, D., Stefanelli, R., and Papa, S. (1979). *Biochem. J.* **182**, 133–147.

Lötscher, H. R., Schwerzmann, K., and Carafoli, E. (1979). *FEBS Lett.* **99**, 194–198.

Mailer, N. (1979). Cited by T. Atkinson (1979). "Rolling Stone." Vol. 298, p. 13. Straight Arrow Publ. Inc., New York.

Massari, S., and Azzone, G. F. (1970). *Eur. J. Biochem.* **12**, 310–318.

Mitchell, P. (1961). *Nature (London)* **191**, 144–148.

Mitchell, P. (1966). "Chemiosmotic Coupling in Oxidative and Photosynthetic Phosphorylation." Glynn Research Ltd., Bodmin, U.K.

Mitchell, P. (1968). "Chemiosmotic Coupling and Energy Transduction." Glynn Research Ltd., Bodmin, U.K.

Mitchell, P. (1972). *Fed. Eur. Biochem. Soc. Symp.* **28**, 353–370.

Mitchell, P. (1976a). *Biochem. Soc. Trans.* **4**, 399–430.

Mitchell, P. (1976b). *J. Theor. Biol.* **62**, 327–367.

Mitchell, P. (1977a). *FEBS Lett.* **78**, 1–20.

Mitchell, P. (1977b). *Symp. Soc. Gen. Microbiol.* **27**, 383–423.

Mitchell, P. (1979). *Eur. J. Biochem.* **95**, 1–20.

Mitchell, P., and Moyle, J. (1967a). *Biochem. J.* **105**, 1147–1162.

Mitchell, P., and Moyle, J. (1967b). In "Biochemistry of Mitochondria" (E. C. Slater, Z. Kaniuga, and L. Wojtczak, eds.), pp. 53–74. Academic Press, New York.

Mitchell, P., and Moyle, J. (1967c). *Nature (London)* **213**, 137–139.

Mitchell, P., and Moyle, J. (1967d). *Biochem. J.* **104**, 588–600.

Mitchell, P., and Moyle, J. (1969). *Eur. J. Biochem.* **7**, 471–484.

Mitchell, P., and Moyle, J. (1978). In "Frontiers of Biological Energetics" (P. L. Dutton, J. S. Leigh, and A. Scarpa, eds.), pp. 342–350. Academic Press, New York.

Mitchell, P., and Moyle, J. (1979a). In "Cytochrome Oxidase" (T. E. King, Y. Orii, B. Chance, and K. Okunuki, eds.), pp. 361–372. Elsevier/North-Holland Biomed. Press, Amsterdam.

Mitchell, P., and Moyle, J. (1979b). *Biochem. Soc. Trans.* **7**, 877–894.

Moyle, J., and Mitchell, P. (1973). *Biochem. J.* **132**, 571–585.

Moyle, J., and Mitchell, P. (1977). *FEBS Lett.* **73**, 131–136.

Moyle, J., and Mitchell, P. (1978a). *FEBS Lett.* **88**, 268–272.

Moyle, J., and Mitchell, P. (1978b). *FEBS Lett.* **90**, 361–365.

Mukohata, Y., and Packer, L., eds. (1979). "Cation Flux across Biomembranes." Academic Press, New York.

Nagle, J. F., and Morowitz, H. J. (1978). *Proc. Natl. Acad. Sci. U.S.A.* **75**, 298–302.

Nicholls, D. G. (1974). *Eur. J. Biochem.* **50**, 305–315.

Nicholls, D. G. (1977). *Biochem. Soc. Trans.* **5**, 203–206.

Nicholls, D. G., and Bernson, V. S. M. (1977). *Eur. J. Biochem.* **75**, 601–612.

Nicholls, D. G., and Garland, P. B. (1969). *Biochem. J.* **114**, 215–225.

Nishibayashi-Yamashita, H., Cunningham, C., and Racker, E. (1972). *J. Biol. Chem.* **247**, 698–704.

Ohnishi, T. (1973). *Biochim. Biophys. Acta* **301**, 105–128.

Ohnishi, T. (1975). *Eur. J. Biochem.* **64**, 91–103.

Owen, C. S., and Wilson, D. F. (1974). *Arch. Biochem. Biophys.* **161**, 581–591.

Padan, E., and Rottenberg, H. (1973). *Eur. J. Biochem.* **40**, 431–437.

Papa, S. (1976). *Biochim. Biophys. Acta* **456**, 39–84.

Papa, S., Scarpa, A., Lee, C. P., and Chance, B. (1972). *Biochemistry* **11**, 3091–3098.

Papa, S., Guerrieri, F., Simone, S., and Lorusso, M. (1973). In "Mechanisms in Bioenergetics" (G. F. Azzone, L. Ernster, S. Papa, E. Quagliariello, and N. Siliprandi, eds.), pp. 451–472. Academic Press, New York.

Papa, S., Guerrieri, F., and Lorusso, M. (1974a). In "Dynamics of Energy-Transducing Membranes" (L. Ernster, R. W. Estabrook, and E. C. Slater, eds.), pp. 417–432. Elsevier, Amsterdam.

Papa, S., Guerrieri, F., and Lorusso, M. (1974b). Biochim. Biophys. Acta 357, 181–192.

Papa, S., Lorusso, M., and Guerrieri, F. (1975). Biochim. Biophys. Acta 387, 425–440.

Papa, S., Guerrieri, F., Lorusso, M., Izzo, G., Boffoli, D., and Capuano, F. (1977). In "Biochemistry of Membrane Transport" (G. Semenza and E. Carafoli, eds.), pp. 502–519. Springer-Verlag, Berlin.

Papa, S., Lorusso, M., Guerrieri, F., Izzo, G., and Capuano, F. (1978a). In "The Proton and Calcium Pumps" (G. F. Azzone, M. Avron, J. C. Metcalfe, E. Quagliariello, and N. Siliprandi, eds.), pp. 227–238. Elsevier/North-Holland Biomed. Press, Amsterdam.

Papa, S., Guerrieri, F., Lorusso, M., Izzo, G., Boffoli, D., and Stefanelli, R. (1978b). Fed. Eur. Biochem. Soc. Symp. 45, 37–48.

Papa, S., Guerrieri, F., Lorusso, M., Capuano, F., Izzo, G., and Boffoli, D. (1978c). In "Frontiers of Biological Energetics" (P. L. Dutton, J. S. Leigh, and A. Scarpa, eds.), pp. 367–374. Academic Press, New York.

Papa, S., Capuano, F., Markert, M., and Altamura, N. (1980). FEBS Lett. 111, 243–248.

Penniston, J. T. (1972). Arch. Biochem. Biphys. 150, 556–565.

Penttilä, T., Saraste, M., and Wikström, M. (1979). FEBS Lett. 101, 295–300.

Petty, K. M., Jackson, J. B., and Dutton, P. L. (1977). FEBS Lett. 84, 299–303.

Pozzan, T., Di Virgilio, F., Bragadin, M., Miconi, V., and Azzone, G. F. (1979). Proc. Natl. Acad. Sci. U.S.A. 76, 2123–2127.

Racker, E. (1972). J. Membrane Biol. 10, 221–235.

Ragan, C. I. (1976). Biochim. kBiophys. Acta 456, 249–290.

Ragan, C. I., and Hinkle, P. C. (1975). J. Biol. Chem. 250, 8472–8476.

Reynafarje, B., and Lehninger, A. L. (1977). Biochem. Biophys. Res. Commun. 77, 1273–1279.

Reynafarje, B. and Lehninger, A. L. (1978). J. Biol. Chem. 253, 6331–6334.

Reynafarje, B., Brand, M. D., and Lehninger, A. L. (1976). J. Biol. Chem. 251, 7442–7451.

Rich, P. R., and Moore, A. L. (1976). FEBS Lett. 65, 339–344.

Rieske, J. S. (1976). Biochim. Biophys. Acta 456, 195–247.

Rossi, C. S., and Lehninger, A. L. (1964). J. Biol. Chem. 239, 3971–3980.

Rossi, C. S., Scarpa, A., and Azzone, G. F. (1967). Biochemistry 6, 3902–3911.

Rossi, E., and Azzone, G. F. (1969). Eur. J. Biochem. 7, 418–426.

Rottenberg, H. (1979). Biochim. Biophys. Acta (in press).

Rottenberg, H., and Gutman, M. (1977). Biochemistry 16, 3220–3226.

Rottenberg, H., Caplan, S. R., and Essig, A. (1967). Nature (London) 216, 610–611.

Ruzicka, F. J., Beinert, H., Schepler, K. L., Dunham, W. R., and Sands, R. H. (1975). Proc. Natl. Acad. Sci. U.S.A. 72, 2886–2890.

Rydström, J. (1977). Biochim. Biophys. Acta 463, 155–184.

Salach, J. I., and Bednarz, A. J. (1973). Arch. Biochem. Biophys. 157, 133–144.

Salerno, J. C., Harmon, H. J., Blum, H., Leigh, J. S., and Ohnishi, T. (1977). FEBS Lett. 82, 179–182.

Salerno, J. C., Maida, T., Blum, H., and Ohnishi, T. (1978). In "Frontiers of Biological Energetics" (P. L. Dutton, J. S. Leigh, and A. Scarpa, eds.), pp. 191–200. Academic Press, New York.

Sigel, E., and Carafoli, E. (1978). Eur. J. Biochem. 89, 119–123.

Sigel, E., and Carafoli, E. (1979). J. Biol. Chem. 254, 10572–10574.

Singer, T. P., and Gutman, M. (1971). Adv. Enzymol. 34, 79–153.

Skulachev, V. P. (1971). *Curr. Top. Bioenerg.* **4**, 127–190.

Slater, E. C. (1967a). *Methods Enzymol.* **10**, 48–57.

Slater, E. C. (1967b). *In* "Biochemistry of Mitochondria" (E. C. Slater, Z. Kaniuga, and L. Wojtczak, eds.), pp. 1–10. Academic Press, New York.

Slater, E. C. (1972a). "Mitochondria/Biomembranes," pp. 133–146. North-Holland Publ., Amsterdam.

Slater, E. C. (1972b). *Biochim. Biophys. Acta* **301**, 129–154.

Slater, E. C., Rosing, J., and Mol, A. (1973). *Biochim. Biophys. Acta* **292**, 534–553.

Sorgato, M. C., and Ferguson, S. J. (1978). *FEBS Lett.* **90**, 178–182.

Sorgato, M. C., Ferguson, S. J., Kell, D. B., and John, P. (1978). *Biochem. J.* **174**, 237–256.

Straub, J. P., and Colpa-Boonstra, J. P. (1962). *Biochim. Biophys. Acta* **60**, 650–652.

Thayer, W. S., and Hinkle, P. C. (1973). *J. Biol. Chem.* **248**, 5395–5402.

Trumpower, B. L., and Edwards, C. A. (1979). *FEBS Lett.* **100**, 13–16.

Trumpower, B. L., and Katki, A. (1979). *In* "Membrane Proteins in Energy Transduction" (R. A. Capaldi, ed.), pp. 89–200. Dekker, New York.

Urban, P. F. and Klingenberg, M. (1969). *Eur. J. Biochem.* **9**, 519–525.

Van Buuren, K. J. H. (1972). Ph.D. Thesis, University of Amsterdam.

Van Dam, K., and Westerhoff, H. V. (1977). *In* "Structure and Function of Energy-Transducing Membranes" (K. Van Dam and B. F. Van Gelder, eds.), pp. 157–168. Elsevier, Amsterdam.

Van Dam, K., Wiechman, A. H. C. H., Hellingwerf, K. J., Arents, J. C., and Westerhoff, H. V. (1978a). *Fed. Eur. Biochem. Soc. Symp.* **45**, 121–132.

Van Dam, K., Casey, R. A., Van der Meer, R., Groen, A. K., and Westerhoff, H. V. (1978b). *In* "Frontiers of Biological Energetics" (P. L. Dutton, J. S. Leigh, and A. Scarpa, eds.), pp. 430–438. Academic Press, New York.

Van Gelder, B. F., Van Rijn, J. L. M. L., Schilder, G. J. A., and Wilms, J. (1977). *In* "Structure and Function of Energy-Transducing Membranes" (K. Van Dam and B. F. Van Gelder, eds.), pp. 61–68. Elsevier/North-Holland Biomed. Press, Amsterdam.

Vercesi, A., Reynafarje, B., and Lehninger, A. L. (1978). *J. Biol. Chem.* **253**, 6379–6385.

Wikström, M. K. F. (1972a). *Biochim. Biophys. Acta* **301**, 155–193.

Wikström, M. K. F. (1972b). *In* "Biochemistry and Biophysics of Mitochondrial Membranes" (G. F. Azzone, E. Carafoli, A. L. Lehninger, E. Quagliariello, and N. Siliprandi, eds.), pp. 147–164. Academic Press, New York.

Wikström, M. K. F. (1973). *Biochim. Biophys. Acta* **301**, 155–193.

Wikström, M. K. F. (1974). *Ann. N. Y. Acad. Sci.* **227**, 146–158.

Wikström, M. K. F. (1977). *Nature (London)* **266**, 271–273.

Wikström, M. K. F. (1978). *In* "The Proton and Calcium Pumps" (G. F. Azzone, M. Avron, J. C. Metcalfe, E. Quagliariello, and N. Siliprandi, eds.), pp. 215–226. Elsevier/North-Holland Biomed. Press, Amsterdam.

Wikström, M. (1980). *Curr. Top. Membranes and Transport* (in press).

Wikström, M. K. F., and Berden, J. A. (1972). *Biochim. Biophys. Acta* **283**, 403–420.

Wikström, M., and Krab, K. (1978a). *In* "Energy Conservation in Biological Membranes" (G. Schäfer and M. Klingenberg, eds.), pp. 128–139. Springer-Verlag, Berlin.

Wikström, M., and Krab, K. (1978b). *In* "Frontiers of Biological Energetics" (P. L. Dutton, J. S. Leigh, and A. Scarpa, eds.), pp. 351–358. Academic Press, New York.

Wikström, M., and Krab, K. (1978c). *FEBS Lett.* **91**, 8–14.

Wikström, M., and Krab, K. (1979a). *Biochim. Biophys. Acta* **549**, 177–222.

Wikström, M., and Krab, K. (1979b). *Biochem. Soc. Trans.* **7**, 880–887.

Wikström, M. K. F., and Saari, H. T. (1976). *Mol. Cell. Biochem.* **11**, 17–33.

Wikström, M. K. F., and Saari, H. T. (1977). *Biochim. Biophys. Acta* **462**, 347–361.
Wikström, M., Saari, H., Penttilä, T., and Saraste, M. (1978). *Fed. Eur. Biochem. Soc. Symp.* **45**, 85–94.
Williams, R. J. P. (1973). *Biochem. Soc. Trans.* **1**, 1–26.
Williams, R. J. P. (1974). *Ann. N.Y. Acad. Sci.* **227**, 98–107.
Williams, R. J. P. (1975). *In* "Electron Transfer Chains and Oxidative Phosphorylation" (E. Quagliariello, S. Papa, F. Palmieri, E. C. Slater and N. Siliprandi, eds.), pp. 417–422. Elsevier/North-Holland, Amsterdam.
Wilson, D. F., Erecińska, M., Leigh, J. S., and Koppelman, M. (1972a). *Arch. Biochem. Biophys.* **151**, 112–121.
Wilson, D. F., Lindsay, J. G., and Brocklehurst, E. S. (1972b). *Biochim. Biophys. Acta* **256**, 277–286.
Wilson, D. F., Erecińska, M., Lindsay, J. G., Leigh, J. S., and Owen, C. S. (1975). *Fed. Eur. Biochem. Soc. Symp.* **40**, 195–210.
Witt, H. T. (1978). *Biochim. Biophys. Acta* **505**, 355–427.
Wyman, J. (1948). *Adv. Protein Chem.* **4**, 407–531.
Wyman, J. (1968). *Quart. Rev. Biophys.* **1**, 35–80.

Note Added in Proof

Papa *et al.* (1980) have recently confirmed our conclusion that the very high $\overleftarrow{H}^+/O$ and $\overleftarrow{q}^+/O$ quotients reported by Azzone *et al.* and Lehninger *et al.* are likely to be largely due to a serious underestimation of the rate of oxygen consumption using a conventional Clark electrode (Wikström and Krab, 1978a, 1979a). Based on a kinetically competent spectrophotometric technique in which the O_2 concentration is monitored from the extent of oxygenation of hemoglobin, Papa *et al.* showed that initiation of respiration by succinate in mitochondria results initially in a fast respiratory burst which is too fast to be monitored by a conventional Clark electrode (cf. also Sigel and Carafoli, 1978, for successful use of a fast-responding Clark electrode).

Using this technique for monitoring the rate of oxygen consumption, Papa *et al.* (1980) also reported that the $\overleftarrow{H}^+/O$ ratio is 4 with succinate as substrate (contrast Fig. 1 and Section III). As discussed in Sections IV,A and V,B (and see Wikström and Krab, 1979a; Krab and Wikström, 1979), it is a paramount importance that the determination of the $\overleftarrow{H}^+/O$ quotient of proton translocation is performed at so-called level flow conditions; i.e., conditions where the force opposing the proton translocation ($\Delta\bar{\mu}_{H^+}$) is zero, or at least very small. If this condition is not satisfied, the measured stoichiometry will inevitably be an underestimate due to significant backflow of H^+ into the mitochondria. The component of $\Delta\bar{\mu}_H$ that is most critical in this respect is no doubt $\Delta\psi$, which develops extremely rapidly unless particular care is taken to prevent this by allowing *kinetically competent* charge compensation (cf., Section V,B). This is usually done by allowing K^+ influx into the mitochondria catalyzed by valinomycin.

The unfortunate choice of experimental conditions by Papa *et al.* (1980) most likely led to a serious underestimation of the $\overleftarrow{H}^+/O$ ratio for the reasons explained above. The rat liver mitochondria were suspended aerobically in 130 mM $LiCl_2$ in the presence of valinomycin, but with only 1 mM of KCl. At this potassium concentration even the slower steady-state rate of respiration and H^+ ejection is limited by the low K^+ concentration (Azzone and Massari, 1971; Massari and Azzone, 1970). Moreover, as shown by the latter authors, $LiCl_2$ inhibits K^+ uptake competitively in the presence of valinomycin. It is, therefore, almost certain that the true rate of H^+ translocation was seriously underestimated in these experiments. We should emphasize that Wikström and Krab (1978a) reported a $\overset{\leftarrow}{H}^+/2e^-$ quotient of 5.76 (±0.22 S.D., 5 determinations) for the oxidation of durohydroquinol by rat liver mitochondria suspended in a medium containing a sufficiently high K^+ concentration (+ valinomycin), determining the rate of electron transfer spectrophotometrically by monitoring the rate of generation of duroquinone. This finding may be related to the report by Capuano *et al.* (1980) that the rates of electron transport are the same whether measured by the hemoglobin or the duroquinone method, during oxidation of durohydroquinol by rat liver mitochondria.

Uptake and Release of Bivalent Cations in Mitochondria[1]

NILS-ERIK SARIS AND KARL E. O. ÅKERMAN

Department of Medical Chemistry
University of Helsinki
Helsinki Finland

[1] Dedicated to Eva.

I. Introduction

The mitochondrial transport of bivalent cations has been studied extensively during the past 20 years. Despite these efforts, the molecular mechanisms involved are still poorly understood. Mitochondria carry out a great number of reactions and contain many enzyme systems. The proteins functioning in the transport therefore certainly constitute only a minuscule fraction of the mitochondrial proteins. It is understandable that the elucidation of the mechanism has been a much more difficult task than, for example, the mechanism of calcium transport in the sarcoplasmic reticulum, which was discovered at about the same time (Ebashi, 1961; Hasselbach and Makinose, 1961). The sarcoplasmic reticulum is specialized in transporting calcium, the transport protein constituting a major part of the membrane (see review by MacLennan, 1975). The challenge to learn more about the mitochondrial transport of bivalent cations despite the complexities of mitochondrial function is spurred by the importance of intracellular Ca^{2+} in vertebrate metabolism and in the control of many physiological processes (see reviews by Carafoli, 1974; Baker, 1976; Lehninger *et al.*, 1978a; Bygrave, 1978). True, mitochondria are not the only membrane system involved, and their relative importance may vary from cell type to cell type (see review by Carafoli and Crompton, 1978). Thus, in some cells mitochondria seem to be involved mainly as a calcium buffer coming into play only when the free Ca^{2+} in the cytosol becomes excessively high, whereas in others it seems to be intimately related to the physiological modulation of the free Ca^{2+} in the cytosol. In addition, the bivalent cation transporting system is involved in the transport of Fe^{2+} for heme synthesis (see Section V,E) and it is implicated in the toxic responses to various heavy metals (see Section V,F). Since cation transport and oxidative phosphorylation both are expressions of energy conversion in mitochondria, the understanding of the mechanism of bivalent cation transport is of great theoretical importance also in relation to the mechanism of oxidative phosphorylation. Indeed, mitochondrial Ca^{2+} transport is one of the tools presently used to test theories on energy coupling (see Section III,B).

The most thoroughly studied cation is Ca^{2+}. The aim of the present review is to present the recent advances in this area. Other cations of interest are also accommodated. The mechanism of the transport system is also treated with particular emphasis on whether one or several transport systems are present in mitochondria, on the control of bivalent cation influx and efflux as well as on differences between different cations. The review includes studies published or brought to our attention before July 1979. The vast number of papers published on the subject make a complete treatise difficult. The reader is advised to consult some of the recent reviews (Carafoli and Crompton, 1976, 1978; Bygrave, 1977). For early work there are two comprehensive reviews (Chance, 1965; Lehninger *et al.*, 1967). We will quote earlier studies only when they are especially pertinent to our topics.

Our interest in bivalent cation transport stems from a visit by one of us to the Reeves Johnson Foundation at the University of Pennsylvania, Philadelphia, in 1959. Dr. Britton Chance then provided an excellent pH meter, hoping that methods could be developed to follow oxidative phosphorylation and ATP hydrolysis (see Saris, 1959; Nishimura *et al.*, 1962). When Ca^{2+}-activated mitochondrial ATPase was studied, an acidification of the medium far in excess of that expected from hydrolysis of ATP ensued. A cycle of a pH drop followed by a rise on addition of Ca^{2+} was observed in coupled mitochondria even in the absence of ATP. Unfortunately, these studies were interrupted by the necessity of returning to Finland, and other responsibilities and lack of suitable equipment delayed the pursuit of this line of research for a couple of years. In a lecture before the Finnish Chemical Society, these results were interpreted as being due to an active ion transport with extrusion of H^+ and uptake of Ca^{2+} leading to gradients of H^+ and Ca^{2+} over the inner membrane (Saris, 1959). To our knowledge, this was the first time that a active transport of H^+ and Ca^{2+} in mitochondria was suggested. Earlier, Slater and Cleland (1953) had shown that Ca^{2+} was accumulated by mitochondria, but this was thought to be due to energy-independent binding. Our studies continued, and the results were presented to the Nordic Biochemical Meeting in 1962 (Saris, 1963a) and published *in extenso* as a thesis monograph (Saris, 1963b). In these studies small pulses of Ca^{2+} were added to energized mitochondria and the uptake of Ca^{2+} could be distinguished from secondary effects leading to the release of Ca^{2+}. These data may be of historical interest, but they had little impact on the scientific community at that time. In the meantime DeLuca and Engström (1961) and Vasington and Murphy (1962) were the first actually to measure uptake of Ca^{2+} by using ^{45}Ca. Their emphasis was on massive uptake of Ca^{2+} in the presence of inorganic phosphate and ATP.

Our knowledge and understanding of mitochondrial systems has been greatly advanced since these early studies. In our opinion the most significant contributions were the introduction of ionophores by Pressman (1965), which has advanced greatly our understanding of ion transport mechanisms; the use of swelling to study permeabilities toward cations and anions by Chappell and Crofts (1965); the stressing of the importance of H^+ and membrane potential in energy coupling and ion transport (Mitchell, 1966); the introduction of spectrophotometric methods for kinetic studies of bivalent cation transport (Chance, 1965); use of the metal indicators murexide (Mela and Chance, 1968) and Arsenoazo III (Scarpa, 1975); the use of the specific inhibitors of bivalent cation transport, La^{3+} (Mela, 1968), and ruthenium red (Moore, 1971); the introduction of more stringent methods for kinetic studies by controlling the extramitochondrial free Ca^{2+} concentration using Ca^{2+} buffers (Carafoli and Azzi, 1971; Bygrave et al., 1971); the demonstration of specific exchange systems for efflux of Ca^{2+} in mitochondria from excitable tissues (Carafoli, 1973), and the demonstration of Ca^{2+} transport by mitochondria in situ in cells (Baker et al., 1971). During the last few years, which this review mainly covers, the emphasis has been shifted from studies of energized uptake of bivalent cations to the efflux mechanisms and the overall regulation of uptake and release of mainly Ca^{2+}.

In our review we will critically treat and examine areas of controversy, e.g., the stoichiometry of $Me^{2+}/0$, Me^{2+}/H^+, the coupling of Me^{2+} fluxes to $\Delta\psi$, ΔpH, and anion fluxes, and the existence of one or several transport systems. To resolve the controversies it is often necessary critically to evaluate the approaches and techniques used in order to become aware of their shortcomings and pitfalls and thereby assess the reliability of the more or less conflicting conclusions of the various groups.

II. Basic Concepts of Ion Transport across Membranes

The molecular mechanisms involved in the transfer of hydrophilic substances across the energy barrier created by the hydrophobic core of biological membranes are as yet far from clear. In this chapter we will make only some brief points on the subject of ion transport relevant to the present review. For more thorough information, the following reviews and monographs should be consulted: Harris (1956), Wilbrandt (1974), Ovchinnikov (1974, 1979), Kotyk and Janáček (1975).

A. Ionophores as Models of Ion Translocators

Much information concerning the transfer of ions across membranes is obtained from studies on substances, either isolated from microorganisms or synthesized chemically, that specifically increase ionic permeabilities in membranes (Pressman, 1965; Chappell and Crofts, 1965; Gómez-Púyou and Gómez-Lojero, 1977). Two types of ionophores can thus be distinguished, namely carriers and channel formers. The carriers can be further classified as electroneutral exchangers and ion conductors. Table I summarizes the properties of some commonly used ionophores. Chemically most ionophores, except some synthesized ones, are small peptides. It is conceivable that similar amino acid groups may also be present in membrane transport proteins. The carrier-type ionophores form a hydrophobic shell around the ion, and the ion–carrier complex may then diffuse freely across the membrane. The interior of the carrier molecule is hydrophilic, its atomic groups substituting for the hydration shell of the ion translocated (Ovchinnikov, 1979). The ionic specificity is thus dependent on the dimensions of the hydrophilic cavity in the interior of the ionophore molecule and its capability for ion transfer depends on the solubility of the complex in the membrane.

The channel formers create pores or holes in the membrane through which ions can diffuse. The ion specificity of the pore is determined by its diameter (Ovchinnikov, 1974, 1979) and also by groups at its mouth (Apell

TABLE I

PROPERTIES OF SOME COMMONLY USED IONOPHORES[a]

Name	Mode of transport	Charge transfer	Selectivity
Valinomycin	Carrier	+	$Rb^+ > K^+ \gg Na^+$
Gramicidin	Channel	+	$H^+ > Rb^+ > K^+ \cong Na^+$
Nigericin	Carrier	H^+/Me^+ exchange	$K^+ > Rb^+ > Na^+$
Dianemycin	Carrier	H^+/Me^+ exchange	$Rb^+ \cong K^+ \cong Na^+$
A23187	Carrier	$2H^+/Me^{2+}$ exchange	$Mg^{2+} > Ca^{2+}$
X537A	Carrier	$2H^+/Me^{2+}$ exchange	$Ba^{2+} > Ca^{2+} > Mn^{2+} > Sr^{2+} \gg Mg^{2+}$

[a] Data were taken from Gómez-Púyou and Gómez-Lojero (1977).

et al., 1977). The molecular conformations of some ionophores and their metal complexes have been throughly studied (Ovchinnikov, 1979).

B. Analysis of the Features of Transport Systems

As in the case of ionophores, translocators in biological membranes may also be classified as either channels or carriers even if often they are more complex than simple ionophores. Transport systems have been characterized using graphical and mathematical methods developed from those used in enzyme kinetics (Kotyk and Janáček, 1975). Thus a channel-mediated transport may be expected to obey first-order kinetics. A carrier, on the other hand, should exhibit saturation kinetics (Wilbrandt, 1974). For several reasons these criteria are far from satisfactory, however, since in certain conditions a channel mechanism may mimic a carrier-type mechanism in this respect. This would be the case when restrictions in the space of diffusion are present —for instance, owing to high saturation of a limited amount of channels (Wilbrandt, 1974). Also osmotic factors might cause such an effect (Wilbrandt, 1974). A carrier-mediated mechanism may, on the other hand, mimic a channel —for instance, at low substrate concentration (Wilbrandt, 1974).

Because the channel mechanism involves diffusion of the ion, it is usually rather insensitive to temperature. The carrier mechanism, on the other hand, involves a diffusion of a carrier–ion complex or a conformational change; hence such a mechanism would be sensitive to the physical state of membrane lipids, which is strongly influenced by temperature (Chapman, 1975). Thus, for instance, the conductance of black lipid membranes is sensitive to temperature in the presence of a carrier type of ionophore, e.g., valinomycin, whereas this is not the case in the presence of a channel former, e.g., gramicidin (Krasne *et al.*, 1971). Other methods of distinguishing channels and carriers involve demonstration of counter movements (Wilbrandt, 1974), i.e., kinetic analysis of the translocator with different concentrations of different substrates on either side of the membrane.

C. Electrical and Chemical Coupling of Transport

Since the transfer of an ion across the membrane involves a transfer of electrical charge across a dielectric medium, net movement of the ion would be retarded and eventually cease because of the development of an electrical potential across the membrane. Therefore, the charge transfer must be compensated for by the movement of a charge of similar sign in the opposite direction or by movement of a charge of opposite sign in the

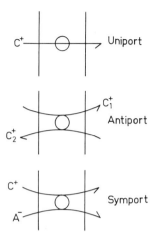

FIG. 1. Transport by uniport, antiport, and symport. C^+ denotes the cation, and A^- the anion.

same direction. Mitchell (1966) has proposed a terminology for classifying the coupling of such movements (Fig. 1). If the translocator transfers the ion from one side of the membrane to the other without direct coupling to the movement of another ion, the translocator is called a uniporter. The uniporter must, however, be coupled to another uniporter in order to get a net movement, and the rate of the transport will depend on the permeability of the more slowly translocated ion. If the translocator exchanges one ion for another, it is called an antiporter. If it moves the ion together with another in the same direction (of the opposite charge) it is called a symporter.

Of the ionophores the carriers, valinomycin and channel gramicidin, are typical examples of uniporters. The H^+/cation exchanger nigericin behaves as an antiporter (Table I).

D. COUPLING OF TRANSPORT TO ENERGY

If the translocation of an ion occurs against its electrochemical potential the translocation is active; i.e., it has to be coupled to an energy-yielding reaction. If the ion diffuses only along its electrochemical gradient, the translocation is passive (Kotyk and Janàćek, 1975).

Active and passive transport processes are usually differentiated by removing the energy source by means of metabolic inhibitors. This does not, however, exclude a passive transport process, since the translocation might be electrically or chemically coupled to an active translocation. Ac-

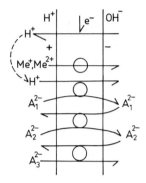

Fig. 2. Coupling of cation uptake to electron flow-induced membrane potential and anion fluxes to H^+ fluxes in energized mitochondria.

cording to Mitchell (1966), only the H^+ ion appears to be actively translocated in the mitochondrial membrane. The transport of all other ions are chemically or electrically coupled to this active process (Fig. 2).

III. General Features of Mitochondrial Bivalent Cation Transport

A. Mitochondrial Responses to Bivalent Cations

This subject has been reviewed extensively by Lenhinger et al. (1967), Lehninger (1970), Carafoli (1974), and Bygrave (1977), and thus will not be accounted for here in detail.

Additions of Ca^{2+} to respiring mitochondria cause a stimulation of respiration (Chance, 1956) (Fig. 3A), redox changes in components of the respiratory chain (Chance, 1965), increase in heat production (Poe, 1969), and proton ejection (Saris, 1959, 1963a,b; Chappell et al., 1962) (Fig. 3B) concomitant with the uptake of this cation. Similar changes have also been observed with other cations, which are translocated by the bivalent cation translocator, namely Sr^{2+}, Ba^{2+}, and Mn^{2+} (Saris, 1963b; Chappell et al., 1963; Drahota et al., 1970; Vainio et al., 1970). With succinate as substrate Ca^{2+}/O ratios varying between 3 (Chance, 1965) and 4 (Lehninger, 1970) have been reported. A more detailed analysis of this is provided by Wikström and Krab in this volume.

In the respiratory chain, cytochrome b becomes more reduced, pyridine nucleotides, and cytochrome $a + a_3$ more oxidized. Cytochrome c is initially reduced and then oxidized (Chance, 1965). The H^+/Ca^{2+} ratio is generally considered to be 1 in the presence of inorganic phosphate and 2

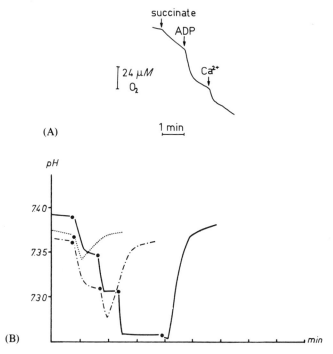

FIG. 3. (A) Ca²⁺-induced respiratory responses. Mitochondria, 1.4 mg protein per milliliter, were suspended in a medium containing sucrose (250 mM), Hepes (10 mM), Pᵢ (3 mM), rotenone (5 μM), pH 7.4. Additions: Succinate (6 mM) ADP (100 μM), and Ca²⁺ (100 μM). (B) Ca²⁺-induced pH changes in a mitochondrial suspension. Mitochondria, 1.9 mg protein per milliliter were in a medium containing sucrose (50 mM); KCl (40 mM); substrate, when present, 4.5 mM, pH 7.4. Ca²⁺ was added in amounts corresponding to 91 μM at the points. ——, Succinate present; — · — · — ·, 2-hydroxybutyrate present; · · · · , no added substrates. Minutes are indicated by dots on the abscissa. From Saris (1963b).

in its absence (Lehninger *et al.*, 1967; Lehninger, 1970). Controversies have recently arisen concerning the H⁺/Ca²⁺ stoichiometry, which will be discussed further in Section III,B.

During respiration in the absence of phosphate, isolated mitochondria take up about 100 nmol of Ca²⁺ per milligram of mitochondrial protein (Lehninger, 1970). However, if endogenous phosphate is completely depleted from the mitochondria (Crompton *et al.*, 1978a) or its movements blocked with *N*-ethylmaleimide (NEM) or Mersalyl, the mitochondrial Ca²⁺ uptake capacity is decreased to 20 nmol per milligram of protein (Bygrave *et al.*, 1977); Ramachandran and Bygrave, 1978; Crompton *et al.*, 1978a) or less (Harris and Zaba, 1977). This point will be further discussed in detail in Section IV,C. In the presence of added phosphate (Lehninger, 1970) or other weak acid anions (Lehninger, 1974) mitochondria take up Ca^{2+} at about 300 nmol per milligram of protein (Lehninger *et al.*, 1967; Lehninger, 1970). When both ATP and phosphate are present the Ca^{2+} uptake capacity may exceed 1000 nmol per milligram of protein. This event is called "massive loading" and leads to the appearance of electron-dense deposits in the mitochondrial matrix space (Lehninger, 1970).

B. Driving Force of Bivalent Cation Uptake in Mitochondria

In 1966 Mitchell postulated that the driving force of mitochondrial bivalent cation uptake is a membrane potential with negative intramitochondrial polarity. According to his "chemiosmotic" hypothesis, a proton electrochemical gradient ($\Delta\bar{\mu}H^+$, PMF) results during respiration from a vectorial transport of protons across the membrane from the inner side of the mitochondrial membrane to the external (Mitchell, 1966, 1968). The $\Delta\bar{\mu}H^+$ consists of a proton gradient (ΔpH, alkaline inside) and a membrane potential ($\Delta\psi$, ΔE, negative polarity inside the mitochondrion) with the following relation

$$\Delta\bar{\mu}H^+ = 60 \,\Delta pH + \Delta\psi \tag{1}$$

If there is a reverse relationship between the respiratory rate and membrane potential (Mitchell, 1966, 1968), then the H^+ ion efflux during Ca^{2+} uptake can be explained as a decrease in $\Delta\psi$ and a compensating increase in respiration and ΔpH. Thus if two H^+ ions are extruded per Ca^{2+} ion taken up and other simultaneous proton movements are excluded, one can predict that Ca^{2+} is transferred across the membrane with two net positive charges.

Before we go into this problem in detail, other reactions in mitochondria that produce or consume protons should be recognized. Proton influx may occur through the H^+ phosphate symporter (Brand *et al.*, 1976b) or with endogenous carbonic acid (Lehninger, 1974; Harris, 1978) leading to low H^+/Ca^{2+} ratios. This can be prevented if phosphate is depleted or its uptake blocked with NEM or Mersalyl (Brand *et al.*, 1976b) and carbonic anhydrase inhibited (Harris, 1978). In the presence of NEM and Mersalyl, far higher H^+/Ca^{2+} (Reynafarje and Lehninger, 1977) and H^+/Mn^{2+} (Pozzan *et al.*, 1976) ratios have been observed than in their absence. On the other hand, NEM and Mersalyl cause an increased K^+ ion permeability (Brierley *et al.*, 1977; Jung *et al.*, 1977), which in some cases might cause charge compensation. Then, measured stoichiometries of H^+/Me^{2+}

might not be valid, especially in steady states. Proton efflux may occur owing to hydrolysis of endogenous ATP if the mitochondrial ATPase is not blocked with oligomycin (Brand and Lehninger, 1975). Surface binding of Ca^{2+} and possible proton release from surface sites (Scarpa and Azzi, 1968) in some cases should be prevented—for instance, by including Mg^{2+} in the medium. Furthermore, some proton influx might occur via influx with endogenous fatty acid unless albumin is used to bind these. Most of these difficulties can be overcome by measuring the ruthenium red-sensitive proton release (Crompton and Heid, 1978). Real initial rate values are also most reliable for measurements of stoichiometries. However, in this case the response time of the equipment used should be known (Wikström and Krab, 1979). These potential difficulties have only recently been stressed. Therefore we cite only the latest papers where adequate precautions have been taken.

Recently Moyle and Mitchell (1977a) reported that only one proton is extruded per Ca^{2+} taken up even in the presence of 30 nmol of NEM per milligram of protein. The workers measured only the steady-state efflux of H^+ using succinate as substrate, and assumed that all Ca^{2+} was taken up. On the basis of these data, they suggested that Ca^{2+} is taken up with a single net charge by a phosphate/Ca^{2+} symporter (Moyle and Mitchell, 1977a,b). The results of Moyle and Mitchell were questioned by Reynafarje and Lehninger (1977), who measured both initial rate values and the steady-state distribution of the ions and arrived at a value of 2 in both conditions. Other workers have also claimed that 30 nmol of NEM per milligram protein does not completely prevent H^+ reuptake via the H^+/phosphate symporter (Pfeiffer et al., 1978). With different experimental approaches using succinate as substrate, several other workers, including ourselves, also have arrived at a value of 2 (Crompton and Heid, 1978; Williams and Fry, 1979) or near 2 (Åkerman and Saris, 1978; Pfeiffer et al., 1978) when initial rate values have been determined both with rat liver and heart mitochondria. In the presence of NEM, a H^+/Mn^{2+} ratio near 2 has also been measured (Pozzan et al., 1976). Using different media we have found a somewhat lower H^+/Ca^{2+} ratio (about 1.5) in sucrose-based media than in the presence of KCl (Åkerman and Saris, 1978). Wikström has also arrived at H^+/Ca^{2+} ratios suggesting the transfer of Ca^{2+} with two charges when he measured Ca^{2+} uptake and proton release in conditions, where only the terminal part of the respiratory chain was active with ferrocyanide as electron donor (Wikström, 1978). This ratio depends on the finding that four electrical charge equivalents are translocated by the cytochrome c oxidase per pair of electrons (Wikström, 1977). Since the techniques for measurements of H^+/Ca^{2+} ratios used by Moyle and Mitchell (1977a) are open to criticism, and other workers (cf. Table II) have

TABLE II

H^+/Me^{2+} Ratios Obtained by Different Workers under Different Conditions

Conditions[a]	H^+/Me^{2+}		Reference
	Initial rate	Steady state	
KCl, 60 μM Ca²⁺, succinate, NEM, RLM	—	1 H⁺/Ca²⁺ in external medium prior to experiment	Moyle and Mitchell (1977a)
KCl, 42 μM Ca²⁺, succinate, NEM, RLM	2H⁺/Ca²⁺	2H⁺/Ca²⁺	Reynafarje and Lehninger (1977)
KCl, 35–74 μM Ca²⁺, succinate, NEM, RaLM, RaHM	2H⁺/Ca²⁺	2H⁺/Ca²⁺	Williams and Fry (1979)
KCl, Ca²⁺, succinate Mersalyl, ruthenium red-sensitive fluxes, RHM	2H⁺/Ca²⁺	<2H⁺/Ca²⁺	Crompton and Heid (1978)
KCl, MgCl₂, 50 μM Ca²⁺, succinate, oligomycin, NEM, BSA, RLM	2H⁺/Ca²⁺	—	Åkerman and Saris (1978)
Sucrose, MgCl₂ 64 nmol Mn²⁺/mg protein, succinate, NEM, RLM	—	1.7H⁺/Mn²⁺	Pozzan et al. (1976)
Mannitol, succinate, 75 μM Ca²⁺, NEM, RLM	—	1.4H⁺/Ca²⁺	Pfeiffer et al. (1978)
Sucrose, MgCl₂, 50 μM Ca²⁺, oligomycin, NEM, BSA, RLM	1.5 H⁺/Ca²⁺	—	Åkerman and Saris (1978)
KCl, succinate, BSA, RLM	—	1.7 β-(OH)butyrate/Ca²⁺	Brand et al. (1976a)

[a] RLM, rat liver mitochondria; RHM, rat heart mitochondria; RaLM, rabbit liver mitochondria; RaHM, rabbit heart mitochondria; NEM, N-ethylmaleimide; BSA, bovine serum albumin.

obtained a H^+/Ca^{2+} stoichiometry of 2, the latter value seems more reliable. Table II compares H^+/Me^{2+} stoichiometries obtained by different workers under different conditions.

Further evidence in favor of the mitochondrial membrane potential being the driving force of bivalent cation uptake comes from the fact that the uptake can be driven by an artificial K^+ ion diffusion potential created by aid of the cation conductor valinomycin (Scarpa and Azzone, 1970). The uptake can also be driven by a diffusion potential of the negatively charged freely permeable anion SCN (Selwyn *et al.*, 1970a). It is of importance in this context that if the ratio of K^+ extrusion/Ca^{2+} uptake is measured during valinomycin-induced uptake, a value near 2 is observed both for initial rate determinations (Åkerman, 1978a) and at a steady state (Azzone *et al.*, 1976; Åkerman, 1978a).

The mitochondrial membrane is depolarized during Ca^{2+} uptake (Åkerman, 1978b), and the uptake rate correlates linearity with the magnitude of membrane potential (Åkerman, 1978b). Furthermore, measurements of the mitochondrial Ca^{2+} conductance in the presence of a $2H^+/Me^{2+}$ exchanger A23187 also are in agreement with an electrogenic uptake of this cation (Heaton and Nicholls, 1976). In this case, the membrane is depolarized and a Ca^{2+} closed-circuit current (electrogenic uptake versus electroneutral release) is induced across the membrane, and the Ca^{2+} stimulated respiration continues until anaerobiosis.

When Ca^{2+} efflux is induced across the mitochondrial membrane by adding the Ca^{2+} chelators EGTA or NTA (nitriloacetate) to deenergized mitochondrial suspensions, a diffusion potential of Ca^{2+} can be recorded (Wikström and Saari, 1976; Åkerman, 1978b) by using spectral changes of cytochrome c oxidase (Wikström and Saari, 1976) or by the safranine method (Åkerman, 1978b) as indicators of charge transfer. The charge stoichiometry as measured with safranine in using different Ca^{2+} gradients appears to be near 1 in these conditions. This might suggest with some reservation that Ca^{2+} efflux occurs by an electroneutral process as well (see Section IV,D).

Measurements of $^{86}Rb^+$ and $^{45}Ca^{2+}$ ratios across the mitochondrial membrane in the presence of valinomycin during respiration at steady state have suggested that Ca^{2+} is distributed across the membrane with two positive charges according to the Nernst equation (Rottenberg and Scarpa, 1974). The predicted relationship between the cation ratio according to the Nernst equation

$$E = \frac{RT}{ZF} \ln \frac{(cation)_{in}}{(cation)_{out}}$$

would be

$$\log \frac{(Ca)_{in}}{(Ca)_{out}} = 2 \log \frac{(Rb)_{in}}{(Rb)_{out}} \qquad (2)$$

at equilibrium. The workers arrived at values close to this prediction. A similar conclusion has been drawn by Crompton and Heid (1978), who kept the intramitochondrial Ca^{2+} concentration constant and varied only the external Ca^{2+} concentration and membrane potential using an uncoupler, carbonyl cyanide p-trifluoromethoxyphenylhydrazone (FCCP). These experiments, however, are open to some criticism. Rottenberg and Scarpa (1974) measured the cation ratios in the presence of acetate and assumed that all Ca^{2+} was in a free state inside the mitochondria under their conditions, which might not have been the case (Azzone et al., 1976; Massari and Pozzan, 1976; Puskin et al., 1976). Crompton and Heid (1978) based their experimental approach on the assumption that the Ca^{2+} distribution ratio at steady state correlates linearly with the membrane potential, which by no means need be the case. Furthermore, they were unable to measure Ca^{2+} distributions at membrane potentials higher than 90 mV. They were, however, able to exclude wrong conclusions due to binding of Ca^{2+} inside mitochondria, and thus their method offers an interesting approach. Other workers have failed to see a simple quantitative correlation between monovalent and bivalent cation distribution ratios when conditions have been varied (Azzone et al., 1976; Massari and Pozzan, 1976; Puskin et al., 1976; Pozzan et al., 1977). Furthermore, if Ca^{2+} is distributed with two net positive charges to steady state with a membrane potential of 180 mV (Rottenberg, 1973; Nicholls, 1974, Åkerman and Wikström, 1976) or more (Mitchell and Moyle, 1969a), very high gradients ($r = 10^6$) of this cation would be created across the mitochondrial membrane (Azzone et al., 1975; Crompton and Carafoli, 1976). This could suggest that measured bivalent cation ratios partially represent internally bound cations. Electron paramagnetic resonance (EPR) measurements with Mn^{2+} have indeed shown that about 97% of this cation is bound to phosphate (Pozzan et al., 1976) or some other substances (Puskin and Gunter, 1972; Puskin et al., 1976). Calorimetric measurements during Ca^{2+} uptake are also in agreement with this (Poe, 1969). Azzone et al. (1976) have shown by measuring volume changes (Fig. 4) during cation uptake in the presence of acetate that the activity coefficient for Ca^{2+} and Sr inside mitochondria could vary between 0.1 and 1. We have also found that the matrix concentration of various bivalent cations accumulated by energized mitochondria is low, since only Ba^{2+} is precipitated by sulfate (see Section IV,C).

It is concluded that the bivalent cations appear to be taken up with two positive charges across the mitochondrial membrane, and that the factors

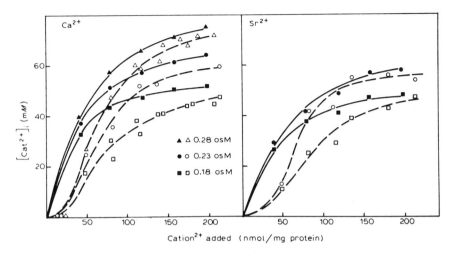

Fig. 4. Calculated matrix Me^{2+} concentrations as a function of added cation. The medium contained 10 mM acetate and various amounts of sucrose; for further experimental details see the original publication. $[Me^{2+}]_{in}$, calculated by assumming an activity coefficient of 1 for the total cation taken up. - - -, $[Me^{2+}]_{in}$, calculated from data on measured matrix volumes. Adapted from Azzone *et al.* (1976).

determining the steady-state ratio of the cations probably are more complex than a simple distribution according to the Nernst equation (Azzone *et al.*, 1976; Massari and Pozzan, 1976; Puskin *et al.*, 1976), possibly involving a separate efflux mechanism (Puskin *et al.*, 1976; Carafoli and Cromptin, 1976; Nicholls, 1978a; Åkerman, 1978c (see Section IV,D).

C. Inhibitors of Bivalent Cation Uptake

Since the uptake of Ca^{2+} and the other bivalent cations is coupled to the energy state of the mitochondrion, the process can be inhibited by agents that interfere with electron transport and coupling.

Trivalent rare earth cations of the lanthanide series, on the other hand, inhibit bivalent cation uptake specifically (Mela, 1968, 1969) in a competitive manner (Reed and Bygrave, 1974b) without interfering with other functions of mitochondria. The apparent K_i for the inhibition is very low (about 20 nM, Reed and Bygrave, 1974b); this would suggest that the amount of bivalent cation translocator in the mitochondria is small (about 1 pmol per milligram of protein, Reed and Bygrave, 1974b). There are some differences in the sensitivity between different bivalent cations toward the inhibition by lanthanides (see Section V,D). Also heavy metal cations, for instance Cd^{2+}, inhibit mitochondrial Ca^{2+} uptake competitively (Saris and Järvisalo, 1977).

Ruthenium red, a hexavalent polysaccharide stain, inhibits Ca^{2+} uptake (Moore, 1971; Vasington *et al.*, 1972) in a noncompetitive manner (Reed and Bygrave, 1974b). With a recrystallized ruthenium red preparation, a K_i near 30 nM has been obtained (Reed and Bygrave, 1974b). The purification of ruthenium red is important, since commerical preparations contain Ru^{3+} and other ruthenium analogs that may affect Ca^{2+} transport or other mitochondrial functions (Vasington *et al.*, 1972; Rossi *et al.*, 1973). It is also important to note that ruthenium red should always be added directly to the mitochondrial suspension in order to get full inhibition (Reed and Bygrave, 1974b). The reason for this is that ruthenium red binds very strongly to glass and plastic materials, and hence its active concentration is decreased. Ruthenium red is also easily inactivated in dilute solutions (Fletcher *et al.*, 1961; Luft, 1971; Reed and Bygrave, 1974b). Furthermore, high concentrations of ruthenium red might inhibit mitochondrial respiration (Vasington *et al.*, 1972). Ruthenium red is oxidized also by mitochondria in some conditions (Schwerzmann *et al.*, 1976).

The mechanism of the inhibition of bivalent cation uptake by La^{3+} and ruthenium red is not known with any certainty at present. It is generally agreed that the inhibition by La^{3+} is competitive (Reed and Bygrave, 1974b), which would suggest that this trivalent cation competes with the bivalent cations at some step of their translocation sequence. In an interesting study using several lanthanide ions, Tew (1977) found that those lanthanides whose ionic radii were closest to that of Ca^{2+} were most potent as inhibitors. This would suggest that a specific space requirement is needed for the inhibition. Ruthenium red is a hexavalent ammonium and ruthenium complex with a high charge density (Fletcher *et al.*, 1961). It has been used as an extracellular marker of acidic polysaccharides and glycoproteins (Luft, 1971), but it is bound also by other negatively charged substances, e.g., nucleic acids and acidic phospholipids (Luft, 1971). Thus, it could interfere with mitochondrial bivalent cation uptake in many different ways—for instance, by screening negative charges and affecting the zeta potential either generally or in a localized specific region. The fact that ruthenium red does not inhibit Ca^{2+} uptake in mitochondria mediated by an electrogenic synthetic uncharged ionophore (Niggli *et al.*, 1978) would suggest that ruthenium red does not inhibit Ca^{2+} uptake by a general effect on the zeta potential. On the other hand, the binding of this inhibitor to some local negative charges is highly likely. It cannot be decided with certainty whether ruthenium red inhibits by binding to components of the transport system or whether its effect is due to interfering with the transport in some other way (see Section VII). Hexamine cobalt, which structurally resembles ruthenium red, also inhibits mitochondrial Ca^{2+} transport specifically (Tashmukhamedov et al., 1972). It has been less used as an inhibitor and therefore its interactions with mitochondria have not been characterized in much detail.

The Mg^{2+} causes some inhibition of mitochondrial Ca^{2+} uptake (Vainio et al., 1970; Sordahl, 1974), especially at low external Ca^{2+} concentrations (Crompton et al., 1976a; Hutson et al., 1976; Åkerman et al., 1977; Åkerman, 1977a). The effect of Mg^{2+} is probably due to its ability to inhibit the surface binding of Ca^{2+} (Åkerman et al., 1977; Åkerman, 1977a) because rather high concentrations are needed. Spermine, a tetravalent polyamine has an effect on Ca^{2+} transport similar to that of Mg^{2+} (Åkerman, 1977a). Spermine is known to interfere with the mitochondrial surface charge, possibly by screening negative charges on phospholipids (Huunan-Seppälä and Nordling, 1971). It also inhibits the surface binding of Ca^{2+} competitively (Åkerman, 1977a). Magnesium and spermine inhibit both Ca^{2+} binding and Ca^{2+} transport at the same concentrations, which are far above the Ca^{2+} concentrations used in experiments (see Section III,D). Uptake of Ba^{2+} is more strongly inhibited by Mg^{2+} than the uptake of other bivalent cations, and Mn^{2+} uptake is slightly stimulated by low concentrations of Mg^{2+} (see Section V,D). Either K^+ does not significantly affect Ca^{2+} uptake (Vainio et al., 1970; Åkerman, 1977a), or it inhibits it slightly (Hutson et al., 1976). In the latter work the slight inhibition by K^+ observed is uncertain at present, since the workers used A23187 in their experimental medium, which also transports K^+ (Pfeiffer and Lardy, 1976). It is of interest, however, that the uptake of Ba^{2+} is almost completely inhibited by 20 mM KCl (see Sections IV,B and V,D). There is some inhibitory effect of Na^+ on Ca^{2+} uptake by mitochondria from heart (Noack and Greeff, 1975). However, as this cation causes Ca^{2+} efflux, the inhibition is uncertain at present (Carafoli, 1973).

As the bivalent cations Ca^{2+}, Sr^{2+}, Ba^{2+}, and Mn^{2+} (see Section V,D) apparently are translocated by the same translocator, they are expected to inhibit the uptake of each other competitively. At least Sr^{2+} (Carafoli, 1965a), Ba^{2+} (Åkerman et al., 1977), and Mn^{2+} (Baker and Schlaepfer, 1978) inhibit mitochondrial Ca^{2+} uptake. The inhibition caused by Ba^{2+} is of a competitive nature only in the presence of K^+ and Mg^{2+}, and its K_i decreases in a medium of low ionic strength. The implications of this result are discussed in Sections III,D, IV,A, and IV,B.

A number of pharmacological agents including β-adrenergic blocking agents (Noack and Greeff, 1971), guanidines (Davidoff, 1974), and diuretics (Gemba, 1974) have been shown to inhibit Ca^{2+} uptake. In most cases, however, very high concentrations are needed, a finding that casts some doubt on the significance from a physiological point of view.

D. KINETICS OF BIVALENT CATION
TRANSPORT IN MITOCHONDRIA

Several different methods have been employed to study the rate of bivalent cation uptake by mitochondria. The methods differ in their specificity and ability to follow fast kinetics. Metallochromic indicators such as murexide, Arsenoazo III, and Apyrazo (Mela and Chance, 1968; Scarpa, 1974; Brinley *et al.*, 1978) have been widely employed in these studies. The spectral changes due to changes in cation concentration outside mitochondria can be monitored in dual-wavelength spectrophotometers. Of these indicators, Arsenoazo III is the most sensitive (K_d for Ca^{2+} about 5 μM, Brinley *et al.*, 1978), whereas murexide is rather insensitive (K_d for Ca^{2+} about 5 mM, Scarpa, 1972). These indicators, however, are not specific for Ca^{2+} and can be used for measurements of other cations as well. One serious difficulty with these methods may be that most media contain considerable amounts of Ca^{2+} and Ca^{2+}-chelating agents. For reliable kinetic measurements, especially at low Me^{2+} concentrations, care must be taken to reduce the endogenous content of Ca^{2+} in mitochondria.

Bivalent cation-complexing agents are often present in experimental media and may cause additional difficulties. The sensitivity of the indicators may also be influenced by the composition of the experimental medium. A recently developed fast-response Ca^{2+} electrode technique has also been used successfully in studies on rates of Ca^{2+} transport (Madeira, 1975; Crompton *et al.*, 1976a). This method is very specific for Ca^{2+} and gives a good estimate of ionized Ca^{2+}. It should be noted that the calibration of this electrode is highly nonlinear.

Rates of Ca^{2+} uptake can be studied with isotope techniques under certain conditions. If the Ca^{2+} concentration is kept constant by the aid of Ca^{2+} buffer systems (ATP, EGTA, NTA), low temperatures are employed, and the reaction is stopped with inhibitor quench methods, information about kinetic parameters of Ca^{2+} uptake can be obtained (Reed and Bygrave, 1974b, 1975; Crompton *et al.*, 1976a). Other methods of measuring Ca^{2+} transport employ monitoring of Ca^{2+}-dependent changes in mitochondria, such as respiration (Chance, 1956). By measuring Ca^{2+}-stimulated respiration in the presence of A23187 (Heaton and Nicholls, 1976; Hutson *et al.*, 1976) real steady-state values of Ca^{2+} transport can be obtained, provided that respiration is not rate limiting. Other indirect methods, such as measurements of pH changes (Saris, 1963b) or redox changes in respiratory components (Chance, 1965) are also useful methods for studies of Ca^{2+} transport with some precautions (Scarpa, 1975). Chlortetracycline has also been used to monitor Ca^{2+} in some membrane phases in mitochondria. Complexing with Ca^{2+} and Mg^{2+} in environments of low dielectricity causes changes in its fluorescence (Caswell, 1972; Schuster and Olson, 1974). The Ca^{2+} and Mg^{2+} can be distinguished by differences in their fluorescence spectrum. There are, however, several limitations with this method, such as difficulties in calibration, nonlinear calibration, and possible migration of the complex (Caswell, 1972). Note that these methods can be used with buffer systems, in contrast to the spectrophotometric or electrode techniques.

Experiments with Ca^{2+} have yielded very conflicting results concerning the kinetic profiles of transport. Thus K_m values between less than 1 μM (Carafoli and Azzi, 1971; Bygrave et al., 1971) and above 50 μM (Vinogradov and Scarpa, 1973) have been reported (see reviews by Carafoli and Crompton, 1976, 1978; Bygrave, 1977). It is evident that such large differences would be due to the use of different conditions and methods. Low K_m values have been obtained by using Ca^{2+} buffers to keep the concentration constant and by measuring the rate of uptake from the kinetics of cytochrome b reduction (Carafoli and Azzi, 1971) or $^{45}Ca^{2+}$ uptake by Millipore filtration (Bygrave et al., 1971). These experiments have mainly been done in sucrose-based experimental media. With the murexide technique a K_m near 50 μM was obtained for rat liver (Vinogradov and Scarpa, 1973) and 75 μM for rat heart (Scarpa and Graziotti, 1973) mitochondria in media containing K^+ and Mg^{2+}. As already mentioned in Section III,C, Mg^{2+} inhibits Ca^{2+} uptake at low Ca^{2+} concentrations that would lead to higher K_m values. The most important point in this context is whether any significant Ca^{2+} transport by mitochondria occurs in conditions prevailing inside the cell where the Ca^{2+} concentration is thought to be below 10^{-6} M. The free cytosolic Mg^{2+} concentration is unknown. Some indirect estimations, however, have been made in different tissues. Results vary between 100 μM and 1 mM, using different methods (Palaty, 1971; Veloso et al., 1973; Endo, 1975), including determinations of Mg flux (Palaty, 1971) and Mg^{2+}-sensitive enzyme activities (Veloso et al., 1973). As an effect of Mg^{2+} is seen already at concentrations near 1 mM, mitochondrial Ca^{2+} uptake in situ would be rather slow. In squid axons some mitochondrial Ca^{2+} transport in situ, however, has been demonstrated (Brinley et al., 1978) with sophisticated methods. Furthermore, in isolated squid axoplasm the mitochondria appear to be quantitatively the main Ca^{2+} buffer, acting together with a protein factor with higher affinity and lower capacity (Baker and Schlaepfer, 1978).

The V_{max} values of Ca^{2+} uptake vary between 2 and 10 nmol per milligram of protein per second for heart (Crompton *et al.*, 1976a; Noack and Heinen, 1977; Carafoli, 1979) and 12 nmol per milligram of protein per second for rat liver mitochondria (Vinogradov and Scarpa, 1973). However, because respiratory chain-linked proton translocation might be rate limiting (Heaton and Nicholls, 1976) (see Section IV,B), the V_{max} values obtained probably do not represent true kinetic parameters of the translocator. Indeed Bragadin *et al.* (1979) and Lejkin and Petushkova (1980) have shown that the V_{max} of Ca^{2+} uptake increases significantly if K^+ diffusion potentials induced by valinomycin are used as a driving force. Furthermore, with extrapolation to an infinite valinomycin concentration, in such conditions a K_m for Ca^{2+} transport above 2 mM is obtained. Therefore the V_{max} values are only apparent or effective and actually give only information about the driving force (see Section IV,B). The same also appears to be the case for values of K_m. When ATP is used as an energy source the rate of uptake is significantly dependent on the ATP concentration, which also suggests that the energy source determines V_{max} (Noack and Heinen, 1977).

Another interesting feature concerning the kinetics of Ca^{2+} uptake is the fact that a sigmoid plot is obtained if the initial rate of uptake is plotted against the Ca^{2+} concentration (Bygrave *et al.*, 1971; Vinogradov and Scarpa, 1973; Reed and Bygrave, 1975). This feature of the kinetics has been suggested to be due to cooperativity in the Ca^{2+} translocator and two-site carrier models have been constructed on this basis (Vinogradov and Scarpa, 1973; Reed and Bygrave, 1975). However, also in this context significant quantitative and qualitative variations occur between results of different workers. In sucrose-based experimental media the sigmoidicity occurs at very low Ca^{2+} concentrations (near 1 μM) (Bygrave *et al.*, 1971; Reed and Bygrave, 1975). In KCl- and $MgCl_2$-based media, however, it occurs at Ca^{2+} concentrations above 10 μM (Vinogradov and Scarpa, 1973). The differences in this context are again apparently due to the ability of Mg^{2+} to cause or increase the sigmoidicity (Crompton *et al.*, 1976a; Hutson *et al.*, 1976; Åkerman *et al.*, 1977). The effect of Mg^{2+} is apparent with several different methods. It is unclear at present, whether Mg^{2+} shifts the point at which the sigmoidicity occurs to higher Ca^{2+} concentrations or whether Mg^{2+} is the cause of the sigmoidicity (Åkerman, 1977a). Endogenous Mg^{2+} in mitochondrial preparations (Bogucka and Wojtczak, 1971) might well cause sigmoidicity in apparently Mg^{2+}-free media. It has been suggested that the effect of Mg^{2+} is due to an interference with the surface binding of Ca^{2+} (Åkerman, 1977a), especially since this cation is not transported by rat liver mitochondria (Brierley, 1976) but inhibits the surface binding of Ca^{2+} (Scarpa and Azzi, 1968). It has been theoretically demonstrated that the kinetics of ion transport across membranes may mimic those of cooperative mechanisms if the surface charge of the membrane is changed toward the charge of the ionic species translocated (Theuvenet and Borst-Pauwels, 1976). Thus Mg^{2+} could simply affect the mitochondrial surface charge. Spermine, a tetravalent polyamine, which shares the membrane-stabilizing properties of Mg^{2+} and significantly af-

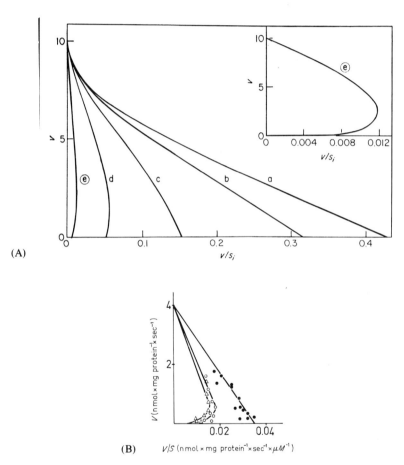

FIG. 5. (A) Hofstee plots for the uptake of a monovalent cation across a negatively charged membrane (curve a) in the presence of increasing concentrations of bivalent cations (curves b–e), which interfere with the surface charge of the membrane. V, initial rate of cation uptake; S_i, monovalent cation concentration. From Theuvenet and Borst-Pauwels (1976). (B) Hofstee plots for Ca^{2+} uptake in rat liver mitochondria in the absence (●—●) or the presence of 1 mM MgCl$_2$ (○—○) or 200 μM spermine (△—△). V, initial rate of Ca^{2+} uptake; S, Ca^{2+} concentration (2.5–100 μM). Data replotted from Fig. 1 of Åkerman (1977a).

fects the mitochondrial surface charge (Huunan-Seppälä and Nordling, 1971), has a similar effect as Mg^{2+} on mitochondrial Ca^{2+} transport (Åkerman, 1977a). The effect of spermine is also seen at concentrations that affect the surface binding of Ca^{2+} (Åkerman, 1977a). It appears unlikely that two cations with very different chemical structure, Mg^{2+} and spermine, would interfere in a similar manner with specific cooperative Ca^{2+} binding sites on a translocator. Figure 5 shows the effect of increasing amounts of bivalent cations, which interfere with the surface charge, on the translocation of a monovalent cation across a negatively charged membrane as compared to the effect of Mg^{2+} and spermine on mitochondrial Ca^{2+} uptake.

A peculiar finding in this context is that Ca^{2+} abolishes the sigmoidicity of Mn^{2+} uptake (Vinogradov and Scarpa, 1973). The reason for this is uncertain at present. However, in many conditions the uptake of Mn^{2+} shows some different features as compared to uptake of the other bivalent cations (see Section V,D). On the other hand, Ba^{2+} increases the sigmoidicity of Ca^{2+} uptake (Åkerman et al., 1977), similarly to Mg^{2+} and spermine. In some tissues sigmoidicity of the Ca^{2+} uptake kinetics is apparently absent even in the presence of Mg^{2+}. These include smooth muscle (Wikström et al., 1975; Batra, 1975; Valliers et al., 1975) and brain mitochondria (Nicholls, 1978a). The reason for this is not known at present. The implications of different features of the kinetics of bivalent cation uptake in mitochondria are discussed further in Sections IV,A, IV,B, and V,D.

IV. Transport Sequence of Bivalent Cations across the Mitochondrial Membrane

A. SURFACE BINDING

Several workers have proposed that Ca^{2+} binds to the outer surface of the mitochondrial membrane before it reaches the transport system (Scarpa and Azzone, 1968; Vainio et al., 1970). Before we go into the problem concerning the surface binding of Ca^{2+} to mitochondria, some inherent experimental difficulties should be mentioned. If low Ca^{2+} concentrations are used, the endogenous Ca^{2+} in the mitochondrial preparation should be accounted for. Most mitochondrial preparations contain about 10 nmol of Ca^{2+} permilligram of protein, most of which is released upon preincubation with inhibitors of the respiratory chain. Furthermore, when binding studies are made in multicompartment systems like mitochondria, redistribution of Ca^{2+} should be excluded, especially because of the high permeability of the mitochondrial membrane toward Ca^{2+}

(Selwyn *et al.*, 1970a; Wikström and Saari, 1976). The matrix space contains some endogenous ATP and other substances capable of binding Ca^{2+}. To avoid this, Ca^{2+} uptake should be excluded using ruthenium red or La^{3+} (Reed and Bygrave, 1974c), in which case possible translocator binding sites cannot be studied. Another possibility is to measure the EGTA-removable part of Ca^{2+} binding (Reed and Bygrave, 1974c). This approach, however, is uncertain and EGTA addition might also lead to redistribution of Ca^{2+} out of the mitochondria (Wikström and Saari, 1976; Åkerman, 1978b) in deenergized conditions.

Some Ca^{2+} and Mn^{2+} binding studies with deenergized mitochondria show that Ca^{2+} is bound at sites with rather low affinity for this cation as compared to the affinity of the translocator (Chappell *et al.*, 1963; Scarpa and Azzi, 1968; Scarpa and Azzone, 1968, 1969; Jacobus and Brierley, 1969; Reed and Bygrave, 1974c). The K_d of this binding is of the order of 100 μM (Reed and Bygrave, 1974c) or higher (Scarpa and Azzone, 1969). The binding is inhibited competitively by Mg^{2+} (Scarpa and Azzi, 1968), Ba^{2+} (Åkerman *et al.*, 1977), K^+ (Scarpa and Azzi, 1968; Reed and Bygrave, 1974c), H^+ (Scarpa and Azzi, 1968), spermine and local anesthetics (Scarpa and Azzi, 1968; Åkerman, 1977a). After acetone extraction of phospholipids from the mitochondrial membrane, the binding sites disappear (Scarpa and Azzi, 1968; Jacobus and Brierley, 1969); upon readdition of phospholipid they reappear, suggesting that this binding occurs mainly at the polar head groups of phospholipid molecules in the mitochondrial membrane.

Evidence in favor of the view that Ca^{2+} binding to the low-affinity sites is the first step in Ca^{2+} transport comes from the finding that Mg^{2+} (Vainio *et al.*, 1970; Crompton *et al.*, 1976a; Hutson *et al.*, 1976; Åkerman *et al.*, 1977; Åkerman, 1977a) and spermine (Åkerman, 1977a), which affect the surface binding, also affect the kinetics of Ca^{2+} uptake at similar concentrations. Furthermore, in a sucrose medium Ba^{2+} affects the Ca^{2+} uptake in a similar way as Mg^{2+} and spermine (Åkerman *et al.*, 1977). In this case, the K_i of Ba^{2+} is rather low (about 10 μM). In the presence of K^+ and Mg^{2+}, the K_i of Ba^{2+} increases to 100 μM. In this case, Ba^{2+} is a purely competitive inhibitor of Ca^{2+} uptake (Åkerman *et al.*, 1977). This would suggest that Ba^{2+} competes with K^+ and Mg^{2+} for surface binding sites. Therefore, it is evident that interference with the surface binding of Ca^{2+} affects the kinetics of Ca^{2+} uptake; hence the surface binding presumably is a step in the Ca^{2+} translocation sequence.

The existence of another type of Ca^{2+} binding sites having higher affinity has also been proposed. These sites were revealed by Scatchard plots for $^{45}Ca^{2+}$ binding to intact mitochondria whose respiration was inhibited (Reynafarje and Lehninger, 1969). Reynafarje and Lehninger suggested that these sites might represent Ca^{2+} binding sites on a carrier. The existence of the high-affinity sites have been questioned, since they are sensitive to high concentrations of inhibitors of the respiratory chain (Åkerman *et al.*, 1974; Southard and Green, 1974; Reed and Bygrave, 1974c) and to a Ca^{2+} ionophore X537A (Åkerman *et al.*, 1974). Especially the results with the ionophore, which should not affect Ca^{2+} binding but ought to alter bulk phase distribution of Ca^{2+}, would suggest that the apparent high-affinity binding represents mainly an uptake of minute amounts of Ca^{2+} into the matrix space. The amount of "high-affinity" binding sites is furthermore far higher than expected from the effect of inhibitors on Ca^{2+} transport (Mela and Chance, 1969). The use of Scatchard plots in a multicompartment system is open to criticism, since the plot has been developed on the assumption of an equilibrium obeying the law of mass action (Scatchard *et al.*, 1957).

Binding studies with the inhibitors of Ca^{2+} transport, La^{3+} and ruthenium red, suggest that La^{3+} binds partially to sites different from ruthenium red binding sites (Reed and Bygrave, 1974b). However, since La^{3+} penetrates the membrane of mitochondria (Reed and Bygrave, 1974a) and liposomes (Lussan and Faucon, 1974), the La^{3+} binding sites might well represent a distribution of La^{3+} into the mitochondria. The fact that high concentrations of Ca^{2+} are unable to remove the bound La^{3+} in similar conditions (Lehninger and Carafoli, 1971) further strengthens this opinion. In this case, the Ca^{2+} translocator would be blocked and hence Ca^{2+} would be unable to remove internally bound La^{3+}. Thus, it is apparent that the inhibitor binding studies have failed to demonstrate Ca^{2+} binding to a translocator and that the binding sites for Ca^{2+} (as well as other bivalent cations), La^{3+}, and ruthenium red all represent the same sites, namely, the low-affinity sites.

Thus the only well documented Ca^{2+} binding sites in the mitochondrial membrane appear to be the polar head groups of phospholipids in the mitochondrial membrane, although it is probable that isolated acidic proteins bind bivalent cations also *in situ* (Sottocasa *et al.*, 1977).

B. THE TRANSLOCATION STEP

Several workers have proposed that the mitochondrial bivalent cation uptake is a carrier-mediated process (Lehninger *et al.*, 1967; Lehninger, 1970; Vinogradov and Scarpa, 1973; Reed and Bygrave, 1975). The following features of transport favor this proposal: (*a*) saturation kinetics (Carafoli and Azzi, 1971; Bygrave *et al.*, 1971; Vinogradov and Scarpa, 1973); (*b*) sigmoidal kinetics, suggesting cooperatively in the carrier molecule (Bygrave *et al.*, 1971; Vinogradov and Scarpa, 1973); (*c*) the existence of specific inhibitors of transport (La^{3+} and ruthenium red (Mela, 1968; Moore, 1971; Vasington *et al.*, 1972); (*d*) the existence of high-affinity binding sites for Ca^{2+} in the mitochondrial membrane (Reynafarje and Lehninger, 1969); (*e*) the fact that high-affinity binding proteins can be extracted from the mitochondrial membrane (Sottocasa *et al.*, 1972); (*f*)evidence for genetic evolution (Lehninger, 1970; Carafoli and Lehninger, 1971; Carafoli, 1973), since no bivalent cation uptake occurs in plant mitochondria (Lehninger, 1970; Moore and Bonner, 1977) or mitochondria from microorganisms (Lehninger, 1970). Even if these features of Ca^{2+} uptake could suggest that there exists a specific carrier for bivalent cations in mitochondria, arguments (*a*)–(*f*) are not conclusive, since a channel mechanism with certain ionic specificity could well account for many features of bivalent cation uptake. As pointed out already in Section II, a channel mechanism would simulate that of a carrier under certain conditions, i.e., limitation of space for diffusion or increased osmotic pressure (Wilbrandt, 1974).

One of the central questions to consider in this context is the rate-limiting step of bivalent cation uptake. It has been suggested that dissociation of the cations (Ca^{2+}) from the translocator at the inner surface of the mitochondrial membrane (Reed and Bygrave, 1975), mitochondrial respiration (Heaton and Nicholls, 1976), or a diffusion from surface binding sites to a translocator (Åkerman, 1977b) is rate limiting.

The first alternative is based on measurements on the effect of extramitochondrial pH on kinetic parameters of Ca^{2+} uptake, and accordingly a two-site carrier model was constructed, where transport of one Ca^{2+} ion is coupled to the exchange for one proton; hence protons in the matrix space cause dissociation of Ca^{2+} ions from the carrier, a step that also was considered to be rate-limiting. This model, however, is unlikely because of the established fact that under most conditions Ca^{2+} appears to be taken up with two net positive charges (see Section III,B). Furthermore, the effects of changes in pH on Ca^{2+} transport are complex. The pH changes affect not only the K_m, but the V_{max} as well as Ca^{2+} efflux (Hutson, 1977).

The second alternative, i.e., that respiratory chain-linked proton translocation is rate limiting under some conditions, appears likely because maximal stimulation of mitochondrial respiration occurs when Ca^{2+} cycling is induced in the presence of A23187 (Heaton and Nicholls, 1976) (see Section III,B). Furthermore, Bragadin *et al.* (1979) and Lejkin and Petushkova (1980) have shown in rat liver mitochondria that when K^+ diffusion potentials generated by valinomycin are used as driving force of Ca^{2+} uptake, a significant increase in V_{max}, which is much higher than that with succinate, can be noted (Lejkin, 1979). This would suggest that V_{max} is determined by the driving force of uptake rather than being a kinetic parameter of the translocator. Interestingly, with extrapolation to an infinite valinomycin concentration, a K_m for Ca^{2+} above 2 mM is obtained (Lejkin and Petushkova, 1980), which is nearly two orders of magnitude higher than those reported in the literature (see Bygrave, 1977; Carafoli and Crompton, 1978) and certainly not a K_m of a "high-affinity" Ca^{2+} carrier.

The third alternative, i.e., that a diffusion of Ca^{2+} from surface sites to the translocator is rate-limiting under some conditions, comes from studies on the rather complex effects of various cations on the kinetics of Ca^{2+} uptake. This could be the case with very low extramitochondrial Ca^{2+} concentrations at the slow phase of the sigmoid kinetic plot or in the presence of Mg^{2+} and spermine (see Sections III,C and III,D and Fig. 5), both of which retard Ca^{2+} uptake at low extramitochondrial Ca^{2+} concentrations. In the presence of Mg^{2+} and spermine, in media of low ionic strength, mitochondrial Ca^{2+} uptake shows features of a classical channel-mediated transport, i.e., a linear relation between rate of uptake and Ca^{2+} concentration (Åkerman, 1977a) and a decrease in the activation energy of transport (Åkerman, 1977b). In the presence of 400 μM spermine, the activation energy is practically 0 kJ per mole. Two possible simple explanations might be presented for the above-mentioned results. A nonspecific diffusion step in the Ca^{2+} uptake sequence might become rate-limiting in the presence of Mg^{2+} and spermine. The second alternative would be that a channel mechanism becomes unmasked in the presence of these agents. As Mg^{2+} and spermine both inhibit Ca^{2+} binding to surface sites (see Sections III,D and IV,A) at concentrations similar to those that affect the kinetics, their effects might well be mediated through a nonspecific surface change rather than an effect on the Ca^{2+} translocator. Furthermore, these effects are not seen in media of high ionic strength containing K^+ (Åkerman, 1977a,b), which also alters the surface binding of Ca^{2+} (Scarpa and Azzi, 1968). This would suggest competition for the surface sites between the cations. Uptake of Ba^{2+} is furthermore much more sensitive to Mg^{2+} than is uptake of Ca^{2+} (Vainio *et al.*, 1970). It is also inhibited completely by 20 mM K^+. Pr^{3+}, which is expected to inhibit only the translocator because of the low concentrations needed is almost equally effective with all bivalent cations (see Section V,D). This would suggest that a nonspecific diffusion step is rate-limiting since Ba^{2+} has the larger crystal ionic radius. Because of this large radius Ba^{2+} uptake would be more strongly affected by such a step (see Section V,D). In contrast to Mg^{2+} and spermine, K^+ alone increases the activation energy of Ca^{2+} uptake (Åkerman, 1977b). The effects of the ions on Ca^{2+} uptake are in agreement with their effects on the physical state of the phospholipid molecules in membranes. Thus bivalent cations like Mg^{2+} compress and decrease the surface charge density of bilayers and monolayers (Papahadjopoulos, 1968; Träuble and Eibl, 1974), whereas monovalent cations like K^+ increase the fluidity of the membrane (Träuble and Eibl, 1974).

All these data would suggest that the bivalent cation uptake is significantly affected by the physical state of the membrane through an effect on a nonspecific diffusion step. Such a step might be a diffusion from the surface of the mitochondrial membrane to a translocator residing in the interior of the membrane. Indeed, changes in temperature and lipid fluidity significantly affect the diffusion of ions across liposomal membranes (Blok et al., 1975). The permeability of liposomes is also affected by bivalent cations such as Mg^{2+} (Papahadjopoulos, 1972), as well as by other agents that change the membrane fluidity or charge density (Haydon and Hladky, 1972). The rate of the uptake of safranine, an organic cation, by liposomes is sensitive to bivalent cations, spermine (Åkerman and Saris, 1976; Åkerman, 1977b), and temperature changes (Åkerman, 1977b) even if this uptake should involve a simple passive diffusion. Interestingly, the sensitivity of safranine uptake to bivalent cations is dependent on the amount of acidic phospholipids in the liposomal membrane (Åkerman and Saris, 1976).

It is concluded that the kinetic evidence in favor of a carrier-type mechanism of bivalent cation uptake is far from conclusive, since none of the kinetic features seem to measure the transport system itself. Under some conditions a nonspecific diffusion step might be rate limiting, and in others the respiratory chain-linked proton translocation. Also since the other results (listed previously) in favor of a carrier mechanism provide no conclusive evidence, we prefer to use the terms translocator or transport system to describe the bivalent cation uptake mechanism in mitochondria. Many features, though, would point to a channel mechanism (see Section VII,C).

C. RETENTION AND CYCLING OF BIVALENT
     CATIONS IN MITOCHONDRIA

One important point concerning mitochondrial bivalent cation uptake is their ability to retain cations and thus their ability to control the cytosolic ionic environment.

1. Ability of Mitochondria to Decrease Extramitochondrial Ca^{2+}

In earlier studies on Ca^{2+} transport it was shown that, depending on experimental conditions, mitochondria can decrease the extramitochondrial Ca^{2+} concentration to $0.2-1$ μM (Drahota et al., 1965; Batra, 1973;

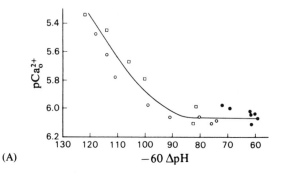

(A)

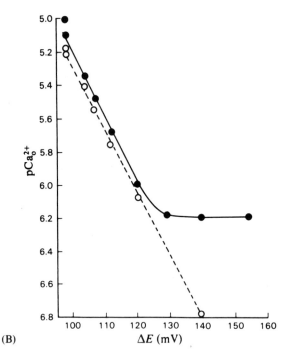

(B)

FIG. 6. (A) Steady-state pCa_0^{2+} as a function of $\triangle pH$: lack of an effect of permeant weak acid. O, Control; □, $+100$ μM N-ethylmaleimide; ●, $+5$ mM potassium acetate. (B) Steady-state pCa_0^{2+} (extramitochondrial free Ca^{2+}) as a function of $\triangle E$ (membrane potential) when the latter is varied by increasing Ca^{2+} in the matrix. ●, Experimental points. For experimental details see original publication; O, theoretical pCa_0^{2+} predicted for thermodynamic equilibrium of a Ca^{2+} uniport assuming a matrix activity coefficient for Ca^{2+} of 0.1. From Nicholls (1978b).

Nicholls, 1978b). Since the mitochondrial membrane potential (see Section III,B) is the driving force for Ca^{2+} uptake, it is important to know the relation of the components of mitochondrial proton electrochemical gradients to extramitochondrial Ca^{2+}. The extramitochondrial Ca^{2+} decrease linearly with an increase in the membrane potential of rat liver mitochondria to about 100–130 mV (Nicholls, 1978b). Thereafter no change in extramitochondrial Ca^{2+} concentration (about 0.8 μM at this point) can be seen. Conversely, extramitochondrial Ca^{2+} increases with an increase in the value of 60 ΔpH above 100 and is constant below this value (Nicholls, 1978b). The effects of $\Delta \psi$ and ΔpH on extramitochondrial Ca^{2+} are shown in Fig. 6.

Measurements of the mitochondrial Ca^{2+} buffering capacity in intact squid axons also indicates that mitochondria may decrease cytosolic Ca^{2+} to about 1 μM (Brinley et al., 1978). However, the Ca^{2+} concentration in the axoplasm is far below 1 μM (Dipolo et al., 1976), and thus Dipolo et al. concluded that the mitochondrial contribution to regulation of axoplasmic Ca^{2+} is negligible. On the other hand, inhibition of mitochondrial respiration with KCN considerably raises the cytosolic Ca^{2+} (Baker et al., 1971). This event can be prevented by ATP in the absence of oligomycin but not in its presence, suggesting indeed that a main part of the intra-axonal Ca^{2+} is buffered within mitochondria. Mitochondria isolated from the squid axoplasm also have a large capacity for Ca^{2+} translocation (Baker and Schlaepfer, 1978). Isolated axoplasm apparently contains two major components capable of decreasing axoplasmic Ca^{2+} during activity, namely, mitochondria and a protein with high affinity for Ca^{2+} (Baker and Schlaepfer, 1978). Therefore it does not seem unreasonable to suggest that mitochondria are involved in the basic regulation of cytosolic Ca^{2+} to about 10^{-6} M whereas other transport systems, such as those in the plasma membrane or endoplasmic reticulum, maintain the fine control (Baker, 1976). Also, in cell fractionation studies on a wide variety of tissues, a main part of cellular Ca^{2+} has been found in the mitochondrial fraction (Patriarca and Carafoli, 1968; Van Rossum et al., 1976; Bygrave, 1977) when particular care has been taken to exclude redistribution during fractionation (Van Rossum et al., 1976).

2. Mitochondrial Bivalent Cation Uptake Capacity

The state of Ca^{2+} in the matrix space of mitochondria in different conditions is unknown at present. From studies on factors that affect the retention of Ca^{2+}, however, much can be learned. As discussed in Section III,A, mitochondria take up about 100 nmol of Ca^{2+} per milligram of protein during respiration in the absence of added anions. This was formerly called membrane loading because it was thought that a saturation of Ca^{2+}

binding sites in the membrane limited the uptake. However, recently several workers have shown that the uptake capacity decreases to about 20 nmol per milligram of protein or less when endogenous phosphate is depleted from the mitochondria (Crompton et al., 1978a) or its uptake blocked with NEM or Mersalyl (Harris and Zaba, 1977; Bygrave et al., 1977; Pfeiffer et al., 1978). Twenty nanomoles of Ca^{2+} per milligram of protein might well represent true membrane loading, since it is of the same order of magnitude as the amount of low-affinity Ca^{2+} binding at the outer surface of the mitochondrial membrane (Reed and Bygrave, 1974c). These results also suggest that under many conditions phosphate is the main factor determining the retention of Ca^{2+} by mitochondria. Phosphate forms soluble complexes and precipitates in the matrix space. This is also in agreement with EPR studies on Mn^{2+} and calorimetric studies on Ca^{2+} (Poe, 1969), which suggest that this cation is mainly bound to phosphate (Pozzan et al., 1976) and some other Ca^{2+} binding substances (Puskin and Gunter, 1972). About 97% of Mn^{2+} appears to be in a bound state (Bragadin et al., 1975; Puskin et al., 1976). From determinations of changes in the mitochondrial volume during uptake of Ca^{2+} and Sr^{2+} in the presence of acetate, a similar conclusion can be drawn for these cations (Azzone et al., 1976) (see Fig. 4). The activity coefficient of the cations increases significantly with an increase in cation and acetate concentration (see Fig. 4). Therefore, an activity coefficient between 0.03 and 1 is expected for bivalent cations inside mitochondria, depending on experimental conditions.

3. Effect of Matrix pH and Weak Acids on Me^{2+} Retention

The stimulating effect of phosphate on bivalent cation uptake is due not only to the formation of Ca^{2+} phosphate salts, but also to the ability of this anion to decrease the pH of the matrix space because of the function of a H^+/phosphate symporter and dissociation of $H_2PO_4^-$. Thus, also weak acid anions, including arsenate, acetate, and bicarbonate (Lehninger, 1974), are able to support bivalent cation uptake. Tributyltin, which causes a Cl^-/OH^- exchange (Selwyn et al., 1970b), also supports Ca^{2+} uptake (Stockdale et al., 1970; Bygrave et al., 1978). Cl^- is not normally able to support Ca^{2+} uptake (Lehninger, 1974). Because weak acid anions, particularly acetate, are accumulated with Ca^{2+} and do not complex Ca^{2+}, swelling of mitochondria can be observed. When sulfate is added to mitochondria swollen in the presence of bivalent cations and acetate, a contraction is seen because of precipitation, but only when Ba^{2+} is accumulated, not with Ca^{2+}, Mn^{2+}, or Sr^{2+} (Fig. 7). This demonstrates that the bivalent cation concentrations in the matrix remain low, since the solubility product of $BaSO_4$ is lower than that of the other bivalent cations

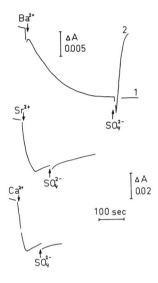

FIG. 7. Contraction of mitochondria by precipitation of accumulated Ba^{2+} as sulfate. Rat liver mitochondria, 0.9 mg of protein per milliliter, were allowed to accumulate Me^{2+} (100 μM) in a medium containing 250 mM sucrose, 10 mM Hepes, pH 6.8, 5 mM potassium acetate, 4 mM succinate, 5 μM rotenone, and oligomycin, 2 μg/ml. K_2SO_4, 1 mM, was added when indicated. Volume changes were followed at 520 nm in an Aminco–Chance dual-wavelength photometer. 1, Control trace without addition of sulfate. Unpublished observation of Saris (1979).

($Ba^{2+} \sim 10^{-10}$, $Sr^{2+} \sim 10^{-6}$, $Ca^{2+} \sim 10^{-2}$ mol^2 × 1^{-2}). Also, in determinations of Ca^{2+}-sensitive enzymes in the matrix, low values of intramitochondrial Ca^{2+} are expected (see Carafoli and Crompton, 1978, for references). These methods, however, have not been systematically used for the purpose of Ca^{2+} determination.

4. Effect of Adenine Nucleotides on Me^{2+} Retention

Apart from the role of weak acid anions in the retention of bivalent cations by mitochondria, several lines of evidence suggest that adenine nucleotides are of importance as well.

If relatively high concentrations of Ca^{2+} are added to mitochondria in the presence of phosphate, uptake of this cation occurs, followed by spontaneous release (Saris, 1963b; Drahota et al., 1965) and swelling of mitochondria (Fig. 8a). This release can be prevented by addition of ATP or ADP (Saris, 1963b; Carafoli et al., 1965a). If ATP is depleted from mitochondria with hexokinase and glucose (Kimura and Rasmussen, 1977) or PP$_i$ (Sordahl and Asimakis, 1978), a spontaneous Ca^{2+} release from

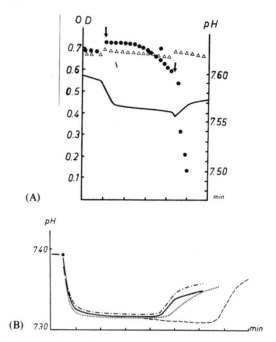

(A)

(B)

FIG. 8. (A) Correlation of extensive swelling induced by Ca^{2+} with the reentry of H^+ in rat liver mitochondria. ——, pH trace; ●, absorbance readings at 540 nm. Ca^{2+}, 65 μM, was added at arrows. △, absorbance of an aged preparation as a control. (B) Effect of Mg^{2+} in delaying the pH rising phase (Ca^{2+} release) of the Ca^{2+}-induced pH cycle. ●, Addition of 166 μM Ca^{2+}. Ca^{2+} was added to mitochondria respiring on succinate as in Fig. 3B. ——, No Mg^{2+}; —·—·, 0.2 mM $MgCl_2$; . . . . , 0.5 mM $MgCl_2$;— — — —, 2 mM $MgCl_2$. From Saris (1963b).

preloaded mitochondria occurs. A similar effect is produced by addition of competitive inhibitors of the adenine nucleotide translocator, atractylate or palmitoyl-CoA (Drahota *et al.*, 1965; Asimakis and Sordahl, 1977). This latter effect is prevented by increasing concentrations of ATP (Drahota *et al.*, 1965). Furthermore, addition of phosphoenolpyruvate to mitochondria causes release of Ca^{2+} (Chudapongse and Haugaard, 1973; Peng *et al.*, 1974), which apparently is due to the depletion of adenine nucleotides from mitochondria (Peng *et al.*, 1977; Sul *et al.*, 1976). These results would thus indicate that adenine nucleotides are of importance in keeping Ca^{2+} inside mitochondria. It is not clear by what mechanism this occurs. Adenine nucleotides may act by forming complexes with Me^{2+}, by stabilizing phosphate precipitates (Lehninger, 1970), or by affecting the efflux at the membrane level. There is, however, to our knowledge no specific evidence in favor of the latter two mechanisms.

An interesting finding is that bongkrekic acid (BA), a noncompetitive inhibitor of the adenine nucleotide translocator (Henderson and Lardy, 1970; Klingenberg and Buchholz, 1973), prevents the dinitrophenol-induced Ca^{2+} efflux from mitochondria (Peng et al., 1977). Since atractylate did not have the same effect, the workers concluded that BA interacts specifically with a transport system involved in Ca^{2+} efflux (Peng et al., 1977). Unfortunately, however, the workers did not measure the total adenine nucleotide pool in mitochondria (only ATP) under their conditions. Atractylate inhibits competitively the adenine nucleotide translocator at the external surface (Bruni et al., 1962; Vignais et al., 1973) and BA noncompetitively at the inner surface (Erdelt et al., 1972; Klingenberg and Buchholz, 1973). Dinitrophenol causes hydrolysis of endogenous ATP, and a retention of ADP might occur, bringing about increased Ca^{2+} retention (Harris, 1979). Indeed BA causes an increased binding of ADP in mitochondria (Erdelt et al., 1972; Klingenberg and Buchholz, 1973). Therefore, it is too early to decide whether BA or adenine nucleotides specifically interact with a Ca^{2+} translocator or merely increase Ca^{2+} retention by trapping Ca^{2+} inside mitochondria. Studies on the effect of adenine nucleotides on mitochondrial Ca^{2+} are invalidated by the very fast metabolism of these substances owing to presence of substantial amounts of adenylate kinase in most mitochondrial preparations. It would therefore be valuable to pursue these kinds of studies using inhibitors of adenylate kinase. Furthermore, studies on the effect of adenine nucleotides on Ca^{2+} retention should always be done simultaneously with determinations of the adenine nucleotide pool.

5. Massive Loading of Ca^{2+} in Mitochondria

Under certain conditions, when both ATP and phosphate are present mitochondria take up massive amounts of Ca^{2+} (about 3000 nmol per milligram of protein). In this case electron dense deposits appear in the matrix space (Lehninger, 1970; Carafoli, 1974). The deposits have been isolated and shown to contain amorphous salts of Ca^{2+} and phosphate. This so-called "massive loading" can be viewed as resulting from the combined effect of increased retention of Ca^{2+} due to adenine nucleotides and precipitation of calcium phosphate; it has been treated in detail in reviews by Lehninger (1970) and Carafoli (1974).

6. Effect of Pyridine Nucleotides on Me^{2+} Retention

Another interesting finding is that mitochondrial Ca^{2+} retention is enhanced when pyridine nucleotides (PN) are kept in a reduced state (Lehninger et al., 1978b). The cation is again spontaneously released when the nucleotides are oxidized. These effects can be obtained when either succinate or ATP are used as an energy source of uptake (Lehninger *et al.*, 1978b). Thus, sequential cycles of Ca^{2+} uptake and release can be induced by reduction and oxidation of PN using various substrates. The importance of the oxidation/reduction state of PN has been questioned by Brand and Nicholls (1980), who could see an effect upon the retention of Ca^{2+} only when the mitochondria were on the verge of spontaneous Ca^{2+} release. The retention of Ca^{2+} is enhanced by rotenone when mitochondria are respiring on endogenous substrates (Dargel, 1974), which may be explained as being due to the prevention of oxidation of PN. This result is also consistent with a role of PN in Ca^{2+} retention. The mechanism by which PN modulate Ca^{2+} retention is uncertain at present, but may be related to the fact that Ca^{2+} interacts more strongly with NADH than with NAD (Vinogradov *et al.*, 1972). Also the decreased retention of Ca^{2+} by mitochondria in the presence of palmitoyl-CoA has been attributed to an effect through pyridine rather than adenine nucleotides (Wolkowicz and Wood, 1979). Therefore, there might exist a link between adenine and pyridine nucleotide pools with Ca^{2+} retention. Further studies are needed to establish the relationship and whether both types of nucleotides affect Ca^{2+} retention independently.

Recently, Panfili *et al.* (1980) have found that their Ca^{2+}-binding glycoprotein is able to bind PN and that its affinity for Ca^{2+} is decreased when NAD^+ is bound. The significance of this finding is not yet clear, especially since there is no evidence that the protein is accessible to NAD^+ and Ca^{2+} from the matrix side. It is interesting that antibodies against the protein prevent the efflux of Ca^{2+} induced by oxidation of NADH, which was obtained by addition of acetoacetate.

7. Other Factors That Affect the Retention of Me^{2+}

Ca^{2+} retention is enhanced and Ca^{2+} release prevented by the presence of agents that stabilize the mitochondrial membrane, such as Mg^{2+} (Saris, 1963b, see Fig. 8b) and spermine (Saris *et al.*, 1969). These agents probably act by preventing the deleterious effects caused by Ca^{2+} in mitochondria, such as swelling and subsequent increase in mitochondrial permeability (Saris, 1963b; Hunter *et al.*, 1976) as well as phospholipase A_2 activation (Scherphof *et al.*, 1972) (see Section V,B).

8. Hormonal Effects on Me^{2+} Retention

Extensive studies have also been made on the effect of different hormones on the content of Ca^{2+} and retention of Ca^{2+} by subsequently isolated mitochondria. In such studies, glucagon, insulin (see Bygrave, 1978, for references), and 1,25-dihydroxycalciferol increase (Guilland and Fleisch, 1974), whereas dexamethasone (Kimura and Rasmussen, 1977) and α-adrenergic stimulants (Blackmore *et al.*, 1979) decrease, mitochondrial Ca^{2+} retention. The effect of insulin may be mediated by the secondary increase in glucagon, which thus appears to be the more important hormone (Dargel, 1978). Borle (1973) has carried out extensive studies on the effect of hormones on kinetic exchange pools (including mitochondrial) of Ca^{2+} in isolated cells. However, these studies on the effect of hormones on mitochondrial Ca^{2+} are outside the scope of this discussion. The effects of hormones by no means prove a role of mitochondrial Ca^{2+} as a trigger of cellular responses, but may merely reflect a metabolic state of the cell.

9. *Cycling and Exchange of* Ca^{2+}

Even if Ca^{2+} thus appears to be mostly bound inside mitochondria, it is to a large extent mobile because Ca^{2+} cycling and exchange can be demonstrated under many conditions. The mobility of Ca^{2+} was first stressed by Drahota *et al.* (1965). Several lines of evidence have been presented supporting the view that there is a steady state of simultaneous uptake and efflux of this cation.

State 4 respiration in the presence of succinate is significantly decreased by ruthenium red or EGTA (Stucki and Ineichen, 1974). This would suggest that a recycling of Ca^{2+} across the membrane increases the resting respiration and causes a dissipation of energy. Such recycling could occur through coupling of an electrogenic uptake mechanism to an electroneutral efflux mechanism, as is the case when mitochondria are treated with the ionophore A23187 (Heaton and Nicholls, 1976). In the presence of A23187, the enhanced efflux causes depletion of mitochondrial Ca^{2+} (Reed and Lardy, 1972), and maximal stimulation of mitochondrial respiration occurs (Heaton and Nicholls, 1976). During resting respiration in the absence of the ionophore and in the presence of only endogenous Ca^{2+}, respiration is only slightly inhibited by EGTA or ruthenium red, suggesting that uptake of Ca^{2+} dominates over efflux owing to its more favorable kinetic properties.

When low concentrations of Ca^{2+} are added to mitochondria in the absence of added permeant anions, a depolarization of the mitochondrial membrane is seen (Åkerman, 1978b; Ramachandran and Bygrave, 1978). This depolarization is followed by a very slow repolarization (Åkerman, 1978b), during which no change in mitochondrial content of Ca^{2+} is observed. Addition of inhibitors of the H^+/phosphate symporter considerably enhances this effect (Ramachandran and Bygrave, 1978). On the other hand, additions of EGTA, phosphate, or ruthenium red notably increase the rate of repolarization (Åkerman, 1978b). This is shown in Fig. 9. The EGTA would complex Ca^{2+} in the extramitochondrial compart-

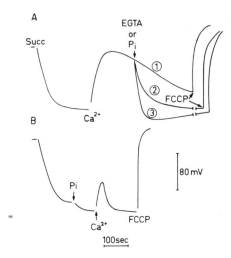

Fig. 9. Effect of phosphate and EGTA on Ca^{2+}-induced depolarization of the mitochondrial membrane. Downward deflection indicates negative polarity inside mitohcondria. The medium was 0.25 M sucrose, 20 mM Tris, 10 mM Hepes, pH 7.4, 10 μM rotenone, oligomycin, 4 μg/ml and 10 μM safranine. Additions: In (A) 8 mM succinate (Succ), 20 μM $CaCl_2$ (Ca^{2+}), 4 mM KH_2PO_4 (3, P_i) or 0.5 mM [ethylenebis(oxyethylenenitrolo)]tetraacetic acid (EGTA) (2), and 7 μM carbonyl cyanide p-trifluoromethoxyphenylhydrazone (FCCP) as indicated; in (B) 4 mM KH_2PO_4 was added before Ca^{2+}. From Åkerman (1978b).

ment, phosphate again would trap Ca^{2+} intramitochondrially and decrease the proton gradient, whereas ruthenium red would block the uniporter, and as a result recycling of Ca^{2+} would be prevented. Thus, these data would suggest that cycling movements of Ca^{2+} across the membrane prolongs depolarization.

Continuous oscillations of Sr^{2+} have been demonstrated in respiring mitochondria (Gylkhandanyan et al., 1976) in media of low osmolarity in the presence of valinomycin.

When high levels of Ca^{2+} are added to mitochondria in the presence of phosphate, a respiratory stimulation occurs that continues until anaerobiosis, even if no change in intramitochondrial Ca^{2+} can be noted (Leblanc and Clauser, 1974). This event is prevented by agents that increase the retention of Ca^{2+} by mitochondria (see Section IV,C,4) ADP or ATP in combination with Mg^{2+}. Interestingly, this event appears to be enhanced in muscle mitochondria from halothane-sensitive pigs, possibly in a temperature-dependent manner (Cheah and Cheah, 1978). In these preparations an increase in the rate of spontaneous Ca^{2+} release was also observed, and both spermine, which increases Ca^{2+} retention by mitochondria (Saris et al., 1969), and bovine serum albumin (BSA) prevented the

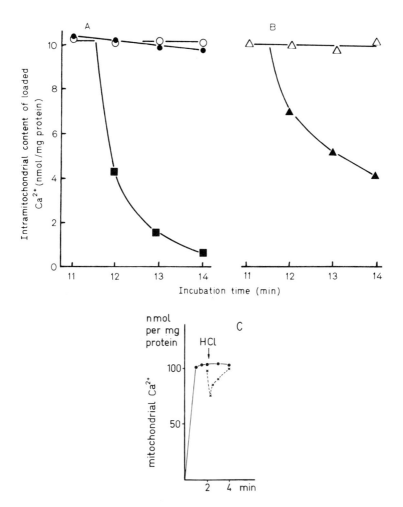

FIG. 10. Ca^{2+} efflux from mitochondria induced by Na^+, Ca^{2+}, and H^+. (A) and (B) Rat heart mitochondria loaded with $^{45}Ca^{2+}$ for 10 minutes; thereafter, addition of ruthenium red (●—●); 20 mM Na^+ (■—■); 20 mM Na^+ and 100 nmol of La^{3+} per milligram of protein (○—○); 80 μM $CaCl_2$ (▲—▲); or 80 μM $CaCl_2$ and 100 nmol of La^{3+} per milligram of protein (△—△). From Crompton *et al.* (1977). (C) Rat liver mitochondria loaded with Ca^{2+}. ●—●; control; ×----×, decrease in medium pH with HCl from 7.4 to 6.8. From Åkerman (1978c).

effects of high Ca^{2+}. Mitochondria from different sources differ in their sensitivities to high concentrations of Ca^{2+}; for instance, mitochondria from Ehrlich ascites tumor cells are resistant (Thorne and Bygrave, 1974). The effect of BSA would thus indicate that free fatty acids produced by activation of mitochondrial phospholipase A_2 (see Section V,B) are somehow involved in the enhanced Ca^{2+} cycling, probably because of their un-coupling action (see Section V,B).

The previously discussed results thus indicate that when intramito-chondrial Ca^{2+} increases to a certain level, the electroneutral efflux mech-anism (see Section IV,D) is activated. As a result, a recycling of Ca^{2+} in and out across the membrane would occur owing to simultaneous func-tioning of the uniporter. This would lead to a decrease in the mitochon-drial membrane potential; subsequently an increase in mitochondrial res-piration would occur, leading to dissipation of energy.

Fast exchange of intramitochondrial to extramitochondrial Ca^{2+} or Ca^{2+} and Sr^{2+} can be demonstrated under several conditions (Leblanc and Clauser, 1974; Crompton et al., 1977; Åkerman, 1978c). This exchange is interestingly unaffected by ruthenium red and inhibited by high concen-trations of La^{3+} (Crompton et al., 1977). Calcium release induced by Ca^{2+} is demonstrated in Fig. 10B. These findings provide further evidence in favor of the mobility of Ca^{2+} inside mitochondria and of a translocator separate from the ruthenium red-sensitive uniporter that might exist in the mitochondrial membrane.

10. Concluding Remarks

Even if mitochondrial Ca^{2+} transport is slow under conditions pre-vailing normally inside the cell, the mitochondria are able to decrease ex-tramitochondrial Ca^{2+} significantly. Inside the mitochondria the free con-centration of the bivalent cations seems to be low, the bulk being in a re-versibly bound, mobilizable state.

D. EFFLUX OF BIVALENT CATIONS FROM MITOCHONDRIA

Release of bivalent cations can be induced in several conditions—for instance, respiratory chain inhibitors, uncouplers of oxidative phosphoryl-ation, or bivalent cation ionophores such as A23187 or X537A (Reed and Lardy, 1972; Caswell and Pressman, 1972). As these perturbations in-volve removal of the energy source or changes in the permeability of the mitochondrial membrane, they are not very interesting physiologically. Several workers have suggested that bivalent cations are extruded from the interior of mitochondria at least partially by a mechanism separate from the uniporter responsible for the uptake. Evidence in favor of this are differences in the effect of inhibitors of Ca^{2+} transport on influx and ef-flux (Crompton et al., 1977; Gunter et al., 1978), the nonequilibrium between the Ca^{2+} gradient and the membrane potential under several con-ditions (Massari and Pozzan, 1976; Puskin et al., 1976; Pozzan et al., 1977), and the fact that Ca^{2+} efflux can be induced under some conditions without affecting other functions of mitochondria (Carafoli, 1973; Åkerman, 1978c). Because of the high effectiveness and activity of the uniporter mechanism, a separate efflux mechanism is often difficult to demonstrate (Nicholls, 1978a,b). Factors that affect mitochondrial bivalent cation retention and thereby cause efflux of the cations are discussed in Section IV,C and will be mentioned here only when it is relevant to the present problem. This distinction, however, at present is not strict, since so little is known about the features of possible separate efflux mechanisms.

1. nNa^+/Ca^{2+} Exchange

Extensive work by Carafoli and co-workers as well as by others have shown that Na^+ promotes release of Ca^{2+} from mitochondria isolated from heart (Carafoli, 1973; Crompton et al., 1976b), brown adipose tissue (Al-Shaikhaly et al., 1979), and other excitable tissues (Crompton et al., 1978; Nicholls, 1978a). Figure 10 demonstrates a typical example of Na^+-induced Ca^{2+} release in the presence of ruthenium red. The Na^+-induced Ca^{2+} release is seen at concentration as low as 4–10 mM Na^+ if further Ca^{2+} uptake is blocked by ruthenium red (Crompton et al., 1976b). The relation of the extent of Ca^{2+} release to the Na^+ concentration is sigmoid. Interestingly, Na^+-induced Ca^{2+} efflux is inhibited by La^{3+}, but unaffected by ruthenium red (Crompton et al., 1977), which would suggest with some reservation that the release is indeed due to a separate transport mechanism other than the Ca^{2+} uniporter. During Na^+-dependent Ca^{2+} efflux no changes in other functions of mitochondria can be noted (Crompton et al., 1977), which indeed shows that this release is not secondary to a deleterious effect on mitochondria.

The nNa^+/Ca^{2+} exchange mechanism seems to be responsible for a ruthenium red-insensitive Ca^{2+}/Ca^{2+} exchange (Fig. 10) in heart mitochondria as well (Crompton et al., 1977). The stoichiometry has not been established and may involve more than 2 Na^+/Ca^{2+} (Crompton et al., 1976b).

It has been reported that the Na^+-induced Ca^{2+} efflux is reversed by addition of oligomycin (Harris, 1979). This does not necessarily prove a link between this efflux mechanism and changes in the adenine nucleotide pool but is certainly worth further characterization. This effect is probably dependent on experimental conditions, and we have not been able to reproduce it using ^{45}Ca (K. E. O. Åkerman and N.-E. L. Saris, unpublished observations). Harris (1979) used Arsenoazo III for determination of Ca^{2+} uptake that might react to nonspecific changes. Furthermore, this indicator might in itself cause Ca^{2+} efflux (Ohnishi, 1979). The physiological significance of the Na^+-dependent Ca^{2+} release is still unclear, but could well be related to the increase in intracellular Ca^{2+} following influx of Na^+ on depolarization. It is of some interest that this mechanism can be seen only in mitochondria from excitable tissues (Crompton *et al.*, 1978b).

2. nH^+/Ca^{2+} Exchange

A transient release of Ca^{2+} from rat liver mitochondria occurs also when the extramitochondrial pH is decreased from 7.4 to 6.8 (Åkerman, 1978c) (see Fig. 10). It occurs without any alteration of other functions of the mitochondrial inner membrane. The release is unaffected by ruthenium red but is inhibited by La^{3+}, as in the case with the Na^+-induced Ca^{2+} release (Åkerman, 1978c). Furthermore, if a proton gradient (acid inside) is induced by aid of the H^+/Me^+ exchanger dianemycin, an uptake of Ca^{2+} by mitochondria occurs (Fiskum and Cockrell, 1978), also in the presence of ruthenium red. It has therefore been suggested that the mitochondrial membrane contains a separate nH^+/Ca^{2+} exchanger that releases this cation when the intramitochondrial Ca^{2+} concentration or the proton gradient across the membrane rises (Åkerman, 1978c; Åkerman and Saris, 1978; Fiskum and Cockrell, 1978). Other workers have also considered the possible existence of an nH^+/Ca^{2+} exchanger in the mitocondrial membrane (Nicholls, 1978a,b). Carafoli (1979) has also claimed that no H^+/Ca^{2+} exchange mechanism is present in heart mitochondria. This suggestion is based on experiments made by Nicholls (1978a). He added 75 mM K^+ together with H^+/Me^+ exchanger nigericin and noted no efflux of Ca^{2+}. However, since mitochondria already contain at least 100 mM K^+ internally (Rottenberg, 1973), no proton gradient would be created upon addition of K^+ + nigericin.

An H^+/Ca^{2+} exchange mechanism could well account for Ca^{2+} cycling across the mitochondrial membrane; i.e., Ca^{2+} uptake would occur by a uniporter, and efflux by an H^+/Ca^{2+} exchange. Similar models for coupling of uniporters to H^+/Me^+ exchange have been proposed for monovalent cation transport in mitochondria (Brierley, 1976) (see Section VII,D). Thus, the mitochondrial membrane potential would drive Ca^{2+} uptake and H^+ efflux. The extramitochondrial Ca^{2+} concentration at steady state is indeed significantly dependent on the external pH and the ΔpH (Fig. 6) across the membrane (Nicholls, 1978b). Thus the bivalent cation distribution ratio would be dependent on the relative kinetic profiles of the translocators as well as upon the magnitude of the membrane potential and ΔpH, which in many cases could explain discrepancies in observed Rb^+ and bivalent cation steady-state distribution ratios (see Section IV,C).

In this context it is also of interest that proteins have been extracted from the mitochondrial membrane that transfer Ca^{2+} into an organic phase only in the presence of a proton gradient (Jeng *et al.*, 1978) or when reconstituted into phospholipid vesicles show H^+/Ca^{2+} exchange (Dubinsky *et al.*, 1979).

Another point of possible interest in this context is that if the cytosolic pH of barnacle muscle fibers is decreased, a rise in the cytosolic Ca^{2+} concentration can be noted (Lea and Ashley, 1978). In squid axons an increase or decrease in axoplasmic Ca^{2+} can be induced by a decrease in axoplasmic pH, depending on conditions (Baker and Honejäger, 1978). A lowering of the cytosolic pH by different means in salivary gland cells or various cultured cells causes an uncoupling of the cells and an increase in cytosolic Ca^{2+} (Rose and Rick, 1978; Flagg-Newton and Loewenstein, 1979). Furthermore, kinetic analysis of Ca^{2+} exchange in isolated rat kidney cells show a decrease in the mitochondrial pool upon induction of acidosis (Studer and Borle, 1979).

Further studies are needed, however, before we can decide whether the mitochondrial membrane contains an nH^+/Ca^{2+} exchanger or whether the effect of extramitochondrial pH is only a functional release of Ca^{2+} due to some other factors, such as lowering of the affinity of Ca-binding sites at lower pH or dissociation of phosphate salts. However, the existence of such a mechanism would provide an interesting regulatory model of mitochondrial bivalent cation transport.

Recently, it has been shown that a ruthenium red-insensitive Ca^{2+} uptake in the presence of phosphate occurs in highly purified preparations of rat liver submitochondrial particles (Lötscher *et al.*, 1979; Carafoli, 1979). The workers suggested that Ca^{2+} efflux in rat liver mitochondria occurs via a $Ca^{2+}/$phosphate symporter. Their results, however, may equally well be explained with a H^+/Ca^{2+} exchange mechanism, and therefore at present there is not enough evidence for a separate $Ca^{2+}/$phosphate symporter mechanism (see Section VII). Wehrle and Pedersen (1979) also concluded that Ca^{2+} uptake in similar conditions was a result of precipitation of calcium phosphate inside the particles.

3. *Effect of Inhibitors on Ca^{2+} Efflux*

As discussed previously, ruthenium red does not inhibit Na^+- or H^+-induced Ca^{2+} efflux (Crompton *et al.*, 1976b; Åkerman, 1978c). Both of those efflux mechanisms, however, are inhibited by La^{3+} (Crompton *et al.*, 1978b; Åkerman, 1978c). Crompton *et al.* (1979) have shown that the Ca^{2+} uptake and release differ in their sensitivities to various lanthanide ions, the release being more strongly inhibited by lanthanides with large ionic radii. In some undefined conditions it has been shown that ruthenium red inhibits Ca^{2+} efflux from mitochondria (Luthra and Olson, 1977). However, this might indicate that efflux in their conditions occurred through the uniporter. Furthermore, they did not purify their ruthenium red prep-aration. Therefore it is not known whether the effect was due to ruthenium red or to some other ruthenium analog (see Section III,C).

Under other experimental conditions ruthenium red is known to induce Ca^{2+} efflux from mitochondria (Rossi et al., 1973). Interestingly, the ruthenium red-induced Ca^{2+} efflux is inhibited by local anesthetics (Dawson et al., 1979), which also increases the rate of Ca^{2+} uptake (Mela, 1968). Whether this effect occurs through an inhibition of Ca^{2+} efflux or through an effect on Ca^{2+} retention remains to be seen.

4. Concluding Remarks

The experiments cited previously, even if they are strongly indicative, do not prove the existence of a translocator separate from the Me^{2+} uni-porter. The efflux of Ca^{2+} under some conditions could only be a result of a nonspecific increase in the permeability of the mitochondrial membrane. Indeed, small concentrations of Ca^{2+} have been shown to increase the mitochondrial permeability toward a large variety of substances (Hunter et al., 1976). It should, furthermore, be stressed that efflux does not nec-essarily occur through the postulated separate mechanism. For instance, when the mitochondrial membrane is depolarized with uncouplers of oxi-dative phosphorylation, it is conceivable that efflux occurs by the uni-porter, which works in both directions depending on conditions (Wikström and Saari, 1976; Åkerman, 1978b). Thus, Pozzan and Azzone (1976) have shown that mitochondria swollen in hypotonic Me^{2+} nitrate media contract by a ruthenium red-sensitive, respiration-driven mecha-nism.

Note that any alteration in factors affecting Me^{2+} retention ($\Delta\psi$, ΔpH, intramitochondrial binding, Me^{2+} concentration, etc.: see Section IV,C), may lead to Me^{2+} efflux; subsequently Me^{2+} cycling would occur with de-polarization of the membrane, total Me^{2+} release, and possible phospholi-pase A_2 activation (in the case of Ca^{2+}). Thus various factors affecting this futile cycle should not be interpreted as acting on an efflux mechanism alone before effects through other mechanisms have been carefully ex-cluded (see Section V,B).

V. Specificity of the Bivalent Cation Uptake

A. General Properties of Transportable Cations

Mitochondria from various sources are able, at least under some exper-imental conditions, to transport in an energy-dependent fashion a number of monovalent cations, the bivalent cations Mg^{2+}, Ca^{2+}, Sr^{2+}, Mn^{2+}, Ba^{2+},

TABLE III
CRYSTAL IONIC RADII OF SOME CATIONS[a]

Cation	Radius (nm)	Cation	Radius (nm)
Mg(II)	0.066	Ca(II)	0.099
Cu(II)	0.072	Hg(II)	0.110
Fe(II)	0.074	Sr(II)	0.112
Zn(II)	0.074	La(III)	0.114
Mn(II)	0.080	Pb(II)	0.120
Na(I)	0.097	K(I)	0.133
Cd(II)	0.097	Ba(II)	0.134
Eu(III)	0.098		

[a] From Weast et al. (1965).

Fe^{2+}, Cu^{2+}, Pb^{2+}, Cd^{2+}, Zn^{2+}, the trivalent cation La^{3+}, and organic cations. Before discussing in detail the specificities of mitochondrial cation transport systems, a brief account of the general properties of these inorganic cations may be useful. From studies of the mechanism of action of ionophores (see Section II,A), it is evident that the nonhydrated radii of the cations are of prime importance for the formation of the close complexes needed with the component of the system regardless of whether it is a carrier type or a channel-forming molecular species. Table III shows the nonhydrated radii of the cations. The best experimental data are obtained from crystallographic measurements. It is of interest that the nonhydrated radius of Na^+ and Cd^{2+} is very close to that of Ca^{2+}, the most likely substrate of the system. Of the earth alkali cations, Sr^{2+} is reasonably close to Ca^{2+}.

Another important factor is the ease of dehydration of the cation. It is highly probable that in the binding of the cation to the transport site, the water of hydration is replaced by ligands, such as O and N atoms. The water molecules as a rule hold more tightly the higher the charge and the smaller the nonhydrated radius of the cation. The difference between the behavior of Mg^{2+} and Ca^{2+} has been largely attributed to the difficulty of removing the last water molecule from Mg^{2+} in contrast to Ca^{2+} (see Williams, 1975).

Coulombic interactions between the cation and negative charges in the transport site may also contribute significantly to the specificity (see review by Diamond and Wright, 1969). Thus the field strength of the intrinsic site will affect the ion–ion or ion–dipole interaction of the cation and the transport site. A site exposed to an aqueous solution containing different cations will selectively bind the species that causes the greatest decrease in free energy upon binding. The main components in the free energy changes are that of hydration of the cation and that of coulombic interaction. If the free energy change of the latter is greater than that of the former, binding is favored. Sites with low field strength, and therefore relatively small free energy changes due to coulombic interactions, will be able to bind only relatively large cations with small free energy change of hydration.

Finally, the ability to bind specifically in multidentate complexes to the transport site seems to be a most important factor. As discussed by Williams (1976) and Carafoli (1977), Ca^{2+} adapts more readily than Mg^{2+} to various complex ligands because of its ability to accommodate a wider range of coordination bond angles and distances. Mg^{2+} is relatively rigid, forming only regular octahedral complexes. Thus, the binding strength of Ca^{2+} generally will increase as the number and complexity of coordination centers in ligands increase whereas the opposite is true of Mg^{2+}. Therefore, Ca^{2+} is better suited to form irregular complexes, and thereby it would be able to penetrate deeper into the membrane than Mg^{2+}. In this context it is pertinent to mention that Ca^{2+} is well known to be able to influence membrane properties profoundly (see Williams, 1975, 1976; Carafoli, 1977).

In a very interesting paper, Tew (1977) has reported the use of the lanthanide series of trivalent cations to probe the Me^{2+} transport site. These potent competitive inhibitors of mitochondrial Me^{2+} transport have very similar chemical properties but vary in their ionic radii and hydration energies. As shown in Fig. 11, the lanthanides with the ionic radii closest to that of Ca^{2+} are the most potent inhibitors. These data do not indicate that strong-field interactions are important in this system, since the lanthanides with small radii then should be the strongest inhibitors. The data are best explained on the basis of complex binding to several coordination centers in a site accommodating an ion of a certain size, that of Ca^{2+}.

Heavy metal cations are even more avid complex formers than Ca^{2+} and may form much stronger and more varied complexes than Ca^{2+}. Correspondingly, they will perturb the membrane structure more strongly than Ca^{2+} and affect the membrane properties more profoundly. From the transport point of view, they may be expected to be bound to the transport site so strongly that release from it is likely to be inhibited. These cations therefore may be expected to be transported slowly and to inhibit Ca^{2+} transport potently.

It is evident that many different bivalent cations may be transported by the mitochondrial Ca^{2+}-transporting system or similar mechanisms. The rate of transport is fastest for Ca^{2+}, almost as fast for Sr^{2+}, far slower for

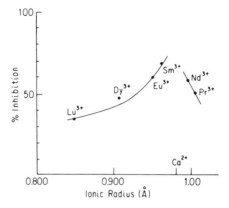

FIG. 11. Inhibition of mitochondrial Ca^{2+} uptake as a function of the ionic radii of different lanthanides. Plotted as percentage of inhibition of the uptake of 125 μM Ca^{2+}. From Tew (1977).

Ba^{2+}, Mn^{2+}, Fe^{2+}, and heavy metal ions. Mg^{2+} is transported very slowly indeed, if at all, by rat liver mitochondria, whereas heart mitochondria have a more active system. From a physiological point of view, transport systems for the uptake of Ca^{2+}, Mg^{2+}, and Fe^{2+} may be significant, whereas transport of the other cations appears to be due to the unspecificity of the transport systems or may be accidental. The transport of Mg^{2+} is distinctly different from that of Ca^{2+}, both in regard to its presence in mitochondria from various sources and to its properties. The other cations are taken up by the mitochondria by mechanisms that show great similarities, and often one may show competition between the various cations. However, there are also some distinct differences. It may be useful, therefore, to discuss separately the uptake of Mg^{2+}, the other alkali earth ions plus Mn^{2+}, Fe^{2+}, and, finally, the heavy metal cations.

B.   SECONDARY EFFECTS OF BIVALENT CATIONS ON MITOCHONDRIAL STRUCTURE AND FUNCTION

The differences between the uptake of the various cations may be due to differences in the transport mechanisms or to secondary effects. Most of the cations have profound effects on mitochondrial functions and the state of the inner membrane, which in its turn may affect the uptake. In most studies net uptake has been measured, and effects on efflux of the cation may then be interpreted as effects upon the uptake. Ca^{2+} and some of the other cations may cause damage to the mitochondria (see Section V,C), whereas other cations, notably Mg^{2+} and Mn^{2+}, will have a protective effect. These various effects (see Section IV,C) may also influence the interpretation of uptake data. Before discussing these, it is pertinent to describe the present knowledge of factors affecting the deleterious effects of Ca^{2+} upon mitochondria.

The Ca^{2+}-induced deterioration of mitochondrial structure and function and the prevention or reversal of it has received considerable attention. Early work was reviewed by Lehninger et al. (1967). It was found that P_i and draining of the mitochondrial ATP pool promoted the damage, whereas Mg^{2+} (or Mn^{2+}), respiration, especially on succinate, and ATP counteracted or reversed it (Saris, 1963b). Liver mitochondria are sensitive and have been most extensively studied. With the swelling, the permeability toward many substances is increased and even nucleotides may be lost from the mitochondria. Two mechanisms merit discussion: that the increased permeability is due to an activation of a Ca^{2+}-stimulated mitochondrial phospholipase A_2 activity, or that it is due to a loss of Mg^{2+} from the inner membrane.

Phospholipase A_2 activity would release fatty acids and lysophosphatides, and by reacyling phosphatides would be re-formed. Wojtczak and Lehninger (1961) showed that both activities occur in mitochondria and are responsible for the increase in the mitochondrial content of fatty acids and their decrease on addition of ATP. They also showed that albumin protected mitochondria against the deleterious effects of fatty acids by binding these. However, the lysophosphatides might be even more important than fatty acids in causing damage to mitochondria (Scherphof et al., 1972). It was interesting that local anesthetics were found to inhibit phospholipase A_2 activities (Seppälä et al., 1971; Scherphof et al., 1972), which provided an explanation for their protective effect, which was even more potent than that of albumin (Scherphof et al., 1972). More recent work has made the phospholipase A_2 mechanism less plausible. While there is no doubt that depletion of energy stores in the presence of Ca^{2+} will activate the phospholipase and inhibit acyltransferase activity, it seems that these changes occur rather late in the swelling process (Parce et al., 1978). Local anesthetics have other effects in addition to that of inhibiting the phospholipase, e.g., inhibition of Ca^{2+} efflux, thereby reducing Ca^{2+} cycling (Dawson et al., 1979), and inhibition of the increased anion permeability observed when the pH is raised above pH 7.5 (Selwyn et al., 1978). In view of these recent findings it appears to be inappropriate to use mitochondrial preparations stabilized by nupercaine in studies of Me^{2+} and anion transport.

Mg^{2+} delays the release of accumulated Ca^{2+} in mitochondria (see Fig. 8b) and decreases their permeability toward monovalent cations (Douglas and Cockrell, 1974; Brierley and Jurkowitz, 1976). These permeabilities may be increased by chelating agents, like EDTA (Packer *et al.*, 1966), that tend to remove some of the mitochondrial Mg^{2+} (Settlemire *et al.*, 1968), presumably from the intermembrane space and the C side of the inner membrane, where most of the mitochondrial Mg^{2+} is found (Bogucka and Wojtczak, 1971). More striking effects have been obtained by selectively removing Mg^{2+} with the bivalent cation ionophore A23187 (Reed and Lardy, 1972), whereby a greatly increased K^+ permeability ensued, presumably owing to the activation of K/H^+ exchange (Duszyński and Wojtczak, 1977). The monitoring of Mg^{2+} in the hydrophobic space of the inner membrane with the aid of the fluorescence of chlorotetracycline (Caswell and Hutchison, 1971) showed that Mg^{2+} was removed from this compartment (Binet and Volfin, 1975). Release of accumulated Ca^{2+} occurred only when Mg^{2+} was substantially reduced (Binet and Volfin, 1975). These data indicate a central role of Mg^{2+} in controlling mitochondrial permeabilities.

Many of the agents that cause damage to mitochondria (evidenced by swelling, lowered control ratios, increased ATPase activities, and loss of matrix components) also cause a release of Mg^{2+}. Thus, accumulation of rather large amounts of Ca^{2+}, even in the absence of permeant anions, reduces the mitochondrial Mg^{2+} in rat liver mitochondria (Lee *et al.*, 1971; Binet and Volfin, 1974). This effect is enhanced by the presence of P_i, and by respiration of endogenous substrates in the absence of rotenone (Höser *et al.*, 1976). The latter finding can now be readily explained as resulting from oxidation of the mitochondrial NADH (Lehninger *et al.*, 1978b). We have also found that sulfate promotes release of Mg^{2+} (N.-E. L. Saris, unpublished observations). Release of Mg^{2+} from rat liver mitochondria occurs in the presence of uncoupling agents and adenine nucleotides (Kun *et al.*, 1969). In these studies the efflux of Mg^{2+} could be retarded by a cytoplasmic factor by a mechanism that remains obscure. This factor may also retard release of Ca^{2+} (Lee *et al.*, 1971).

Bogucka and Wojtczak (1979) showed that organic mercurials also cause a release of Mg^{2+}, which might be the mechanism for the enhanced permeability toward K^+ induced by heavy metals and organic mercurials (see review by Brierley, 1976). There seems to be a connection between blocking of thiol groups in the membrane and its permeability properties (Scott *et al.*, 1970; Brierley *et al.*, 1971). Pfeiffer *et al.* (1978) have reported that NEM, which can react with —SH groups also on the matrix side, will promote the release of accumulated Ca^{2+} in rat liver mitochondria. NEM may alter mitochondrial permeabilities and must be used with caution.

The mechanism by which Mg^{2+} exerts its effects might be the formation of ternary complexes with anionic groups in the membrane, whereby negatively charged phospholipids and proteins would tend to become immobilized (Binet and Volfin, 1975). Mg^{2+} might also act by immobilizing free fatty acids in the membrane that have been shown to be able to act as ionophores for monovalent cations (Wojtczak, 1974). These effects would be caused by the interaction of Mg^{2+} with surface charges. An interesting possibility is that the small amount of Mg^{2+} that is localized in the inner region of the membrane (less than 2 nmol per milligram of protein; Binet and Volfin, 1975) is involved in the control of mitochondrial permeability. Also, a Ca^{2+}-dependent increased anion permeability in rat liver mitochondria has been described (Selwyn et al., 1979). Mg^{2+} could act by competing with Ca^{2+} for binding to this "anion-conducting pore." At present, there is not enough evidence in favor of any of the abovementioned mechanisms to make them more than interesting speculations.

C. TRANSPORT OF MAGNESIUM

Even if much is known about the role of Mg^{2+} in cellular function (Bygrave, 1967; Aikawa, 1978), little is known about the regulation of this cation at the cellular level. One of the main reasons for this is the lack of suitable isotopes for such studies. The only available isotope is ^{28}Mg, which unfortunately has a half-time of about 21 hours. Therefore most studies are made using atomic absorption spectrometry, in which case kinetic analysis on the exchangeability and mobility of Mg^{2+} is difficult, especially since cellular Mg^{2+} is mostly bound (Veloso et al., 1973). Spectroscopic methods have been developed for the determination of Mg^{2+} fluxes based upon Mg^{2+}-sensitive indicators (Scarpa, 1974).

Fractionation studies on the compartmentalization of Mg^{2+} in different mitochondrial membrane fractions indicate that the main part of Mg^{2+} is present in the matrix space and intermembrane space (Bogucka and Wojtczak, 1971). The intermembranously localized Mg^{2+} has been suggested to be mostly bound to certain protein species (Bogucka and Wojtczak, 1976). A peculiarity in this context, though, is that most of the mitochondrial Mg^{2+} is released by treatment with A23187 (Reed and Lardy, 1972), which would suggest that the main part of the mitochondrial Mg^{2+} is sequestered in a membrane-bounded compartment (or compartments) because the ionophore should only affect bulk phase distributions of Mg^{2+} across membranes, not binding of it to proteins.

It has long been known that mitochondria isolated from heart muscle take up massive amounts of Mg^{2+} during respiration (Schuster and Olson, 1974; Brierley, 1976). This uptake of Mg^{2+} by heart mitochondria is completely insensitive to ruthenium red (Brierley, 1976), a finding that would suggest that the uniport involved in the uptake of other bivalent cations is not involved. On the other hand, Mg^{2+} is only slowly taken up by rat liver mitochondria, except when acetate and very high extramitochondrial Mg^{2+} concentrations are present (Brierley, 1976). An energy-dependent Mg^{2+} release mechanism has been demonstrated by several workers. In liver mitochondria, ADP in combination with an uncoupler (Kun et al., 1969) or endogenous Ca^{2+} and phosphate (Höser et al., 1976; D. Siliprandi et al., 1977; N. Siliprandi et al., 1978) are necessary for the respiration-linked Mg^{2+} efflux. The phosphate (and endogenous Ca^{2+})-stimulated Mg^{2+} efflux in rat liver mitochondria is inhibited by ruthenium red or EGTA (Höser et al., 1976; D. Siliprandi et al., 1977; N. Siliprandi et al., 1978), which would suggest that uptake of Ca^{2+} is necessary for this mechanism. This efflux, furthermore, is inhibited by an uncoupler, FCCP, and an inhibitor of phosphate transport, NEM (Höser et al., 1976; Siliprandi et al., 1977).

In heart mitochondria, on the other hand, respiration-linked Mg^{2+} efflux occurs even in the presence of ruthenium red (Crompton et al., 1976c), and with these mitochondria the efflux is inhibited by Ca^{2+} (Crompton et al., 1976c). This efflux occurs at extramitochondrial Mg^{2+} concentrations below 2 mM (Crompton et al., 1976c). Above this concentration an uptake of Mg^{2+} occurs. Since most workers have arrived at a value of $0.1-1$ mM of free cytosolic Mg^{2+} (Palaty, 1971; Veloso et al., 1973; Endo, 1975) in various tissues, one might expect that Mg^{2+} extrusion from heart mitochondria could occur in vivo under appropriate conditions. Mg^{2+} efflux from heart mitochondria is stimulated by phosphate and inhibited by FCCP, an uncoupler of oxidative phosphorylation (Crompton et al., 1976c), as in the case of liver mitochondria. Therefore, the movements of Mg^{2+} both in and out across the mitochondrial membrane appear to be energy-linked.

Respiration-linked Mg^{2+} release also occurs in smooth muscle mitochondria (Sloane et al., 1978). However, this event was not characterized in detail, and therefore it is not known whether it has the same properties as efflux in heart or liver mitochondria.

These experiments would indicate that Mg^{2+} movements occur by mechanisms separate from those involved in the transport of other bivalent cations.

D. Transport of Alkali Earth Cations and Mn^{2+}

In early studies of Ca^{2+} transport it was observed that Sr^{2+} and Mn^{2+} behaved in the same way as Ca^{2+} in causing acidification of the medium upon energized uptake (Chappell et al., 1962, 1963; Saris, 1963b). Figure 12 shows a comparison between rates of acidification caused by Ca^{2+},

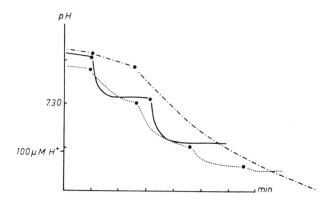

FIG. 12. Comparison between the rate of acidification of the medium produced by addition of 91 μM Ca^{2+} (——), 91 μM Sr^{2+} ($\cdots\cdots$), and 340 μM Mn^{2+} ($\cdot-\cdot-\cdot$) at points indicated (●) to mitochondria respiring on succinate. From Saris (1963b).

Sr^{2+}, and Mn^{2+}. The uptake of Sr^{2+} was then studied in great detail by Carafoli *et al.* (1965b) and Carafoli (1965a,b). In these studies Sr^{2+} was found to behave essentially like Ca^{2+} in regard to the energy source, stoichiometric stimulation of respiration, and coaccumulation of P$_i$ when present. There was competition between Ca^{2+} and Sr^{2+} for transport (Carafoli, 1965a). These data leave no doubt that Sr^{2+} and Ca^{2+} indeed are transported by the same system.

Early in the investigations, it was observed that injected Mn^{2+} became localized in liver mitochondria (Maynard and Cotzias, 1955). Chappell *et al.* (1962) showed that Mn^{2+} was accumulated by mitochondria in an energy-dependent reaction, which was stimulated by respiration and coaccumulation of P$_i$. From these studies it was clear that the affinity of the transporting system was rather low for Mn^{2+}. Drahota *et al.* (1969) and Vainio *et al.* (1970) have systematically compared these cations and in addition studied Ba^{2+} transport. Ba^{2+} was found to be accumulated at a slow rate that had not been detected earlier (Saris, 1963b). Both from initial rate and apparent K_m values, as well as from their effects on respiration and proton production, the following order of selectivity was observed: Ca^{2+} > Sr^{2+} ≫ Mn^{2+} > Ba^{2+} (Saris, 1963b; Drahota *et al.*, 1969; Vainio *et al.*, 1970). No transport or responses were observed with Mg^{2+}. Figure 12 compares the rate of proton production with Ca^{2+}, Sr^{2+}, and Mn^{2+}.

Vainio *et al.* (1970) also compared effects of various inhibitors on the uptake and responses of the bivalent cations. A 50% inhibition was observed with the same concentration of Pr^{3+}, except in the case of Mn^{2+} (see below). With Ca^{2+} and Sr^{2+}, however, much higher concentrations were needed for maximal inhibition than with Ba^{2+}. Vainio *et al.* (1970)

also showed that Mg^{2+} inhibits the uptake of bivalent cations. Half-maximal inhibition of Ba^{2+} uptake was observed at much lower concentrations of Mg^{2+} than with the other cations. Only Ba^{2+} uptake was also sensitive to K^+. 20 mM K^+ completely inhibited the Ba^{2+} uptake (Vainio et al., 1970). This is probably the reason why Saris (1963b) observed no Ba^{2+} uptake in mitochondria, since he used a KCl-containing medium. Interestingly, the crystal ionic radius of Ba^{2+} and K^+ is about the same (see Table III). As discussed in Section IV,A, K^+ probably interferes with the surface binding of Ba^{2+}. This would indicate that the selectivity of the transport process is partially determined by the surface binding step (see Section IV,A) and partially by the translocator (see Section VI).

The difference between the effect of various inhibitors on the uptake of different bivalent cations is thus compatible with the two-step mechanism of uptake suggested by Scarpa and Azzone (1968), Vainio et al. (1970), Åkerman et al. (1977), and Åkerman (1977a,b): i.e., an initial binding to surface sites (sensitive to Mg^{2+} and spermine, and in case of Ba^{2+} also to K^+), a subsequent diffusion to a translocator, and a transfer across the membrane (sensitive to La^{3+} and ruthenium red). Vainio et al. (1970) reported some pecularities of Mn^{2+} transport, including stimulation of Mn^{2+} transport by other cations, at least at low concentration. Among these cations were K^+, Mn^{2+}, Ca^{2+}, and even a lanthanide, Pr^{3+}, which at higher concentrations is an inhibitor of Me^{2+} transport. The reason for this is unclear, but one explanation may be the lowering of the free Mn^{2+} concentration by binding to some sites from which it may be released by these cations. Nevertheless, there is little doubt that all these cations are transported by the same mechanism.

Drahota et al. (1969) demonstrated some release of K^+ following uptake of large amounts of Mn^{2+} and Ba^{2+}. The release was slower than the uptake of Me^{2+}. These cations thus seem to induce increased permeability toward K^+, an effect similar to that induced by small amounts of heavy metals (see review by Brierley, 1976).

Unfortunately, there are no up-to-date careful studies on the kinetic parameters of the transport of these cations, whereby a more detailed comparison could be made.

E. TRANSPORT OF IRON

The uptake of Fe^{2+} by mitochondria shows many similarities to the uptake of Ca^{2+} (Romslo and Flatmark, 1973; Romslo, 1975a), e.g., energy-dependence, saturation kinetics, and inhibition by ruthenium red as well as by La^{3+}. There is a competitive inhibition by Ca^{2+} (Romslo and Flatmark, 1973). The energy-dependent uptake of Fe^{2+} is difficult to study because of chelation of Fe^{2+} by substrate ions and ATP, but uptake is stimulated by induction of a diffusion potential by addition of valinomycin to mitochondria suspended in a K^+-free medium (Romslo, 1975b). There are, however, several special features indicating that the transport system has been developed especially to meet the specific requirements and needs of transport of Fe^{2+} for the synthesis of heme, the final stage of which occurs in the matrix space with the aid of ferrochelatase. In mitochondria from reticulocytes, cells with an especially high rate of heme synthesis, the ratio of transport of Fe^{2+} to that of Ca^{2+} is higher than in other mitochondria in corresponding experimental conditions (Romslo, 1974). The energy-dependent transport of Fe^{2+} in liver mitochindria, which also have a comparatively high rate of heme synthesis, is inhibited by hemin and stimulated by isonicotinic acid hydrazide (Koller *et al.*, 1976) when transferrin is the substrate. It seems therefore plausible that one controlled step in the pathway of heme synthesis is the mitochondrial transport of Fe^{2+}.

The transport of iron has to overcome several obstacles due to its chemical properties. It is present both in transferrin and ferritin as Fe^{3+}, which is easily bound or precipitated at intracellular pH. Prior to the transport of iron through the hydrophobic barrier, it is bound by ligands in a microenvironment giving it a sufficiently high half-reduction potential to establish redox equilibrium with cytochrome *c* (Flatmark and Romslo, 1975) and to be capable of being reduced to Fe^{2+}. Iron transport, therefore, cannot be supported by ATP alone but requires a supply of reducing equivalents. A schematic model of iron transport is shown in Fig. 13.

Iron transport is inhibited by *N*-ethylmaleimide (Romslo and Flatmark, 1973; Ulvik *et al.*, 1976) as well. Up to 30 nmol of Fe per milligram of pro-

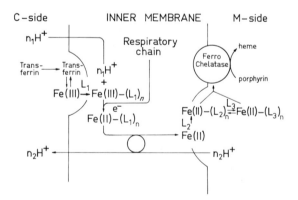

FIG. 13. Scheme of iron transport in mitochondria. C-Side, cytosolic side; M-side, matrix side of the inner membrane; L, iron-binding components. Adapted from Flatmark and Romslo (1975).

tein can be accumulated. The transport is not reversible, presumably because of binding of iron to components in the matrix, or M side, of the membrane (Flatmark and Romslo, 1975).

In addition to the energy-dependent transport of Fe^{2+}, there is an energy-independent, nonsaturable uptake of Fe^{2+}. In this regard, iron behaves similarly to the cations of heavy metals (see Section V,F).

F. TRANSPORT OF HEAVY METAL CATIONS

Brierley and co-workers (see reviews by Brierley, 1974, 1976, 1978) have shown that mercurials and heavy metal cations (Pb^{2+}, Zn^{2+}, Cd^{2+}, Cu^{2+}, and Hg^{2+}) drastically change the permeability properties of mitochondria, inhibiting P_i/OH^- exchange and increasing K^+ and Mg^{2+} permeabilities. They also report energy-dependent accumulation of Pb^+ (Scott et al., 1971) in heart mitochondria, which occurs in acetate media. In Cl^- or NO_3^- media energy-independent binding is extensive (up to 150 nmol/per milligram of protein), and no further uptake is obtained upon energization. In energized conditions, addition of Pb^{2+} causes similar reactions as Ca^{2+}, e.g., apparent alkalinization of the matrix. Pb^{2+} also inhibits Ca^{2+} uptake. These data are compatible with the hypothesis that Pb^{2+} is transported with the aid of the Ca^{2+}-transporting system. The solubility of Pb^{2+} is enhanced by sucrose, dextran, and especially ATP, whereby the deleterious effects upon oxidative phosphorylation and respiration are enhanced (Parr and Harris, 1976). This is seen even in the presence of P_i, which under other conditions precipitates Pb^{2+}. It is of interest that mitochondria seem to be a target when Pb^{2+} is administrated in vivo (Krall et al., 1971).

Zn^{2+} also seems to be accumulated in an energy-dependent manner by heart mitochondria with matrix alkalinization and inhibition of Ca^{2+} transport in massive loading conditions (Scott et al., 1971). We have studied Cd^{2+} in kidney mitochondria and shown that it is taken up by an uncoupler- and ruthenium red-sensitive process (Saris and Järvisalo, 1977). In addition, there is an energy-independent, ruthenium red-insensitive uptake. In contrast to previous workers, we used very small concentrations of the cation, which did not induce marked permeability changes or uncoupling. There was also a clear inhibition of Ca^{2+} transport at 1 μM concentration of Cd^{2+} or less. These studies leave little doubt that Cd^{2+}, and the chemically very similar Zn^{2+}, are transported by the Ca^{2+} transporting system. When Cd^{2+} was administered in vivo, we found no effects on kidney mitochondria though they contained substantial amounts of Cd^{2+} (Järvisalo et al., 1980). These data could indicate a protective role of mitochondria in the kidney.

Cu^{2+} has been shown to be taken up in massive amounts by nonenergized heart mitochondria (Cederbaum and Vainio, 1972). Energization decreases the amount taken up (Zaba and Harris, 1976). Depending on the medium used, the rate of penetration of Cu^{2+} may increase with time. Cu^{2+} will inhibit mitochondrial Ca^{2+} transport. These data do not, however, indicate any energy-linked transport of Cu^{2+} by the Me^{2+}-transporting system; presumably this would be masked by the extensive nonenergized uptake.

Summarizing the data on heavy metals, one may conclude that at least Cd^{2+}, but probably Pb^{2+} and Zn^{2+} as well, are transported by the Me^{2+} transporting system. Studies of energized transport of these cations are difficult owing to their strong perturbing effects upon mitochondria and the appreciable energy-independent uptake.

G. Specificity of Efflux of Bivalent Cations

The efflux mechanisms for bivalent cations have received attention only during the last few years, and they are still only poorly understood (see Sections IV,D and VII).

The efflux can be studied in mitochondria by interrupting the generation of the driving force (inhibition of respiration or ATPase or addition of an uncoupling agent) or by inhibiting the influx with ruthenium red. Alternatively, uptake of bivalent cations can be studied in submitochondrial particles with inverted membrane polarity, using ruthenium red to prevent the release of accumulated cations by the normal uptake mechanism (Lötscher et al., 1979). The studies so far have centered upon Ca^{2+}, and little information is available on other cations.

Different efflux mechanisms have been proposed based on ruthenium red insensitivity and stimulation of efflux by possible antiports. The nNa^+/Ca^{2+} exchange system found by Carafoli and co-workers (Carafoli, 1973) in heart and other excitable tissues is well documented. It is not present in liver mitochondria, where an H^+/Ca^{2+} exchange (Åkerman, 1978c; Fiskum and Cockrell, 1978) or P_i/Ca^{2+} symport (Lötscher et al., 1979; Carafoli, 1979) might be operative. There is no information on other bivalent cations in this system. Both systems are sensitive to La^{3+}, which suggests that other bivalent cations might interact with it.

Pozzan and Azzone (1976) have used a very interesting experimental approach. When mitochondria are energized after swelling in $Sr(NO_3)_2$ media, there is respiration-dependent extrusion of nitrate and Sr^{2+} and contraction. This is ruthenium red-sensitive. It seems that in these conditions the normal Me^{2+}-transport system is acting in reverse (see Section IV). There is no formation of membrane potential by respiration (Azzone et al., 1978) under such conditions because of the extrusion of NO_3^- electrophoretically, Sr^{2+} efflux being coupled to NO_3^- movements. It is therefore probable that the cation specificity of this type of efflux is similar to that of uptake.

Gunter *et al.* (1978) have reported differences in the efflux of Ca^{2+} and Mn^{2+} in rat liver mitochondria. Efflux of cations was induced after loading the mitochondria by addition of uncouplers. The efflux of Mn^{2+} in contrast to Ca^{2+} was retarded in these conditions by ruthenium red or EGTA. However, some of these effects could be seen on Ca^{2+} efflux as well when much lower amounts of uncouplers were used. Mn^{2+} efflux was also slower when induced by addition of EGTA or ruthenium red in the presence of respiratory inhibitors, whereas Ca^{2+} efflux was unaffected under these conditions. The efflux properties of these two cations are thus quite distinct, but it is not clear whether this is due to differences in access of Me^{2+} to the efflux system, to different sensitivities of the two cations to factors regulating the activity of the system, to the different rates of efflux, or whether the two cations are transported predominantly by different systems. Efflux of heavy metal cations has not been studied, partly because they are bound almost irreversibly by mitochondrial membranes.

H. Concluding Remarks

The dominant Me^{2+} uptake mechanism seems to have low specificity. Other alkali earth cations, Mn^{2+}, Fe^{2+}, heavy metal bivalent cations, and even trivalent lanthanide ions may be transported by it. The transport system for Fe^{2+} may have evolved to meet the specific requirements of Fe^{2+} transport in mitochondria from reticulocytes. Under some experimental conditions the bivalent cation uptake mechanism appears to be able to act in reverse. There are other, ruthenium red-insensitive, systems for efflux, notably nNa^+/Ca^{2+} exchange, nH^+/Ca^{2+} exchange and possibly Ca^{2+}/nA^- symport with poorly studied specificities. In rat liver mitochondria Ca^{2+} and Mn^{2+} efflux have distinctly different properties.

VI. Attempts to Isolate Components of the Me^{2+} Transporting Systems

The Me^{2+} transporting systems of mitochondria can be understood at the molecular level only when their components have been isolated and characterized and the transport reconstituted in a phospholipid membrane. Earlier attempts to isolate proteins involved in the system were based on the working hypothesis that high-affinity binding of Ca^{2+} or La^{3+} and binding of ruthenium red were characteristic properties of these components, which need not necessarily be true. Several proteins meeting these criteria were purified from various sources, the most interesting being an acidic sialoprotein easily detached from mitochondria by hypoosmotic shock (Lehninger, 1971; Sottocasa *et al.*, 1972). Other proteins were highly hydrophobic and difficult to purify (Gómez-Púyou *et al.*, 1972). However, Carafoli *et al.* (1978) have purified one such protein [molecular weight (M_r) 35,00–40,000]. A small hydrophobic protein (M_r 3000) with Ca^{2+} ionophoretic properties has been isolated by Shamoo *et al.* (1978). Blondin (1974) has succeeded in isolating substances with ionophoretic properties for Ca^{2+} and Mg^{2+} or K^+ and Ca^{2+} from a similar protein fraction (Blondin, 1974; Blondin *et al.*, 1977). We thus have several candidates for components of mitochondrial Me^{2+} transport. Progress along these lines will be discussed below.

A. Ca^{2+}-BINDING GLYCOPROTEIN(S)

Glycoproteins similar to that of Sottocasa *et al.* (1972) have been purified from various mitochondrial sources (Evtodienko *et al.*, 1971; Tashmukhamedov *et al.*, 1972). Kimura *et al.* (1972) have purified from adrenal cortex mitochondria a glycoprotein with lower affinity for Ca^{2+}.

It is difficult to visualize how such a hydrophilic glycoprotein, which is easily detached from the inner membrane, could serve as a transport protein capable of transferring Me^{2+} across the hydrophobic core of the membrane. No evidence of transmembrane transport mediated by the protein has been produced despite serious endeavors (see Carafoli and Sottocasa, 1974). It has been reported that in the presence of rather high concentrations of Ca^{2+} it is able to associate with the inner membrane and with artificial phospholipid membranes, causing increase in the electrical conductance of bilayers (Prestipino *et al.*, 1976), but this might be an unspecific response. It has therefore been suggested that the protein could serve as a Ca^{2+}-binding and -concentrating component transferring the cation to the translocating system (Carafoli *et al.*, 1978). It is present mainly in the mitochondrial intermembrane phase, which is compatible with such a function. It could also function as a signal-conferring protein in analogy with calmodulin, the cytosolic Ca^{2+}-sensitive protein that is able to modulate phosphodiesterase activity and to activate the plasma membrane Ca^{2+} pump (see Larsen and Vincenzi, 1979).

Interest in the glycoprotein has been revived by the finding of Panfili *et al.* (1976) that antibodies against it inhibited Ca^{2+} uptake in rat liver mitochondria. It has been found that antibodies against it also inhibited the efflux induced by uncoupling agents in some conditions and, most interestingly, the efflux induced by oxidation of NADH (Panfili *et al.*, 1980). Glycoprotein-depleted mitochondria had a lowered Ca^{2+}-transport activity, which could be restored by addition of the protein in the presence of small amounts of Mg^{2+} (Sandri *et al.*, 1979). These data suggest that the protein is involved in Ca^{2+} transport, but the mechanism still remains obscure.

The glycoprotein has a relative molecular mass of 33,000 and contains about 10% carbohydrate including sialic acid; it is rich in aspartate and glutamate and has two classes of Ca^{2+} binding sites, the high-affinity sites having a K_D of 0.1 μM (Sottocasa *et al.*, 1972; Carafoli and Sottocasa, 1974). Ca^{2+} binding is inhibited by La^{3+} and ruthenium red. It has been found that it also binds NAD^+ and NADH, the former more strongly. When NAD^+ is bound, the affinity for Ca^{2+} is lowered (Sottocasa *et al.*, 1979). This is of special interest in view of the finding that the redox state of mitochondrial NADH is one factor affecting efflux of Ca^{2+} (Lehninger *et al.*, 1978b). However, in order to be accessible to intramitochondrial NAD the protein should reach the matrix side of the inner membrane, which seems unlikely, even if some of the protein remains associated with the inner membrane on hypoosmotic treatment and sonication.

B. Hydrophobic Proteins

The state of research in this area was well reviewed by Shamoo and Goldstein (1977). Progress has been made in the laboratory of Carafoli *et al.* (1978), who have purified one ruthenium red-binding protein from rat liver mitochondria. At this time, however, there is no further evidence linking it to Me^{2+} transport. Shamoo *et al.* (1978) have described a low-molecular protein isolated from calf heart mitochondria. With the aid of this protein it was possible to transfer Ca^{2+} from an aqueous layer to an immiscible organic solvent. When the phospholipids had been removed from it, it was able to extract Ca^{2+} into an organic phase only in the presence of an ion pair-forming lipophilic anion (picrate or tetraphenylboride). This would indicate that the protein–Ca^{2+} complex is positively charged. Extraction of Ca^{2+} was inhibited competitively by a number of cations and also by ruthenium red. The properties of this protein thus are very interesting, but evidence of Ca^{2+} transport mediated by it in biological or artificial membranes is still lacking.

C. Ionophores

From the fraction of hydrophobic proteins obtained from beef heart mitochondria, Blondin and co-workers (1977) have isolated a number of ionophoric substances after extensive treatment of the mitochondrial membranes with mercurials and proteolytic enzymes. In 1974 Blondin reported that he had succeeded in obtaining a fraction exhibiting iono-phoretic activity toward Mg^{2+} and Ca^{2+}. It was able to induce swelling in

MgNO$_3$ media and to increase the rate of swelling in CaNO$_3$-containing media. It was also able to release Ca^{2+} and Mg^{2+} from mitochondria into media containing EDTA and to effect transfer of these cations across a bulk phase of an organic solvent. More recently a similar K$^+$/Ca^{2+} iono-phore was described (Blondin et al., 1977). The Mg^{2+} and Ca^{2+} ionophore would effect an Me^{2+}/2H$^+$ neutral exchange. From the fraction a number of active components have been identified, all being unsaturated fatty acids of the octadecadienoic acid class containing hydroxy or keto groups in positions 9 or 13 (Blondin, 1975). These fatty acids are structurally re-lated to prostaglandins that have been shown to be able to release Ca^{2+} from mitochondria and to cause cycling of Ca^{2+}, at least in comparatively high concentrations (Malmström and Carafoli, 1975).

In order to evaluate the possible significance of Blondin's ionophores, more data are needed on the distribution and amounts of the substances in various mitochondria. In view of the minuscule amounts present and the heroic efforts involved in their isolation, it is not likely that the studies will continue in this direction. The fatty acids are covalently bound in the proteins, and there is no evidence that they are indeed able to act in the suggested fashion. The specificity of Me^{2+} transport is not compatible with the specificity of these ionophores. At least Me^{2+} uptake by mito-chondria seems to be mediated by an electrogenic process, not by a neu-tral one. The increased permeability brought about by administration of mercurials is compatible with the suggested mechanism, but the alterna-tive mechanism, that this is due to loss of Mg^{2+} (Bogucka and Wojtczak, 1979), seems more plausible.

D. Concluding Remarks

The glycoprotein isolated and characterized by Sottocasa et al. (1972) has been implicated both in the uptake and release of Ca^{2+} from liver mitochondria. The transport system probably involves other compo-nents also, the nature of which is not known. Both the hydrophobic pro-tein of Carafoli et al. (1978) and that of Shamoo et al. (1978) could be involved as could some still unknown substances. The role of the iono-phores of Blondin (1975) still remains obscure.

VII. Models of Bivalent Cation Transport in Mitochondria

A. Requirements of the Model

From the preceding sections certain features of Me^{2+} transport emerge that any model should be able to account for. Some of these features are accepted by all workers in the field whereas others may be disputed. In the summary of the main features given below, we will indicate when this is the case, but then mainly give our judgment.

In the light of the present knowledge the Me^{2+} transport shows the following features:

1. The specificity of the uptake is rather low and is mainly determined by the nonhydrated radius of the cation, Ca^{2+} being most rapidly transported.

2. The uptake is mainly by a specific mechanism: in addition, there is an unspecific uptake in the case of heavy metal cations.

3. The specific mechanism is inhibited by strongly positively charged cations, competitively by trivalent cations of the lanthanide series, and noncompetitively by a few ammonium complexes, ruthenium red, and cobalt hexaminechloride. As judged from the inhibitor sensitivity, the number of transporting sites seems to be small, less than 1 pmol per milligram of protein.

4. The specific mechanism shows saturability; however, some workers point out that in some mitochondrial preparations the apparent V_{max} is due not to the transport system but to some other factor that becomes rate limiting, e.g., the respiratory chain.

5. The K_m of the transport system generally is rather high, but some groups obtain low K_m values, depending upon the experimental conditions and possible underestimation of the V_{max}.

6. In most preparations the rate of transport is strongly influenced by other cations, capable of binding to low-affinity sites, the most important cation being Mg^{2+}. Then the sigmoidal dependence of the rate of uptake upon Me^{2+} concentration will be accentuated. Physiologically, these considerations are more important than the apparent V_{max} and K_m.

7. The uptake is driven by an electric field, negative inside, down the electrochemical potential.

8. The uptake occurs by a mechanism involving a transfer of two positive charges, though some workers still maintain that only one net charge is moved per Me^{2+}.

9. In favorable conditions 2 H^+ may be extruded per Ca^{2+} taken up. When compensating ion movements occur, any value lower than this may be obtained.

10. Compensating ion movements may be efflux of cations or influx of anions depending upon the experimental conditions.

11. The amount of Me^{2+} taken up is dependent upon the number of intramitochondrial binding sites, soluble and membrane bound, or by the presence of a sink, such as precipitation of phosphates.

12. The Me^{2+} gradient during respiration is generally lower than expected from a distribution according to the Nernst equation.

13. Efflux may occur by exchange mechanisms involving Na^+ or H^+, depending upon the source of mitochondria.

14. Efflux is influenced by the energy state of the mitochondria, the number and affinity of intramitochondrial binding sites, influx of H^+ or Na^+, the redox state of pyridine nucleotides, adenine nucleotides, and certain metabolites. Many of these factors are interrelated.

B. MODELS OF Me^{2+} UPTAKE IN RELATION TO ENERGY COUPLING

The chemiosmotic hypothesis (Mitchell, 1966, 1968) predicts formation of a membrane potential due to electron transfer-linked translocation of protons from the matrix to the extramitochondrial space. If the membrane potential is the driving force of Me^{2+} uptake (Mitchell, 1966), certain stoichiometric relationships between Me^{2+} uptake and H^+ extrusion as well as O_2 consumption (e^- transfer) should exist according to mechanisms of Me^{2+} uptake and charge separation in relation to electron transfer. This would be the case also if the membrane potential is localized as suggested by Williams (1978).

As discussed in Section III,D, most evidence would suggest that Ca^{2+} is translocated with two positive charges and that the H^+/Ca^{2+} stoichiometry is about 2, with succinate as substrate.

Much controversy exists concerning charge/$2e^-$ stoichiometries in the respiratory chain (see Brand et al., 1976b; Wikström, 1977; Wikström and Krab, this volume, Chapter 2). As Ca^{2+} is translocated with two positive charges, measurements of $Ca^{2+}/2e^-$ ratios might throw some light on this problem.

In earlier studies $Ca^{2+}/2e^-$ ratios near 2.6 (Chance, 1965) or above 3 (see Rossi and Lehninger, 1964; Lehninger, 1970) have been obtained for sites II + III (succinate O_2). It is obvious that such high values are incompatible with the loop hypothesis of Mitchell (1966), which predicts a charge/$2e^-$ stoichiometry of 2 (2 $Ca^{2+}/2e^-$, sites II + III) at each site in the respiratory chain. More recently $Ca^{2+}/2e^-$ stoichiometries of about 4 have been measured for sites II + III by Brand et al. (1976a), Vercesi et al. (1978), and Pozzan et al. (1979). A $Ca^{2+}/2e^-$ value of 4 would indicate a separation of 8 charges/$2e^-$ sites II + III (2 + 6, respectively). Nicholls (1977), on the other hand, has obtained lower values (about 3) by measuring the Ca^{2+} remaining after EGTA + ruthenium red treatment. Wikström and Krab (1979), however, have evaluated the techniques used in measurements of stoichiometries. They showed that oxygraph techniques are generally too slow for kinetic measurements and hence the above-mentioned values might be questionable. At site III $Ca^{2+}/2e^-$ ratios of 2 (Wikström, 1978; Siegel and Carafoli, 1978) and $K^+/2e^-$ values of 4 in

TABLE IV
REPORTED $Ca^{2+}/2e^-$ RATIOS AT DIFFERENT SITES

	Site II		Site III		Site II + III	
	$Ca^{2+}/2e^-$	$(q^+/2e^-)^g$	$Ca^{2+}/2e^-$	$(q^+/2e^-)$	$Ca^{2+}/2e^-$	$(q^+/2e^-)$
Ca^{2+}	1	(2)	1^a	(2)	2^a	(4)
Ca^{2+}	2^a	(2)	2^a	(2)	4^a	(4)
Ca^{2+}	1^b	(2)	2^c	(4)	3^d	(6)
Ca^{2+}	1^b	(2)	3^e	(6)	4^f	(8)

[a] Expected from loop hypothesis (Mitchell, 1966, 1968).
[b] Lehninger et al. (1979); Pozzan et al. (1979); Mitchell and Moyle (1979); M. F. K. Wikström (unpublished).
[c] Wikström (1978); Siegel and Carafoli (1978).
[d] Brand et al. (1976a).
[e] Pozzan et al. (1979).
[f] Brand et al. (1976b); Vercesi et al. (1978); Lehninger et al. (1979); Pozzan et al. (1979).
[g] q^+ = charge.

the presence of valinomycin have been obtained. These determinations are not invalidated by slow equipment because they were made by spectroscopic determinations of e^- transfer or by a fast responding O_2 electrode. These values for site III are in disagreement with values of 4 $Ca^{2+}/2e^-$ for site II + III, since this ratio would predict a value of 3 $Ca^{2+}/2e^-$ at site III providing that the value at site II alone is 1. A value near 1 $Ca^{2+}/2e^-$ for site II alone has recently been obtained by Lehninger et al. (1979), Pozzan et al. (1979), Mitchell and Moyle (1979), and Wikström and Krab (unpublished, cf. Wikström and Krab, 1978). It is thus generally agreed that the charge/$2e^-$ stoichiometry of site II is 2 (1 $Ca^{2+}/2e^-$). Table IV summarizes the different stoichiometries determined by different workers.

Measurements of relative charge/2e ratios by relating the membrane potential to respiratory rate at various sites (Brand et al., 1978) yield a ratio of charge transfer for site II/site III near 1/2. This agrees with the notion that the charge stoichiometry at site III is 4 per $2e^-$, since the stoichiometry of site II is settled at 2, but does not agree with the stoichiometries of 6 charges/$2e^-$ (3 $Ca^{2+}/2e^-$) at site III. Note that these determinations involve measurements of steady states and are independent of response times of equipment or of the presence of valinomycin.

From the above discussion it is obvious that further measurements of $Ca^{2+}/2e$ ratios have to be made using different experimental approaches and techniques. For the time being the stoichiometries of 1 $Ca^{2+}/2e^-$ at site II and 2 $Ca^{2+}/2e^-$ at site III appear to be the best estimates.

C. Models of Molecular Mechanisms of Me²⁺ Transport in Mitochondria

1. Molecular Mechanisms of Me²⁺ Uptake

As discussed in Section V efforts to isolate and subsequently reconstitute the mitochondrial bivalent cation translocator have yielded little information, if any, concerning the molecular mechanisms of bivalent cation uptake. The main problem with the isolation is probably the fact that the amount of translocator/mitochondrion is extremely small (about 1 pmol per milligram of protein) (Reed and Bygrave, 1974b). From features of the Me^{2+} uptake, something about molecular mechanisms can, however, be learned.

As discussed in Section III,B, a channel or carrier mechanism of Me^{2+} uptake cannot be distinguished with certainty even if a channel mechanism appears more likely.

From the effects of various inhibitors on the kinetics of uptake it can be concluded that a surface binding, unrelated to transport, and a subsequent diffusion to a translocator is a step in the translocation sequence (see Sections III,C, III,D, IV,A, and V,D).

The selectivity of the transport system, namely, $Ca^{2+} > Sr^{2+} \gg Mn^{2+} > Ba^{2+}$ (with Mg^{2+} not being translocated), would suggest certain requirements of ionic size, loss of water of hydration, and formation of coordination complexes during transport. Mg^{2+} would not be transported, since it is too small (Table III) and the most difficult to dehydrate (see Section V,A).

The fact that lanthanides whose ionic radii are closest to that of Ca^{2+} are the most potent inhibitors of transport (Tew, 1977) also suggests that coordination complex formation is of importance.

The inhibition of Me^{2+} uptake by ruthenium red, which is expected to interact with strong coulombic forces at negative sites, would indicate that electrostatic binding is of importance somewhere in the transport sequence. The K_i of ruthenium red is as low as that of La^{3+}, which suggests an interaction in a localized region in the membrane (see Section III,C).

Figure 14 shows models of Me^{2+} uptake taking these considerations into account. Model A is a channel with electrostatic bonding of Me^{2+} at the outer mouth and coordination in the interior. Model B shows coordination at the mouth and coulombic interactions in the interior. Model C is a mobile carrier analogous to model A. Model D is a carrier involving a conformational change. Of these models, A and C are most likely, since they explain several features of the interaction of inhibitors with Me^{2+} transport. They would explain the uptake of La^{3+} by mitochondria (Reed and

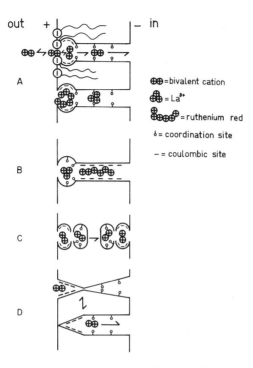

FIG. 14. Models of molecular mechanisms of Me^{2+} uptake. Translocation should involve both coulombic and coordination interactions as well as a diffusion step from the surface to the translocator. Models: (A) A channel with negative charges at the outer mouth and coordination forces in the interior. The bivalent cation uptake sequence, i.e., surface binding → binding to negative sites → dehydration → and diffusion across the membrane is shown. The interaction of La^{3+} (coordination) and ruthenium red (coulombic) is also shown. Note that La^{3+} is expected to interact also with the coulombic sites. (B) A channel mechanism with coordination binding at the external mouth and negative charges in the interior. (C) A mobile carrier model compatible with model A. Note that the carrier has always to be linked to a negatively charged substructure. (D) A carrier model involving a conformational change or a gated channel.

Bygrave, 1974a). Because of uptake of La^{3+}, maximal inhibition is never achieved with Ca^{2+} and Sr^{2+}, in contrast to Ba^{2+} (Vainio *et al.*, 1970), which also is in accordance with model A. Note also the analogy of model A to the modified gramicidin channel with negative charges at the mouth (Apell *et al.*, 1977). The negative charges significantly increase the channel conductivity at low Cs$^+$ concentrations.

In the case of model B, it is difficult to imagine how a bulky molecule like ruthenium red could penetrate into a narrow channel. Model D, with several modifications, certainly could also explain features of Me^{2+} uptake as well as models A and C. However, no evidence for conformational changes has as yet been presented. The model could explain the apparent cooperativity of transport (Bygrave *et al.*, 1971) if one assumes that the conformational change occurs at a certain occupancy of the coulombic sites. On the other hand, apparent cooperativity might simply be a result of nonspecific alterations at the membrane surface (see Section III,D).

From the results concerning the Ca^{2+} binding (glyco)protein(s) isolated from mitochondria (Sottocasa *et al.*, 1972; Gómez-Púyou *et al.*, 1972; Panfili *et al.*, 1976), one might speculate that the external ruthenium red binding site in Models A and C could be identical with the carbohydrate moiety of the protein. An interesting finding in this context is that Tb^{3+} appears to bind mainly to the protein moiety of the glycoprotein(s) (at least to that of Gómez-Púyou *et al.*, 1972) to sites close to each other (Mikkelsen and Wallach, 1976). Carbohydrate and phospholipid binding was excluded by neuraminidase and acetone treatment. This would indicate that ruthenium red and lanthanides bind to different sites. The low affinity of the Tb^{3+} sites would favor rather low-affinity coordination bonding. Interestingly, similar effects were obtained using isolated mitochondria (Mikkelson and Wallach, 1976). Therefore if the glycoprotein(s) are involved in Me^{2+} uptake, both parts of the translocator might be present in the preparation. However, it is obvious that further studies are needed before any relation of the glycoprotein to Me^{2+} uptake can be ascertained (see Section V).

2. Mechanisms of Me^{2+} Efflux and Cycling

From the experiments cited in Sections IV,C and IV,D, much evidence for separate Me^{2+} efflux mechanisms in mitochondria exist even if so far they are not conclusive. Figure 15 shows models for the coupling of an Me^{2+} uniport to different anti- and symports according to models presented in the literature.

Model A represents cycling caused by a coupling of the Me^{2+} uniport to a Na^+/Me^{2+} and H^+/Na^+ antiport. Much evidence for the existence of such a mechanism in some types of mitochondria (not in liver) has been presented in the literature. Evidence for this way of coupling is that in the presence of ruthenium red all Ca^{2+} in mitochondria is released by Na^+. This would not occur unless the H^+/Na^+ antiport would constantly recycle Na^+ driven by the H^+ gradient.

In model B the coupling of an Me^{2+} uniport to a nH^+/Me^{2+} antiport is shown. Some evidence exists for such a mechanism. According to the model, induction of a proton gradient would cause only a deviation from a steady state, not total release of Me^{2+}, because of an equilibration of the proton gradient, which appears to be the case (Åkerman, 1978c). Simi-

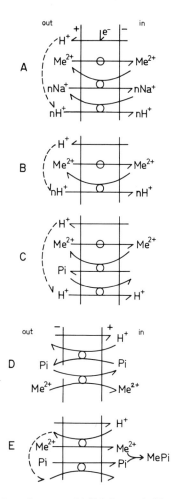

Fɪɢ. 15. Models for coupling of separate Me²⁺ influx and efflux pathways and for Me²⁺ up-take by submitochondrial particles. (A) Model to explain Na⁺-linked Ca²⁺ release from mito-chondria. A coupling of the Me²⁺ uniport nNa⁺/Me²⁺ and Na⁺/H⁺ antiports. (B) Model to explain H⁺ ion linked Ca²⁺ fluxes in mitochondria. Coupling of an Me²⁺ uniport to an nH⁺/Me²⁺ antiport. (C) Coupling of an Me²⁺ uniport to an Me²⁺/phosphate and nH⁺/phos-phate symport. (D) The same model as C, to explain respiration-linked Ca²⁺ uptake by in-verted membrane particles when uniport is blocked. (E) Model to explain Ca²⁺ uptake by inverted membrane particles by coupling of a nH⁺/Me²⁺ exchanger (proton gradient acid inside driving force) and a nH⁺/phosphate symporter (to restore proton gradient and pre-cipitate cation in the interior).

larly, induction of a proton gradient (acid inside mitochondria) would result in Me^{2+} influx, which indeed also appears to be the case (Fiskum and Cockrell, 1978). Note that in order to obtain net uptake with such a mechanism the kinetic properties of both translocators should be different, the nH^+/Me^{2+} antiport being far less effective. The ΔpH-induced efflux is very fast; therefore the apparent K_m should be lower for the antiport.

An electroneutral Me^{2+} phosphate symport (see model C) involved in efflux of Ca^{2+} from liver mitochondria has been proposed by Carafoli (1979). No evidence for such a mechanism has been presented. The only circumstantial evidence is that respiration-dependent Ca^{2+} uptake occurs in highly purified submitochondrial particles in the presence of ruthenium red and high phosphate concentrations. This result could be equally well explained by an nH^+/Ca^{2+} antiport and a precipitation of Ca^{2+} and phosphate inside the particles (see models D and E). Distinction between these alternatives could easily be made by measurements of phosphate in such conditions. According to model C, inhibition of the $H^+/phosphate$ symport with NEM would prevent Ca^{2+} recycling, since the $Ca^{2+}/phosphate$ symport would soon reach a steady state because no reuptake of P_i would occur. The opposite, however, is the case, since NEM enhances cycling (Ramachandran and Bygrave, 1978).

All the models presented above need a coupling to the proton gradient in order to achieve a constant recycling.

D. MODELS OF MONOVALENT CATION TRANSPORT IN MITOCHONDRIA

Brierley (1976, 1978) has presented models according to which mitochondria would possess both a rather unspecific uniport for C^+ favoring K^+ over Na^+ and a C^+/H^+ antiport favoring Na^+ over K^+. The operation of the former would be favored by the formation of a high membrane potential, whereas the operation of the antiport would come into play with the development of a pH gradient. This model is consistent with many experimental findings (see Brierley, 1974, 1976, 1978).

In nonenergized conditions swelling occurs in isoosmolar sodium acetate and lithium acetate solution due to the operation of the C^+/H^+ antiport (Fig. 16A), with acetate entering as acetic acid and the dissociated proton being exchanged against C^+. In contrast, the bivalent Ca^{2+} and Sr^{2+} do not cause appreciable swelling in corresponding conditions, and stimulation of swelling is obtained with uncoupling agents (Selwyn et al., 1970a). These data show that the bivalent cations indeed enter by uniport, not by exchange against H^+ in these conditions.

In energized conditions swelling is obtained also in potassium acetate

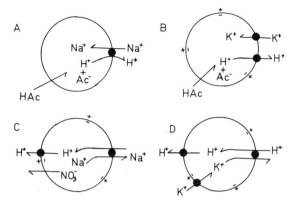

Fig. 16. Models of transport of monovalent cations in mitochondria. (A) Swelling in sodium acetate solution in nonenergized conditions. Acetic acid diffuses to the matrix compartment, dissociates, and the H$^+$ is exchanged against Na$^+$ on the C$^+$/H$^+$ antiporter. (B) Swelling in potassium acetate solution in energized conditions. Acetic acid diffuses to the matrix compartment and dissociates, and H$^+$ is extruded on the respiration-driven H$^+$ pump. K$^+$ enters by uniport, driven by the membrane potential, negative inside. (C) Contraction of mitochondria in energized conditions. Mitochondria have been induced to swell in sodium nitrate solution. When energized, mitochondria extrude nitrate, presumably electrogenically, and Na$^+$ on the C$^+$/H$^+$ antiporter. H$^+$ is also extruded by the H$^+$ pump, resulting in cycling of H$^+$. (D) Model of regulation of mitochondrial K$^+$ by the operation of a $\Delta\psi$-activated K$^+$ uniporter and a ΔpH-activated K$^+$/H$^+$ antiporter. Adapted from Brierley (1976, 1978).

solution. Figure 16B shows entry of K$^+$ by a uniport mechanism driven by the membrane potential in analogy with the Me^{2+} uniport. We have obtained more direct evidence for the electrophoretic movements of C$^+$ by following the decay of the membane potential associated with the influx of the K$^+$ analog Tl$^+$ (Skulskii *et al.*, 1978).

Bivalent cations cause swelling in nonenergized conditions when nitrate (Azzone *et al.*, 1975) or thiocyanate anions are present (Selwyn *et al.*, 1970a). These anions enter the matrix by a uniport mechanism. In contrast, mitochondria do not swell in the presence of the corresponding monovalent cation salts unless ionophores or uncoupling agents or both, are also present in order to bring about electrogenic cation movements or H$^+$ cycling (Mitchell and Moyle, 1969b). Swelling can, however, be induced in special experimental conditions (hypoosmolarity, high pH or decrease of mitochondrial Mg^{2+} content). Figure 16C shows the model for the respiration-dependent contraction obtained when swollen mitochondria are supplemented with a respiratory substrate. Surprisingly, the ion movements are reversed, and K$^+$ and nitrate are pumped out of the matrix. It seems plausible that nitrate is driven out by the membrane potential, which therefore remains low during the process. H^+ would enter in exchange for C^+ and be pumped out by the proton pump(s) of the respiratory chain (see Wikström and Krab, in this volume, Chapter 2). It is interesting to note that the same phenomenon occurs also with bivalent cations (Azzone *et al.*, 1975).

The model also explains why K^+ ratios do not change with the membrane potential as would be expected if only electrophoretic uniport was operative. Furthermore, a futile cycle of K^+ entry by the uniport and efflux by the antiport may be avoided (Brierley, 1978) by a gating mechanism (Mueller, 1975) whereby the uniport becomes operative only when $\Delta\psi$ reaches a certain level. The uniport again would come into play when ΔH^+ becomes significant (Fig. 16D). This is consistent with the finding that both $K^{\cdot}$ influx and efflux are stimulated by respiration, especially in the presence of P_i, and inhibited by uncoupling agents, ADP in the presence of P_i, and Mg^{2+} (Jung *et al.*, 1977; Chavez *et al.*, 1977). The net result then would be maintenance of matrix K^+ at a level influenced mainly by the number of anionic sites.

Brierley (1978) pointed out the hazards of using unphysiologically high, isoosmolar concentrations of acetate, which is relevant also in the study of bivalent cation transport. At lower, <40 mM K^+ acetate concentrations, K^+ uniport shows features of specificity, such as saturability (Diwan and Harrington, 1975), while uptake becomes unspecific at higher concentrations.

Doubt has been raised as to whether C^+/H^+ antiport is present in native mitochondria, at least as far as K^+ is concerned. Thus, Duszynski and Wojtczak (1977) found that treatment with EDTA or the ionophore A23187 caused activation of the K^+/H^+ antiport, presumably mediated by the loss of Mg^{2+}. Since EDTA is commonly used in homogenization media in the preparation of mitochondria, there is obvious cause for caution. Azzone *et al.* (1978) have confirmed these findings and suggested that Na^+/H^+ exchange also may be an induced phenomenon. Brierley *et al.* (1978) showed that the C^+/H^+ antiport was extremely sensitive to Mg^{2+} (K_i 5–10 μM), but part of the activity was not Mg^{2+} sensitive, suggesting the presence of an additional antiport with little cation specificity.

In heart mitochondria, Mg^{2+} makes the kinetics of energized Li^+ transport sigmoidal (Brierley *et al.*, 1978) in analogy with its effects upon Ca^{2+} transport (Crompton *et al.*, 1976a).

It is evident that there are many similarities between monovalent and bivalent cation transport in mitochondria. A number of exchange systems may exist, including the nNa^+/Ca^{2+} antiport. Cations may enter energized mitochondria electrophoretically by various uniport mechanisms.

ACKNOWLEDGMENTS

Our sincere thanks are expressed to those of our colleagues who have sent us their reprints, preprints, manuscripts, and comments: Drs. G. F. Azzone, F. L. Bygrave, E. Carafoli, R. Dargel, E. J. Harris, N. Haugaard, A. L. Lehninger, D. G. Nicholls, M. S. Olson, C.-F. Peng, M. J. Selwyn, A. L. Shug, D. Siliprandi, N. Siliprandi, L. A. Sordahl, G. L. Sottocasa, and L. Wojtczak. We are also indebted to Dr. M. K. F. Wikström for valuable discussions, to Mrs. Sirkka Rönnholm and Miss Maria Saariluoma for typing the manuscript.

REFERENCES

Aikawa, J. K. (1978). *World Rev. Nutr. Diet.* **28**, 112–142.

Åkerman, K. E. O. (1977a). *J. Bioenerg. Biomembr.* **9**, 65–72.

Åkerman, K. E. O. (1977b). *J. Bioenerg. Biomembr.* **9**, 141–149.

Åkerman, K. E. O. (1978a). *FEBS Lett.* **93**, 293–296.

Åkerman, K. E. O. (1978b). *Biochim. Biophys. Acta* **502**, 359–366.

Åkerman, K. E. O. (1978c). *Arch. Biochem. Biophys.* **189**, 256–262.

Åkerman, K. E. O., and Saris, N.-E. L. (1976). *Biochim. Biophys. Acta* **426**, 624–629.

Åkerman, K. E. O., and Saris, N.-E. L. (1978). In "Frontiers of Biological Energetics" (P. L. Dutton, J. S. Leigh, and A. Scarpa, eds.), Vol. 2, pp. 1187–1195. Academic Press, New York.

Åkerman, K. E. O., and Wikström, M. K. F. (1976). *FEBS Lett.* **68**, 191–197.

Åkerman, K. E. O., Saris, N.-E. L., and Järvisalo, J. O. (1974). *Biochem. Biophys. Res. Commun.* **58**, 801–807.

Åkerman, K. E. O., Wikström, M. K. F., and Saris, N.-E. L. (1977). *Biochim. Biophys. Acta* **464**, 287–294.

Al-Shaikhaly, M. H. M., Nedergaard, J., and Cannon, B. (1979). *Proc. Natl. Acad. Sci. U.S.A.* **76**, 2350–2353.

Apell, H. J., Bamberg, E., Alpes, H., and Läuger, P. (1977). *J. Membr. Biol.* **31**, 171–188.

Asimakis, G. K., and Sordahl, L. A. (1977). *Arch. Biochem. Biophys.* **179**, 200–210.

Azzone, G. F., Bragadin, M., Dell'Antone, P., and Pozzan, T. (1975). In "Electron Transfer Chains and Oxidative Phosphorylation" (E. Quagliariello, S. Papa, F. Palmieri, E. C. Slater, and N. Siliprandi, eds.), pp. 423–429. North-Holland Publ., Amsterdam.

Azzone, G. F., Bragadin, M., Pozzan, T., and Dell'Antone, P. (1976). *Biochim. Biophys. Acta* **459**, 96–109.

Azzone, G. F., Zanotti, A., and Colonna, R. (1978). *FEBS Lett.* **96**, 141–147.

Baker, P. F. (1976). *Symp. Soc. Exp. Biol.* **30**, 67–88.

Baker, P. F., and Honejäger, P. (1978). *Nature (London)* **273**, 160–161.

Baker, P. F., and Schlaepfer, W. W. (1978). *J. Physiol. (London)* **276**, 103–125.

Baker, P. F., Hodgin, A. L., and Ridgeway, E. B. (1971). *J. Physiol. (London)* **218**, 709–755.

Batra, S. (1973). *Biochim. Biophys. Acta* **305**, 428–432.

Batra, S. (1975). In "Calcium Transport in Contraction and Secretion" (E. Carafoli et al., eds.), pp. 87–94. North-Holland Publ., Amsterdam.

Binet, A., and Volfin, P. (1974). *Arch. Biochem. Biophys.* **164**, 756–764.

Binet, A., and Volfin, P. (1975). *FEBS Lett.* **49**, 400–403.

Blackmore, P. F., Dehaye, J.-P., Strickland, W. G., and Exton, J. H. (1979). *FEBS Lett.* **100**, 117–120.

Blok, M. C., Van Der Neut-Kok, E. C. M., Van Deenen, L. L. M., and De Gier, J. (1975). *Biochim. Biophys. Acta* **406**, 187–196.

Blondin, G. A. (1974). *Biochem. Biophys. Res. Commun.* **56,** 97–105.
Blondin, G. A. (1975). *Ann. N.Y. Acad. Sci.* **264,** 98–111.
Blondin, G. A., Kessler, R. J., and Green, D. E. (1977). *Proc. Natl. Acad. Sci. U.S.A.* **74,** 3667–3671.
Bogucka, K., and Wojtczak, L. (1971). *Biochem. Biophys. Res. Commun.* **44,** 1330–1336.
Bogucka, K., and Wojtczak, L. (1976). *Biochem. Biophys. Res. Commun.* **71,** 161–167.
Bogucka, K., and Wojtczak, L. (1979). *FEBS Lett.* **100,** 301–303.
Borle, A. B. (1973). *Fed. Proc., Fed. Am. Soc. Exp. Biol.* **32,** 1944–1950.
Bragadin, M., Pozzan, T., and Azzone, G. F. (1979). *Biochem.* **18,** 5972–5978.
Bragadin, M., Dell'Antone, P., Pozzan, T., Volpato, O., and Azzone, G. F. (1975). *FEBS Lett.* **60,** 354–358.
Brand, M. D., and Lehninger, A. L. (1975). *J. Biol. Chem.* **250,** 7958–7960.
Brand, M. D., and Nicholls, D. G. (1980). *Biochem.* **19,** (in press).
Brand, M. D., Chen, C.-H., and Lehninger, A. L. (1976a). *J. Biol. Chem.* **251,** 968–974.
Brand, M. D., Reynafarje, B., and Lehninger, A. L. (1976b). *J. Biol. Chem.* **251,** 5670–5679.
Brand, M. D., Harper, W. G., Nicholls, D. G., and Ingledew, W. J. (1978). *FEBS Lett.* **95,** 125–129.
Brierley, G. P. (1974). *Ann. N.Y. Acad. Sci.* **227,** 398–411.
Brierley, G. P. (1976). *Mol. Cell. Biochem.* **10,** 41–62.
Brierley, G. P. (1978). *In* "The Molecular Biology of Membranes" (S. Fleischer, Y. Hatefi, D. H. MacLennan, and A. Tzagoloff, eds.), pp. 295–308. Plenum, New York.
Brierley, G. P., and Jurkowitz, M. (1976). *Biochem. Biophys. Res. Commun.* **74,** 235–241.
Brierley, G. P., Scott, K. M., and Jurkowitz, M. (1971). *J. Biol. Chem.* **246,** 2241–2251.
Brierley, G. P., Jurkowitz, M., Chavez, E., and Jung, D. W. (1977). *J. Biol. Chem.* **252,** 7932–7939.
Brierley, G. P., Jurkowitz, M., and Jung, D. W. (1978). *Arch. Biochem. Biophys.* **190,** 181–192.
Brinley, F. J., Jr., Tiffert, T., and Scarpa, A. (1978). *J. Gen. Physiol.* **72,** 101–127.
Bruni, A., Contessa, A. R., and Luciani, S. (1962). *Biochim. Biophys. Acta* **60,** 301–311.
Bygrave, F. L. (1967). *Nature (London)* **214,** 667–671.
Bygrave, F. L. (1977). *Curr. Top. Bioenerg.* **6,** 259–316.
Bygrave, F. L. (1978). *Biol. Rev. Cambridge Philos. Soc.* **53,** 43–79.
Bygrave, F. L., Reed, K. C., and Spencer, T. E. (1971). *Nature (London), New Biol.* **230,** 89.
Bygrave, F. L., Ramachandran, C., and Smith, R. L. (1977). *FEBS Lett.* **83,** 155–158.
Bygrave, F. L., Ramachandran, C., and Robertson, R. N. (1978). *Arch. Biochem. Biophys.* **188,** 301–307.
Carafoli, E. (1965a). *Biochim. Biophys. Acta* **97,** 99–106.
Carafoli, E. (1965b). *Biochim. Biophys. Acta* **97,** 107–117.
Carafoli, E. (1973). *Biochimie* **55,** 755–762.
Carafoli, E. (1974). *Biochem. Soc. Symp.* **39,** 89–109.
Carafoli, E. (1977). *In* "Living Systems as Energy Converters" (R. Buvet *et al.*, eds.), pp. 153–174. Elsevier/North-Holland Biomedical Press, Amsterdam.
Carafoli, E. (1979). *FEBS Lett.* **104,** 1–5.
Carafoli, E., and Azzi, A. (1971). *Experientia* **27,** 906–909.
Carafoli, E., and Crompton, M. (1976). *Symp. Soc. Exp. Biol.* **30,** 89–115.
Carafoli, E., and Crompton, M. (1978). *Curr. Top. Membr. Transport* **10,** 151–216.
Carafoli, E., and Lehninger, A. L. (1971). *Biochem. J.* **122,** 681–690.
Carafoli, E., and Sottocasa, G. (1974). *In* "Dynamics of Energy-Transducing Membranes" (L. Ernster, R. W. Estabrook, and E. Slater, eds.), pp. 455–469. Elsevier, Amsterdam.
Carafoli, E., Rossi, C. S., and Lehninger, A. L. (1965a). *J. Biol. Chem.* **240,** 2254–2261.

Carafoli, E., Weiland, S., and Lehninger, A. L. (1965b). *Biochim. Biophys. Acta* **97**, 88–98.

Carafoli, E., Schwerzmann, K., Roos, I., and Crompton, M. (1978). *In* "Transport by Proteins" (G. Blaner and H. Sund, eds.), pp. 171–186. de Gruyter, Berlin.

Caswell, A. H. (1972). *J. Membr. Biol.* **7**, 345–364.

Caswell, A. H., and Hutchison, J. D. (1971). *Biochem. Biophys. Res. Commun.* **43**, 625–630.

Caswell, A. H., and Pressman, B. C. (1972). *Biochem. Biophys. Res. Commun.* **49**, 292–298.

Cederbaum, A. I., and Vainio, W. W. (1972). *J. Biol. Chem.* **247**, 4593–4603.

Chance, B. (1956). *Proc. Int. Congr. Biochem., 3rd, 1955* p. 300.

Chance, B. (1965). *J. Biol. Chem.* **240**, 2729–2748.

Chapman, D. (1975). *Q. Rev. Biophys.* **8**, 185–235.

Chappell, J. B., and Crofts, A. R. (1965). *Biochem. J.* **95**, 393–402.

Chappell, J. B., Greville, G. D., and Bicknell, K. E. (1962). *Biochem. J.* **84**, 61P.

Chappell, J. B., Cohn, M., and Greville, G. D. (1963). *In* "Energy-Linked Functions of Mitochondria" (B. Chance, ed.), pp. 219–231. Academic Press, New York.

Chavez, E., Jung, D. W., and Brierley, G. P. (1977). *Arch. Biochem. Biophys.* **183**, 460–470.

Cheah, K. S., and Cheah, A. M. (1978). *FEBS Lett.* **95**, 307–310.

Chudapongse, P., and Haugaard, N. (1973). *Biochim. Biophys. Acta* **307**, 599–606.

Crompton, M., and Heid, I. (1978). *Eur. J. Biochem.* **91**, 599–608.

Crompton, M., Siegel, E., Salzmann, M., and Carafoli, E. (1976a). *Eur. J. Biochem.* **69**, 429–434.

Crompton, M., Capano, M., and Carafoli, E. (1976b). *Eur. J. Biochem.* **69**, 453–462.

Crompton, M., Capano, M., and Carafoli, E. (1976c). *Biochem. J.* **154**, 735–742.

Crompton, M., Künzi, M., and Carafoli, E. (1977). *Eur. J. Biochem.* **79**, 549–558.

Crompton, M., Hediger, M., and Carafoli, E. (1978a). *Biochem. Biophys. Res. Commun.* **80**, 540–546.

Crompton, M., Moser, R., Lüdi, H., and Carafoli, E. (1978b). *Eur. J. Biochem.* **82**, 25–31.

Crompton, M., Heid, I., Baschera, C., and Carafoli, E. (1979). *FEBS Lett.* **104**, 352–354.

Dargel, R. (1974). *FEBS Lett.* **42**, 57–60.

Dargel, R. (1978). *In* "Bioenergetics at Mitochondrial and Cellular Levels" (L. Wojtzcak *et al.*, eds.), pp. 133–151. Nencki Inst. Exp. Biol., Warsaw.

Davidoff, F. (1974). *J. Biol. Chem.* **249**, 6406–6415.

Dawson, A. P., Selwyn, M. J., and Fulton, D. V. (1979). *Nature (London)* **277**, 484–486.

DeLuca, H. F., and Engström, G. W. (1961). *Proc. Natl. Acad. Sci. U.S.A.* **47**, 1744–1754.

Diamond, J. M., and Wright, E. M. (1969). *Annu. Rev. Physiol.* **39**, 581–646.

Dipolo, R., Requena, J., Brinley, F. J., Jr., Mullins, L. J., Scarpa, A., and Tiffert, T. (1976). *J. Gen. Physiol.* **67**, 433–467.

Diwan, J. J., and Harrington, P. (1975). *Fed. Proc., Fed. Am. Soc. Exp. Biol.* **34**, 518.

Douglas, M. G., and Cockrell, R. S. (1974). *J. Biol. Chem.* **249**, 5464–5471.

Drahota, Z., Carafoli, E., Rossi, C. S., Gamble, R. L., and Lehninger, A. L. (1965). *J. Biol. Chem.* **240**, 2712–2720.

Drahota, Z., Gazzotti, P., Carafoli, E., and Rossi, C. S. (1969). *Arch. Biochem. Biophys.* **130**, 267–273.

Dubinsky, W., Kandrach, M. A., and Racker, E. (1979). *Fed. Proc., Fed. Am. Soc. Exp. Biol.* **38**, 248.

Duszyński, J., and Wojtczak, L. (1977). *Biochem. Biophys. Res. Commun.* **74**, 417–424.

Ebashi, S. (1961). *J. Biochem. (Tokyo)* **50**, 236–244.

Endo, M. (1975). *Proc. Jpn. Acad.* **51**, 479–484.

Erdelt, H., Weidmann, M. J., Buchholz, M., and Klingenberg, M. (1972). *Eur. J. Biochem.* **30**, 107–122.

Evtodienko, J. V., Peskova, L. V., and Shchipakin, V. N. (1971). *Ukr. J. Biochem.* **43**, 98–104.

Fiskum, G., and Cockrell, R. S. (1978). *FEBS Lett.* **92**, 125–128.

Flagg-Newton, J., and Loewenstein, W. R. (1979). *J. Membr. Biol.* **50**, 65–100.

Flatmark, T., and Romslo, I. (1975). *J. Biol. Chem.* **250**, 6433–6438.

Fletcher, J. M., Greenfield, B. F., Hardy, C. J., Scargill, D., and Woodhead, J. L. (1961). *J. Chem. Soc.* pp. 2000–2006.

Gemba, M. (1974). *Jpn. J. Pharmacol.* **24**, 271–277.

Gómez-Púyou, A., and Gómez-Lojero, C. (1977). *Curr. Top. Bioenerg.* **6**, 221–257.

Gómez-Púyou, A., de Gómez-Púyou, T. M., Becker, G., and Lehninger, A. L. (1972). *Biochem. Biophys. Res. Commun.* **47**, 814–819.

Guilland, D. F., and Fleisch, H. (1974). *Biochem. Biophys. Res. Commun.* **61**, 906–911.

Gunter, T. E., Gunter, K. K., Puskin, J. S., and Russell, P. R. (1978). *Biochemistry* **17**, 339–345.

Gylkhandanyan, A. V., Evtodienko, J. V., Zhabotinsky, A. M., and Kondrashova, M. N. (1976). *FEBS Lett.* **66**, 44–47.

Harris, E. J. (1956). "Transport and Accumulation in Biological Systems." Butterworth, London.

Harris, E. J. (1978). *Nature (London)* **274**, 820–821.

Harris, E. J. (1979). *Biochem. J.* **178**, 673–680.

Harris, E. J., and Zaba, B. (1977). *FEBS Lett.* **79**, 284–290.

Hasselbach, W., and Makinose, M. (1961). *Biochem. Z.* **333**, 518–528.

Haydon, D. A., and Hladky, S. B. (1972). *Q. Rev. Biophys.* **5**, 187–282.

Heaton, G. M., and Nicholls, D. G. (1976). *Biochem. J.* **156**, 635–646.

Henderson, P. J. F., and Lardy, H. A. (1970). *J. Biol. Chem.* **245**, 1319–1326.

Höser, N., Dargel, R., Dawczynski, H., and Winnefeld, K. (1976). *FEBS Lett.* **72**, 193–196.

Hunter, D. R., Haworth, R. A., and Southard, J. H. (1976). *J. Biol. Chem.* **251**, 5069–5077.

Hutson, S. M. (1977). *J. Biol. Chem.* **252**, 4539–4545.

Hutson, S. M., Pfeiffer, D. R., and Lardy, H. A. (1976). *J. Biol. Chem.* **251**, 5251–5266.

Huunan-Seppälä, A. J., and Nordling, S. (1971). *In* "Energy Transduction in Respiration and Photosynthesis" (E. Quagliariello *et al.*, eds.), pp. 317–328. Adriatica Editrice, Bari.

Jacobus, W. E., and Brierley, G. P. (1969). *J. Biol. Chem.* **243**, 5133–5138.

Järvisalo, J. O., Kilpiö, J., and Saris, N.-E. L. (1980). *Environ. Res.* (in press).

Jeng, A. Y., Ryan, T. E., and Shamoo, A. E. (1978). *Proc. Natl. Acad. Sci. U.S.A.* **75**, 2125–2129.

Jung, D. W., Chavez, E., and Brierley, G. P. (1977). *Arch. Biochem. Biophys.* **183**, 452–459.

Kimura, S., and Rasmussen, H. (1977). *J. Biol. Chem.* **252**, 1217–1225.

Kimura, T., Chu, J. W., Mukai, R., and Ishizuka, I. (1972). *Biochem. Biophys. Res. Commun.* **49**, 1678–1683.

Klingenberg, M., and Buchholz, M. (1973). *Eur. J. Biochem.* **38**, 346–358.

Koller, M. E., Prante, P. H., Ulvik, R., and Romslo, I. (1976). *Biochem. Biophys. Res. Commun.* **7**, 339–345.

Kotyk, A., and Janáček, K. (1975). "Cell Membrane Transport, Principles and Techniques." Plenum, New York.

Krall, A. R., Meng, T. T., Harmon, S. J., and Dougherty, W. J. (1971). *Fed. Proc., Fed. Am. Soc. Exp. Biol.* **30**, 1285.

Krasne, S., Eiseman, G., and Szabo, G. (1971). *Science* **174**, 412–415.

Kun, E., Kearney, E. B., Wiedmann, I., and Lee, N. M. (1969). *Biochemistry* **8**, 4443–4450.

Larsen, F. C., and Vincenzi, F. F. (1979). *Science* **204**, 306–308.

Lea, T. J., and Ashley, C. C. (1978). *Nature (London)* **275**, 236–238.

Leblanc, P., and Clauser, H. (1974). *Biochim. Biophys. Acta* **347**, 87–101.

Lee, N. M., Wiedemann, I., and Kun, E. (1971). *Biochem. Biophys. Res. Commun.* **42**, 1037–1034.

Lehninger, A. L. (1970). *Biochem. J.* **119**, 129–138.

Lehninger, A. L. (1971). *Biochem. Biophys. Res. Commun.* **42**, 312–318.

Lehninger, A. L. (1974). *Proc. Natl. Acad. Sci. U.S.A.* **71**, 1520–1524.

Lehninger, A. L., and Carafoli, E. (1971). *Arch. Biochem. Biophys.* **143**, 506–515.

Lehninger, A. L., Carafoli, E., and Rossi, C. S. (1967). *Adv. Enzymol.* **29**, 259–319.

Lehninger, A. L., Reynafarje, B., Vercesi, A., and Tew, W. P. (1978a). *Ann. N.Y. Acad. Sci.* **307**, 160–176.

Lehninger, A. L., Vercesi, A., and Bababunmi, E. A. (1978b). *Proc. Natl. Acad. Sci. U.S.A.* **75**, 1690–1694.

Lehninger, A. L., Reynafarje, B., and Alexandre, A. (1979). In "Cation Flux across Biomembranes" (Y. Mukohaty and L. Packer, eds.), pp. 343–354. Academic Press, New York.

Lejkin, Yu. N., and Petushkova, N. A. (1980). *Biokhimiya* **45**, (in press).

Lötscher, H. R., Schwerzmann, K., and Carafoli, E. (1979). *FEBS Lett.* **99**, 194–198.

Luft, J. H. (1971). *Anat. Rec.* **171**, 347–368.

Lussan, C., and Faucon, J.-F. (1974). *Biochim. Biophys. Acta* **345**, 83–90.

Luthra, R., and Olson, M. S. (1977). *FEBS Lett.* **81**, 142–146.

MacLennan, D. H. (1975). *Can. J. Biochem.* **53**, 251–261.

Madeira, V. M. C. (1975). *Biochem. Biophys. Res. Commun.* **64**, 870–876.

Malmström, K., and Carafoli, E. (1975). *Arch. Biochem. Biophys.* **171**, 418–423.

Massari, S., and Pozzan, T. (1976). *Arch. Biochem. Biophys.* **173**, 332–340.

Maynard, L. S., and Cotzias, G. L. (1955). *J. Biol. Chem.* **214**, 489–495.

Mela, L. (1968). *Arch. Biochem. Biophys.* **123**, 286–293.

Mela, L. (1969). *Biochemistry* **8**, 2481–2486.

Mela, L., and Chance, B. (1968). *Biochemistry* **7**, 4059–4063.

Mela, L., and Chance, B. (1969). *Biochem. Biophys. Res. Commun.* **35**, 556–559.

Mikkelsen, R. B., and Wallach, D. F. H. (1976). *Biochim. Biophys. Acta* **433**, 674–683.

Mitchell, P. (1966). "Chemiosmotic Coupling in Oxidative and Photosynthetic Phosphorylation." Glynn Res., Bodmin.

Mitchell, P. (1968). "Chemiosmotic Coupling and Energy Transduction." Glynn Res., Bodmin.

Mitchell, P., and Moyle, J. (1969a). *Eur. J. Biochem.* **7**, 471–484.

Mitchell, P., and Moyle, J. (1969b). *Eur. J. Biochem.* **9**, 149–155.

Mitchell, P., and Moyle, J. (1979). *Biochem. Soc. Trans.* **7**, 887–894.

Moore, A. L., and Bonner, W. D., Jr. (1977). *Biochim. Biophys. Acta* **460**, 455–466.

Moore, C. L. (1971). *Biochem. Biophys. Res. Commun.* **42**, 298–305.

Moyle, J., and Mitchell, P. (1977a). *FEBS Lett.* **73**, 131–136.

Moyle, J., and Mitchell, P. (1977b). *FEBS Lett.* **77**, 136–145.

Mueller, P. (1975). *Ann. N.Y. Acad. Sci.* **264**, 247–264.

Nicholls, D. G. (1974). *Eur. J. Biochem.* **50**, 305–315.

Nicholls, D. G. (1977). *Biochem. Soc. Trans.* **5**, 203–206.

Nicholls, D. G. (1978a). *Biochem. J.* **170**, 511–522.

Nicholls, D. G. (1978b). *Biochem. J.* **176**, 463–474.

Niggli, V., Grazzotti, P., and Carafoli, E. (1978). *Experientia* **34**, 1136–1137.

Nishimura, M., Ito, T., and Chance, B. (1962). *Biochim. Biophys. Acta* **59**, 172–182.

Noack, E., and Greeff, K. (1971). *Experientia* **27**, 810–811.

Noack, E., and Greeff, K. (1975). *Recent Adv. Stud. Card. Struct. Metab.* **5**, 165–170.

Noack, E., and Heinen, E. M. (1977). *Eur. J. Biochem.* **79**, 245–250.

Ohnishi, S. T. (1979). *Biochim. Biophys. Acta* **585**, 315–319.
Ovchinnikov, Yu.A. (1974). *FEBS Lett.* **44**, 1–21.
Ovchinnikov, Yu.A. (1979). *FEBS Lett.* **94**, 321–336.
Packer, L., Utsumi, K., and Mustafa, M. G. (1966). *Arch. Biochem. Biophys.* **117**, 381–393.
Palaty, V. (1971). *J. Physiol. (London)* **218**, 353–368.
Panfili, E., Sandri, G., Sottocasa, G. L., Lunazzi, G., Lint, G., and Graziossi, G. (1976). *Nature (London)* **264**, 185–186.
Panfili, E., Sottocasa, G. L., Sanori, G., and Liut, G. F. (1980). *Eur. J. Biochem.* (in press).
Papahadjopoulos, D. (1968). *Biochim. Biophys. Acta* **163**, 240–254.
Papahadjopoulos, D. (1972). *Biochim. Biophys. Acta* **265**, 169–186.
Parce, J. W., Cunningham, C. C., and Waite, M. (1978). *Biochemistry* **17**, 1634–1639.
Parr, D. R., and Harris, E. J. (1976). *Biochem. Soc. Trans.* **3**, 951–953.
Patriarca, P., and Carafoli, E. (1968). *J. Cell. Physiol.* **72**, 29–37.
Peng, C.-F., Price, D. W., Bhuvaneswaran, C., and Wadkins, C. L. (1974). *Biochem. Biophys. Res. Commun.* **56**, 134–141.
Peng, C.-F., Straub, K. D., Kane, J. J., Murphy, M. L., and Wadkins, C. L. (1977). *Biochim. Biophys. Acta* **462**, 403–413.
Pfeiffer, D. R., and Lardy, H. A. (1976). *J. Biol. Chem.* **15**, 935–943.
Pfeiffer, D. R., Kauffman, R. F., and Lardy, H. A. (1978). *J. Biol. Chem.* **253**, 4165–4171.
Poe, M. (1969). *Arch. Biochem. Biophys.* **132**, 377–387.
Pozzan, T., and Azzone, G. F. (1976). *FEBS Lett.* **71**, 62–66.
Pozzan, T., Bragadin, M., and Azzone, G. F. (1976). *Eur. J. Biochem.* **77**, 93–99.
Pozzan, T., Bragadin, M., and Azzone, G. F. (1977). *Biochemistry* **16**, 5618–5623.
Pozzan, T., DiVirgilio, F., Bragadin, M., Miconi, V., and Azzone, G. F. (1979). *Proc. Natl. Acad. Sci. U.S.A.* **76**, 2123–2127.
Pressman, B. C. (1965). *Proc. Natl. Acad. Sci. U.S.A.* **53**, 1076–1082.
Prestipino, G. F., Coccarelli, D., Conti, F., and Carafoli, E. (1976). *FEBS Lett.* **45**, 99–103.
Puskin, J. S., and Gunter, T. E. (1972). *Biochim. Biophys. Acta* **275**, 302–307.
Puskin, J. S., Gunter, T. E., Gunter, K. K., and Russel, P. R. (1976). *Biochemistry* **15**, 3834–3842.
Ramachandran, C., and Bygrave, F. L. (1978). *Biochem. J.* **174**, 613–620.
Reed, K. C., and Bygrave, F. L. (1974a). *Biochem. J.* **138**, 239–252.
Reed, K. C., and Bygrave, F. L. (1974b). *Biochem. J.* **140**, 143–155.
Reed, K. C., and Bygrave, F. L. (1974c). *Biochem. J.* **142**, 555–566.
Reed, K. C., and Bygrave, F. L. (1975). *Eur. J. Biochem.* **55**, 497–504.
Reed, P. W., and Lardy, H. A. (1972). *J. Biol. Chem.* **247**, 6970–6977.
Reynafarje, B., and Lehninger, A. L. (1969). *J. Biol. Chem.* **244**, 584–593.
Reynafarje, B., and Lehninger, A. L. (1977). *Biochem. Biophys. Res. Commun.* **77**, 1273–1279.
Romslo, I. (1974). *Biochim. Biophys. Acta* **357**, 34–42.
Romslo, I. (1975a). Thesis, University of Bergen, Bergen, Norway.
Romslo, I. (1975b). *Biochim. Biophys. Acta* **387**, 69–79.
Romslo, I., and Flatmark, T. (1973). *Biochim. Biophys. Acta* **325**, 38–46.
Rose, B., and Rick, R. (1978). *J. Membr. Biol.* **44**, 377–415.
Rossi, C. S., and Lehninger, A. L. (1964). *J. Biol. Chem.* **239**, 3971–3980.
Rossi, C. S., Vasington, F. D., and Carafoli, E. (1973). *Biochem. Biophys. Res. Commun.* **50**, 846–852.
Rottenberg, H. (1973). *J. Membr. Biol.* **11**, 117–137.
Rottenberg, H., and Scarpa, A. (1974). *Biochemistry* **13**, 4811–4817.

Sanori, G., Sottocasa, G. L., Panfili, E., and Liut, G. F. (1979). *Biochim. Biophys. Acta* **558**, 214–220.

Saris, N.-E. L. (1959). *Suom. Kemistiseuran Tied.* **68**, 98–107.

Saris, N.-E. L. (1963a). *Acta Chem. Scand.* **17**, 882.

Saris, N.-E. L. (1963b). *Comment. Phys.-Math., Soc. Sci. Fenn.* **28**, Fasc. 11,1.

Saris, N.-E. L., and Järvisalo, J. O. (1977). *In* "Clinical Chemistry and Toxicology of Metals" (S. S. Brown, ed.), pp. 109–112. Elsevier-North-Holland Biomedical Press, Amsterdam.

Saris, N.-E. L., Wikström, M. K. F., and Seppälä, A. J. (1969). *In* "Mitochondria: Structure and Function" (L. Ernster and Z. Drahota, eds.), FEBS Symp., Vol. 17, pp. 363–368. Academic Press, New York.

Scarpa, A. (1972). *In* "Methods in Enzymology" (A. San Pietro, ed.), Vol. 24, Part B, pp. 343–351. Academic Press, New York.

Scarpa, A. (1974). *Biochemistry* **13**, 2789–2794.

Scarpa, A. (1975). *In* "Calcium Transport in Contraction and Secretion" (E. Carafoli *et al.*, eds.), pp. 65–72. North-Holland Publ., Amsterdam.

Scarpa, A., and Azzi, A. (1968). *Biochim. Biophys. Acta* **150**, 473–481.

Scarpa, A., and Azzone, G. F. (1968). *J. Biol. Chem.* **243**, 5132–5138.

Scarpa, A., and Azzone, G. F. (1969). *Biochim. Biophys. Acta* **173**, 78–85.

Scarpa, A., and Azzone, G. F. (1970). *Eur. J. Biochem.* **12**, 328–335.

Scarpa, A., and Grazziotti, P. (1973). *J. Gen. Physiol.* **62**, 756–764.

Scatchard, G., Coleman, J. S., and Shen, A. L. (1957). *J. Am. Chem. Soc.* **79**, 12–17.

Scherphof, G. L., Scarpa, A., and van Toorenenberg, A. (1972). *Biochim. Biophys. Acta* **270**, 226–240.

Schuster, S. M., and Olson, M. S. (1974). *J. Biol. Chem.* **249**, 7151–7158.

Schwerzmann, K., Gazzotti, P., and Carafoli, E. (1976). *Biochem. Biophys. Res. Commun.* **69**, 812–815.

Scott, K. M., Knight, V. A., Settlemire, C. T., and Brierley, G. P. (1970). *Biochemistry* **9**, 714–723.

Scott, K. M., Hwang, K. M., Jurkowitz, M., and Brierley, G. P. (1971). *Arch. Biochem. Biophys.* **147**, 557–567.

Selwyn, M. J., Dawson, A. P., and Dunnet, S. J. (1970a). *FEBS Lett.* **10**, 1–5.

Selwyn, M. J., Dawson, A. P., Stockdale, M., and Gains, N. (1970b). *Eur. J. Biochem.* **14**, 120–126.

Selwyn, M. J., Fulton, D. W., and Dawson, A. P. (1978). *FEBS Lett.* **96**, 148–151.

Selwyn, M. J., Dawson, A. P., and Fulton, D. V. (1979). *Biochem. Soc. Trans.* **7**, 216–219.

Seppälä, A. J., Saris, N.-E. L., and Gauffin, M. L. (1971). *Biochem. Pharmacol.* **20**, 305–313.

Settlemire, C. T., Hunter, G. R., and Brierley, G. P. (1968). *Biochim. Biophys. Acta* **162**, 487–499.

Shamoo, A. E., and Goldstein, D. A. (1977). *Biochim. Biophys. Acta* **472**, 13–53.

Shamoo, A. E., Jeng, A. Y., and Tivol, W. F. (1978). *In* "Frontiers of Biological Energetics" (P. C. Dutton, J. S. Leigh, and A. Scarpa, eds.), pp. 1197–1203. Academic Press, New York.

Siegel, E., and Carafoli, E. (1978). *Eur. J. Biochem.* **89**, 119–123.

Siliprandi, D., Toniello, A., Zoccarato, F., and Siliprandi, N. (1977). *Biochem. Biophys. Res. Commun.* **78**, 23–27.

Siliprandi, N., Siliprandi, D., Toniello, A., Rugolo, M., and Zoccarato, F. (1978). *In* "Proton and Calcium Pumps'' (G. F. Azzone *et al.*, eds.), pp. 263–271. Elsevier/North-Holland Biomedical Press, Amsterdam.

Skulskii, I. A., Savina, M. V., Glasunov, V. V., and Saris, N.-E. L. (1978). *J. Membr. Biol.* **44**, 187–194.

Slater, E. C., and Cleland, K. W. (1953). *Biochem. J.* **55**, 566–572.

Sloane, B. F., Scarpa, A., and Somlyo, A. P. (1978). *Arch. Biochem. Biophys.* **189**, 409–416.

Sordahl, L. A. (1974). *Arch. Biochem. Biophys.* **167**, 104–115.

Sordahl, L. A., and Asimakis, G. K. (1978). *Dev. Bioenerg. Biomembr.* **1**, 273–283.

Sottocasa, G. L., Sandri, G.,Panfili, E., De Bernard, B., Gazzotti, P., Vasington, F. D., and Carafoli, E. (1972). *Biochem. Biophys. Res. Commun.* **47**, 808–813.

Sottocasa, G. L., Panfili, E., and Sandri, G. (1977). *Bull. Mol. Biol. Med.* **2**, 1–28.

Southard, J. H., and Green, D. E. (1974). *Biochem. Biophys. Res. Commun.* **59**, 30–37.

Stockdale, M., Dawson, A. B., and Selwyn, M. J. (1970). *Eur. J. Biochem.* **15**, 342–351.

Stucki, J. W., and Ineichen, E. A. (1974). *Eur. J. Biochem.* **48**, 365–375.

Studer, R. K., and Borle, A. B. (1979). *J. Membr. Biol.* **48**, 325.

Sul, H. S., Shrago, E., and Shug, A. L. (1976). *Arch. Biochem. Biophys.* **172**, 230–237.

Tashmukhamedov, B. A., Gagelgans, A. J., Mamatkulov, K. H., and Makhmudova, E. M. (1972). *FEBS Lett.* **28**, 239–245.

Tew, P. W. (1977). *Biochem. Biophys. Res. Commun.* **78**, 624–629.

Theuvenet, A. P. R., and Borst-Pauwels, G. W. F. H. (1976). *J. Theor. Biol.* **57**, 313–329.

Thorne, R. F. W., and Bygrave, F. L. (1974). *Biochem. J.* **144**, 551–558.

Träuble, H., and Eibl, H. (1974). *Proc. Natl. Acad. Sci. U.S.A.* **71**, 214–219.

Ulvik, R., Prante, P. H., Koller, M. E., and Romslo, I. (1976). *Scand. J. Clin. Lab. Invest.* **36**, 539–546.

Vainio, H., Mela, L., and Chance, B. (1970). *Eur. J. Biochem.* **12**, 387–391.

Vallieres, J., Scarpa, A., and Somlyo, A. P. (1975). *Arch. Biochem. Biophys.* **170**, 659–669.

Van Rossum, G. D. V., Smith, K. P., and Beeton, P. (1976). *Nature (London)* **260**, 335–337.

Vasington, F. D., and Murphy, J. V. (1962). *J. Biol. Chem.* **237**, 2670–2676.

Vasington, F. D., Gazzotti, P., Tiozzo, T., and Carafoli, E. (1972). *Biochim. Biophys. Acta* **256**, 43–54.

Veloso, D., Guynn, R. W., Oskarsson, M., and Veech, R. L. (1973). *J. Biol. Chem.* **248**, 4811–4819.

Vercesi, A., Reynafarje, B., and Lehninger, A. L. (1978). *J. Biol. Chem.* **253**, 6379–6385.

Vignais, P. V., Vignais, P. M., and Defaye, G. (1973). *Biochemistry* **12**, 1508–1519.

Vinogradov, A., and Scarpa, A. (1973). *J. Biol. Chem.* **248**, 5527–5531.

Vinogradov, A., Scarpa, A., and Chance, B. (1972). *Arch. Biochem. Biophys.* **152**, 646–654.

Weast, R. C., Selby, S. M., and Hodgman, C. D. (1965). ''Handbook of Chemistry and Physics,'' 46th ed., p. F117. Chemical Rubber Publ. Co., Cleveland, Ohio.

Wehrle, J. P., and Pedersen, P. C. (1979). *J. Biol. Chem.* **254**, 7269–7275.

Wikström, M. K. F. (1977). *Nature (London)* **266**, 271–273.

Wikström, M. K. F. (1978). *Dev. Bioenerg. Biomembr.* **1**, 215–226.

Wikström, M. K. F., and Krab, K. (1978). *In* ''Energy Conservation in Biological Membranes'' (G. Schäfer and M. Klingenberg, eds.), pp. 128–139. Springer-Verlag, Berlin and New York.

Wikström, M. K. F., and Krab, K. (1979). *Biochim. Biophys. Acta* **549**, 177–222.

Wikström, M. K. F., and Saari, H. T. (1976). *Mol. Cell. Biochem.* **11**, 17–34.

Wikström, M. K. F., Ahonen, P., and Luukkainen, T. (1975). *FEBS Lett.* **56**, 120–123.

Wilbrandt, W. (1974). *Biomembranes* **7**, 11–31.

Williams, A. J., and Fry, C. H. (1979). *FEBS Lett.* **97**, 288–292.

Williams, R. J. P. (1975). *In* "Biological Membranes" (D. S. Parsons, ed.), pp. 106–124. Oxford Univ. Press (Clarendon), London and New York.

Williams, R. J. P. (1976). *In* "Calcium in Biological Systems" (C. J. Duncan, ed.), pp. 1–26. Cambridge Univ. Press, London and New York.

Williams, R. J. P. (1978). *FEBS Lett.* **85,** 9–19.

Wojtczak, L. (1974). *FEBS Lett.* **44,** 25–30.

Wojtczak, L., and Lehninger, A. L. (1961). *Biochim. Biophys. Acta* **51,** 442–456.

Wolkowicz, P. E., and Wood, J. M. (1979). *FEBS. Lett.* **101,** 63–66.

Zaba, B. N., and Harris, E. J. (1976). *Biochem. J.* **160,** 707–714.

CURRENT TOPICS IN BIOENERGETICS, VOLUME 10

Role of Subunits in Proton-Translocating ATPase (F_0-F_1)

MASAMITSU FUTAI AND HIROSHI KANAZAWA

Department of Microbiology
Faculty of Pharmaceutical Sciences
Okayama University
Okayama, Japan

I. An Overview of Proton-Translocating ATPase

All forms of living cells conserve energy in chemical compounds, especially in ATP. The proton-translocating ATPase in membranes of chloroplasts, mitochondria, and bacteria synthesizes this high energy compound utilizing energy from the electron transfer chain. The overall reactions of ATP synthesis in these organellae are now well explained by the chemiosmotic hypothesis. This hypothesis was proposed in 1961 by Peter Mitchell and is now well accepted in principle after almost two decades of critical experimentation. This hypothesis proposes that ATP is synthesized by the ATPase complex utilizing an electrochemical gradient of protons. This electrochemical gradient of protons or proton-motive force (transmembrane pH gradient and associated electrical potential) is formed by the unidirectional movement of protons across membranes during the flow of electrons through the respiratory or photosynthetic electron transfer chain. The ATPase complex phosphorylates ADP to form ATP driven by a reverse flow of protons. The complex can work reversibly and form an electrochemical gradient of protons coupled with the hydrolysis of ATP. Although the basic features of the mechanism of phosphorylation have been established, it is still unknown at the molecular level how synthesis or hydrolysis of ATP by the enzyme complex is coupled to vectorial translocation of protons.

The proton-translocating ATPase complex consists of two main portions, coupling factor 1, F_1, and a membrane component, F_0.[1] This terminology was introduced by Racker and his associates, who first isolated F_1 from beef heart mitochondria (Racker, 1976). F_1, the catalytic portion of the complex, is an extrinsic membrane protein. Thus it can easily be released from membranes by washing them with dilute buffer; when once solubilized, it behaves like other soluble proteins. The F_1 portions purified from various sources have striking similarities in structure. They consist of five subunits with ATPase activity but no ability to synthesize ATP. The ADP phosphorylating activity can be reconstituted by binding F_1 to the F_0 portion, which is apparently a transmembrane complex mediating proton translocation between two compartments.

The proton passage through F_0 is regulated by the F_1 portion. Protons flow passively through F_0 in membrane vesicles depleted of F_1. Thus, such vesicles are unable to form a proton gradient during electron transfer through the cytochrome chain because of proton leakage, but they become capable of forming a respiratory proton gradient on rebinding of F_1. The defect of depleted membranes was first recognized as a loss of the structural role of F_1. The F_0 portion has so far been studied less extensively than the F_1 portion, but preparations of F_0 from bacteria, plants, and animals all contain a protein with a similar function, and this subunit, dicyclohexyl carbodiimide (DCCD) binding protein, has been isolated from various sources and studied in detail. The binding of DCCD to this subunit in membranes depleted of F_1 prevents leakage of protons.

The essential feature of the ATPase complex is that it is universally

---

[1] *Abbreviations used:* DCCD, dicyclohexyl carbodiimide; F_1, catalytic portion of the proton-translocating ATPase (also defined in Fig. 1 and the text): F_0, membrane sector or ionophore portion (also defined in Fig. 1 and the text); TF_1, F_1 from thermophilic bacterium PS3; TF_0, F_0 from thermophilic bacterium PS_3; CF_1, F_1 from chloroplasts (prepared from spinach unless otherwise specified); EF_1, F_1 from *Escherichia coli;* SDS, sodium dodecyl sulfate; SDS–polyacrylamide gel electrophoresis, polyacrylamide gel electrophoresis in the presence of SDS; NBD-Cl, 7-chloro-4-nitrobenzo-2-oxo-1,3-diazole; OSCP, oligomycin sensitivity-conferring protein; AMPPNHP, β,γ-imidoadenosine 5'-triphopshate; P_i, phosphoric acid. ATP, ADP, AMP, CTP, ITP, EDTA, and DNA have their usual meanings.

present in all living things from mammals to bacteria. Even in a simple organism like *Streptococcus faecalis,* which has no electron transfer chain, F_0-F_1 forms a proton-motive force by hydrolysis of ATP, which is synthesized by glycolysis. The proton motive force in bacteria is utilized for vectorial functions, such as motility or active transport. The universal presence of the energy-transducing apparatus in all living organisms provides us with the opportunity to study its structure and function in different ways by using preparations from organisms with different unique features. Thus, for instance, we can study thermostable F_0-F_1 of thermophilic bacteria and F_0-F_1 of *Escherichia coli* of which the genetic background is well known. Results of studies on these organisms can then be extrapolated to other animal or plant organelles, although care must be taken in making generalizations.

There have been several excellent reviews of the complex: comprehensive reviews concerning mainly coupling factors of chloroplasts (Nelson, 1976; McCarty, 1978; Baird and Hammes, 1979), mitochondria (Senior, 1973b; Pedersen, 1975; Racker, 1976; Panet and Sanadi, 1976), and bacterial membranes (Abrams, 1976; Harold, 1977; Haddock and Jones, 1977; Wilson and Smith, 1978; Kagawa, 1978; Kagawa *et al.,* 1979) are available: the principle of the mechanism of phosphorylation by the complex has been extensively discussed by several authors (Boyer *et al.,* 1977; Kozlov and Skulachev, 1977; Hinkle and McCarty, 1978); there are also reviews available on special aspects of the complex, such as the tightly bound nucleotides in F_1 (Harris, 1978), and the biogenesis of the complex (Sebald, 1977). In this review we discuss the role of the subunits and their assembly into a functional complex. Most of the discussion is centered on the F_1 portion, since this has been studied more extensively than the F_0 portion. However, we also discuss recent exciting developments in studies on the F_0 portion. A more detailed review of work on this portion is to appear in this series of publications (Fillingame, 1980). We have tried to cover the literature up to the spring of 1979, and have relied on previous reviews for details of earlier work. We offer apologies to those whose contributions have been unintentionally overlooked or have not been discussed fully.

II. Coupling Factor 1 (F_1) Portion of the Complex

A. Structure and Subunit Composition of F_1

1. Electron Microscopic Studies on F_1

Negatively stained electron micrographs of the membranes from chloroplasts (Howell and Moudrianakis, 1967; Lien and Racker, 1971; Garber and Steponkus, 1974), mitochondria (Kagawa and Racker, 1966; Hinkle and McCarty, 1978), *E. coli* (Hinkle and McCarty, 1978; Yamato *et al.*, 1978), and thermophilic bacteria (Kagawa *et al.*, 1976) all show spheres of about 90 Å diameter attached to the bilayer through a portion called the stalk. These structures have also been observed by other electron microscopic techniques such as positive staining of thin sections (Telford and Racker, 1973; Oleszko and Moudrianakis, 1974) or freeze etching (Garber and Steponkus, 1974; Miller and Staehelin, 1976). The identity of this structure with F_1 has been confirmed by various procedures (Kagawa and Racker, 1966; Racker, 1969; Lien and Racker, 1971; Garber and Steponkus, 1974). For instance, no spherical particles can be seen in electron micrographs of F_1-depleted membranes, but they appear when these membranes are reconstituted with purified F_1.

Pictures of F_1 also revealed spheres with similar characteristics. Kagawa and collaborators (Kagawa *et al.*, 1976) crystallized F_1 from a thermophilic bacterium PS3 (TF_1) and observed the periodic array of the molecules under an electron microscope (Wakabayashi *et al.*, 1977). The image of the TF_1 molecule reconstructed from the light diffraction pattern showed considerable six-fold and three-fold symmetry and had a hexagonal structure, which is consistent with a subunit stoichiometry of the $\alpha 3$-$\beta 3$ type as discussed below. They also observed a low-density region, or hole, near the center of the molecule, and they suggested that this hole may be a channel through which H^+ passes, although this has not yet been confirmed. F_1 from beef heart (Spitsberg and Haworth, 1977) and rat liver (Amzel and Pedersen, 1978) have also been crystalized, and the rat liver crystals seem to be especially suitable for X-ray diffraction studies, because they show at least 3.5 Å diffraction.

2. Subunit Composition and Stoichiometry

The F_1 released from membranes has been purified by conventional procedures for purification of soluble proteins, after the purification by measurement of ATPase activity. Usually 20- to 30-fold purification from membranes is sufficient to obtain a homogeneous preparation, suggesting that the F_1 content of energy-transducing membranes is quite high. Homogeneous F_1 has five subunits, named α, β, γ, δ, and ϵ in order of decreasing molecular weight. Only F_1 with all these subunits is capable of binding to the F_0 portion and of energy transduction, although ATPase lacking the γ, δ, and/or ϵ subunit can be prepared, as discussed later. The molecular weights of the α, β, γ, and δ subunits from different sources, determined from the mobilities of the denatured subunits on polyacrylamide gel electrophoresis, were shown to be quite similar, regardless of their source: α, 62,000–57,000; β, 56,000–50,000; γ, 37,000–31,000; δ,

18,000–15,000. The molecular weight of the ϵ subunits varies somewhat depending on the source: chloroplasts, 13,000 (Nelson *et al.*, 1972); bovine mitochondria, 5700 (Knowles and Penefsky, 1972b); *E. coli*, 12,000 (Futai *et al.*, 1974); thermophilic bacteria PS3, 11,000 (Yoshida *et al.*, 1975). The main reason for this variation may be that polyacrylamide gel electrophoresis is not an accurate method for determining the molecular weights of small proteins. Lists of the molecular weights of the subunits from different sources measured in this way have been given in previous reviews (Abrams, 1976; Baird and Hammes, 1979), and the values obtained by other procedures are discussed below.

Although the molecular weights of the subunits of F_1 from different sources were found to be similar, discrepant results have been reported for their stoichiometries. There is even uncertainty about the stoichiometry of the best characterized F_1, that from mitochondria; the minimal subunit stoichiometries of $\alpha_3 \beta_3 \gamma \delta \epsilon$ (Catterall *et al.*, 1973) and $\alpha_2 \gamma_2 \epsilon_2$ (Senior, 1975) have been obtained, respectively, from the intensity of staining in polyacrylamide gel in the presence of SDS and by analysis of sulfhydryl groups. It seems particularly difficult to determine the exact number of δ and ϵ subunits, because these subunits dissociate from the enzyme rather easily, as discussed below.

The stoichiometry of the subunits of CF_1 has been shown in several laboratories to be of the $\alpha_2 \beta_2$ type. Recently Binder *et al.* (1978) concluded that CF_1 has a subunit stoichiometry of $\alpha_2 \beta_2 \gamma_1 \delta_1 \epsilon_2$ by staining the subunits isolated on SDS–polyacrylamide gel. These numbers are consistent with their values for the cysteine content and amino acid composition; Binder *et al.* found 2 cysteines in α, 2 in β, 3 in γ, 1 in δ, and 1 in ϵ. The sum of these residues in CF_1 with the above stoichiometry is 14, which is in agreement with the value of 13 obtained for the entire complex. The values for the cysteine contents of the α, β, and ϵ subunits are the same as those reported previously (Nelson *et al.*, 1972, 1973), but the values for γ and δ are different. Essentially the same subunit ratio was reported for CF_1 from pea plants grown in $^{14}CO_2$ (Nelson, 1976) and for the cross-linking of purified CF_1 (Baird and Hammes, 1976). A stoichiometry of the $\alpha_2 \beta_2$ type is consistent with the molecular weight of CF_1 (325,000) determined by sedimentation equilibrium centrifugation and small angle X-ray scattering as discussed by Baird and Hammes (1979) in their review.

The stoichiometry of TF_1 from thermophilic bacteria PS3 has been extensively analyzed (Kagawa *et al.*, 1976; Yoshida *et al.*, 1978). TF_1 is known to be thermostable, and it does not easily dissociate into subunits. Kagawa and his associates concluded that the subunit stoichiometry of this F_1 is of the $\alpha_3 \beta_3$ type from analysis of the ratio of subunits in radioactively labeled TF_1, the cysteine content (3 cysteines in TF_1 and 1 in α), and the tryptophan content. They determined the molecular weights of the subunits by four different procedures (low- and high-speed equilibrium centrifugation, amino acid analysis, and high-speed liquid chromatography) and finally concluded that the stoichiometry was $\alpha_3 \beta_3 \gamma_1 \delta_1 \epsilon_1$. Their results are quite convincing, and the stoichiometry is consistent with the molecular weight of the entire complex (380,000). Stoichiometry of the $\alpha_3 \beta_3$ type has been obtained for $E.\ coli$ F_1 (EF_1) by analysis of the radioactively labeled complex (Bragg and Hou, 1975). Stoichiometry of the $\alpha_2 \beta_2$ type has also been suggested for EF_1 from results on its reconstitution from partially resolved fragments (Vogel and Steinhart, 1976); the highest ATPase activity was obtained by mixing F_1 fragments $IA(\beta)$ and $II(\alpha, \gamma,$ and $\epsilon)$ in a molar ratio of $1:1$, suggesting a stoichiometry of $(IA)_2$ $(II)_2$ for the basic F_1 ATPase complex. In contrast, when isolated individual subunits were used for the reconstitution, a mixture of $\alpha_3 \beta_3$ and γ_1 had the highest ATPase activity (Dunn and Futai, 1980). However, the subunit stoichiometry cannot be determined definitely from the results of these reconstitution experiments, because the ATPase activities reconstituted in both cases were lower than that of native F_1. The stoichiometry of F_1 from $S.\ faecalis$ was also formulated as $\alpha_3 \beta_3$ (Abrams $et\ al.$, 1976b).

Kagawa and his colleagues claim that one reason for the discrepancy in results on subunit stoichiometry is that the subunits readily dissociate from F_1 during experiments. They have reexamined the molecular weights of CF_1 and mitochondrial F_1 in buffer containing methanol, which prevented dissociation of subunits during high- and low-speed sedimentation centrifugation and high-speed liquid chromatography, obtaining values of 380,000 for both mitochondrial and chloroplast F_1 (Yoshida $et\ al.$, 1979). Furthermore they have obtained molecular weights of about 50,000 for the α and β subunits of CF_1 and mitochondrial F_1 by high-speed liquid chromatography. Their values for subunits are at least 5000 daltons lower than previous values (Baird and Hammes, 1979). In this regard Knowles and Penefsky (1972b) have already pointed out that SDS–polyacrylamide gel electrophoresis overestimates the molecular weight of α or β subunit. On the basis of values discussed above, a subunit stoichiometry of $\alpha_3 \beta_3$ is possible for CF_1 and mitochondrial F_1, although it is not consistent with the cysteine content of CF_1 (Binder $et\ al.$, 1978), as discussed earlier in this section.

Although it is well recognized that δ and ϵ dissociate from the enzyme rather easily, no dissociation of the α and β subunits has been detected during molecular weight determination or purification. In this connection, however, we have made interesting observations on F_1 from an $E.\ coli$ mutant (Kanazawa $et\ al.$, 1980a). The F_1 of this mutant could not be purified by the published procedure (Futai $et\ al.$, 1974): it separated into an

α-rich peak and β-rich peak during chromatography, whereas no dissociation of wild-type F_1 was observed. The mutant F_1 could, however, be purified without dissociation of the main subunits by a modified procedure in which methanol was used instead of glycerol, and 1.0 mM MgCl$_2$ was added to the buffer for chromatography. Therefore, it is quite possible that even the two major subunits dissociate from F_1 under some conditions.

For resolving the discrepancy between values for the stoichiometry of different F_1's, it is important to reexamine the properties of these F_1's prepared by a procedure in which dissociation of the subunits does not occur. Until agreement is reached on the stoichiometry, we cannot exclude the possibility that different F_1's may have different subunit stoichiometries: in other words that species specificities of stoichiometry may exist.

B. Catalytic Portion (ATPase) of F_1: α, β, and γ Subunits

1. Partial Digestion of F_1 with Proteases

Various approaches have been used to study the role of each subunit in the F_1 molecule. One obvious method is to study the properties of F_1 after partial digestion with proteases. Deters *et al.* (1975) showed that CF$_1$ still had ATPase activity after prolonged treatment with trypsin (free from contaminating chymotrypsin), although only two subunits, α and β, remained in the complex. This two-subunit complex no longer served as a coupling factor, because it had no subunits capable of binding to the F_0 portion. The two-subunit enzyme still showed cold sensitivity, which is a universal property of F_1. However, the complex was not sensitive to natural inhibitor protein, which is one of the subunits of CF$_1$ (ϵ subunit) isolated as an inhibitor to CF$_1$ ATPase. These results indicate that the α and β subunits are sufficient for the ATPase reaction, although other subunits are required for coupling factor activity. Similar complexes of F_1 were obtained from *E. coli* (Nelson *et al.*, 1974; Bragg and Hou, 1975), *Bacillus megatherium* (Mirsky and Barlow, 1973), and mitochondria (Kozlov and Mikelsaar, 1974). An α and β ATPase was also obtained from *Micrococcus lysodeikticus* (Salton and Schor, 1974) by treating the membrane fraction with butanol.

Höckel *et al.* (1976) treated F_1 of *Micrococcus* sp. with trypsin and obtained two complexes, depending on the time of incubation: complex α' (about 4000 daltons smaller than intact α) and unchanged β had the same specific activity of ATPase as intact F_1. On the other hand, a complex consisting of α', β, and two polypeptides (38,000 and 22,000 dalton polypeptides derived from α') had no ATPase activity. Both complexes could bind to purine riboside triphosphate linked to Sepharose 6B and could be eluted with 5 mM ATP, which is essentially the same concentration as that required for eluting intact F_1 from the matrix. Höckel *et al.* suggested from these studies that some quaternary structure of α' and the β subunit is necessary for the ATPase activity, although it is not necessary for ATP binding. An interesting finding was that conversion of about one-third of α' to two polypeptides was enough for complete loss of activity. Brief treatment of F_1 with proteases has interesting effects on the subunit interactions of the entire F_0–F_1 complex, as shown by Abrams *et al.* (1976a). On partial digestion of F_1 from *S. faecalis* with chymotrypsin under carefully controlled conditions, Abrams *et al.* observed that after brief treatment (15 minutes, at 38°C) the F_1 became unable to reattach to the depleted membranes (without F_1), although it had full ATPase activity. SDS-polyacrylamide gel electrophoresis indicated that the partially digested F_1 contained modified α subunits (about 2000 daltons smaller than native α subunit), but that other subunits were unaltered. From this, they suggested that a short chymotrypsin-sensitive α chain "tail" protruding from the F_1 surface is required for membrane attachment.

Different conclusions were reached from similar experiments on EF_1. Dunn and Heppel (1979) treated F_1 (four-subunit enzyme, see Section II,C) with a small amount of trypsin or chymotrypsin [1:1000, protease/F_1(weight ratio)] and showed by SDS-polyacrylamide gel electrophoresis that both proteases caused a detectable decrease in molecular weight of α subunit. These protease-treated F_1's had full ATPase activity but were unable to restore ATP-driven transhydrogenase when incubated with the δ and ϵ subunit and depleted membranes. Cleavage of the α subunit was proved to be responsible for this failure to restore transhydrogenase by reconstitution experiments using α subunit isolated from trypsinized F_1. The defect was shown to result from loss of ability of the catalytic portion to bind the δ subunit. Complexes of α, β, and γ were reconstituted using native and trypsinized α subunits, and these complexes were incubated with the δ and ϵ subunits (see Section III,B for details of the reconstitution). The complex containing trypsinized α could bind the ϵ but not the δ subunit, although the complex containing native α bound both subunits. These results suggest that trypsinized F_1 could not bind to depleted membranes because it could not interact with the δ subunit, possibly through the α subunit. This does not necessarily rule out the possibility of direct interaction of the α subunit of *E. coli* with membranes, but it provides a simpler model, as shown in Fig. 1.

The exact nature of the limited proteolysis was studied by Dunn and Heppel (1979, 1980). They determined the sequence of the first 20 residues from the amino terminal of the native α subunit; from a comparison

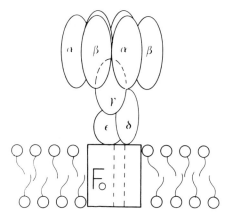

FIG. 1. Models of proton-translocating ATPase (F_0–F_1) from *Escherichia coli*, mainly based on the results of reconstitution experiments (see Section III for details). A complex with ATPase activity could be obtained by mixing the α, β, and γ (optimum reconstitution from a mixture of α, β, and γ of 3 : 3 : 1) (Futai, 1977; Dunn and Futai, 1980). The complete F_1 molecule could be reconstituted by adding δ and ϵ. The spherical shape of ϵ and elongated shape of δ were deduced from physical studies (Smith and Sternweis, 1977; C. H. H. Paradies, private communication). The position of the γ subunit is based on the finding that three low molecular weight subunits are sensitive to trypsin (Nelson *et al.*, 1974). Subunit α and δ are drawn in close contact, because the three-subunit complex reconstituted from β, γ, and trypsinized α (lacking the first 16 N-terminal amino acids) could not bind δ (Dunn and Heppel, 1979, 1980). The proton channel of the F_0 portion is shown by dashed lines because the topology of proteins in *E. coli* F_0 is unknown.

of this sequence with the amino terminal of the proteolyzed α subunit, they concluded that trypsin and chymotrypsin removed the first 15 and 19 residues, respectively, from the amino terminus. The carboxyl terminal seems to remain intact during proteolysis, because the terminal amino acid was tryptophan both before and after treatment. These results suggest that the amino terminal sequence is important in subunit interaction, possibly between α and δ subunits. Dunn and Heppel (1979) isolated peptides composed of residues 1–13 and 1–19 by treatment with trypsin and chymotrypsin, respectively, by high performance liquid chromatography. It will be very interesting to study the interactions of these polypeptides with other subunits, especially δ.

2. *Immunochemical Studies on the Catalytic Portion of* F_1

The functional roles of the subunits of CF_1 have been studied by immunochemical techniques. Nelson *et al.* (1973) dissociated CF_1 with pyridine and urea, separated the individual subunits, and raised antibodies to them in rabbits. Antibodies against the α and γ subunits inhibited ATP synthesis and light-triggered Mg^{2+}-ATPase in chloroplasts. Anti-α also inhibited the stimulation of H^+ uptake in chloroplasts by ATP. Antibodies against the α and β subunits agglutinated chloroplasts, although antibodies against the smaller subunits did not. A combination of anti-α and anti-γ inhibited the ATPase activity of activated chloroplasts, but neither antibody alone was effective. Divalent antibodies against the β subunit were not inhibitory, but monovalent anti-β inhibited photophosphorylation (Gregory and Racker, 1973). CF$_1$ is known to take up tritium dependent on light (Ryrie and Jagendorf, 1971, 1972), presumably owing to change of conformation, and this activity was also inhibited by anti-α or anti-β (both monovalent type). These studies indicate that the three major subunits α, β and γ are intimately involved in catalysis in the coupling factor. Antibody against β subunit of TF$_1$ inhibited ATPase and energy-transducing activity of TF$_1$ (Yoshida et al., 1979), suggesting that β is the catalytic subunit in this F$_1$.

Baird et al. (1979) made dansyl-labeled monovalent antibody against solubilized CF$_1$ and against four of the isolated CF$_1$ subunits, α, β, γ, and ϵ, and found that the dansyl group served as a specifically bound energy donor in singlet–singlet energy transfer. They also prepared phospholipid vesicles containing reconstituted DCCD-sensitive ATPase prepared from chloroplasts. Hexadecanoyl-aminofluorescein molecules were incorporated into the lipid bilayer as energy acceptors. The energy transfer parameters were analyzed in terms of a model consisting of two spheres with uniformly labeled surfaces, one with an energy donor and one with an energy acceptor. The results indicate that the antigenic site for monovalent anti-CF$_1$ is located more than 35Å away from the surface of the phospholipid vesicle. The antigenic sites for anti-α, anti-γ, and anti-ϵ also appeared to be farther than 35 Å from the vesicles, and the antigenic site for anti β was located about 30 Å from the vesicles. These results are consistent with a model in which a portion of F$_1$ extends far from the membrane, as seen by electron microscopy.

C. CHEMICAL MODIFICATION AND AFFINITY LABELING OF SUBUNITS

1. Chemical Modification

The involvement of tyrosine residues in the ATPase activity of mitochondrial F$_1$ was suggested by Senior (1973a) because modification of 9 or 10 tyrosine residues of F$_1$ with tetranitromethane was accompanied by loss of activity. 7-Chloro-4-nitrobenzo-2-oxa-1,3-diazole (NBD-Cl) was found to react more specifically than tetranitromethane with tyrosine residues in F$_1$. NBD-Cl is a potent inhibitor of F$_1$-ATPase activity; when CF$_1$ (Deters et al., 1975) or EF$_1$ (Nelson et al., 1974) was incubated with two molar equivalents of NBD-Cl, ATPase activity was inhibited almost completely. This inhibition was completely reversed by dithiothreitol. One molecule of NBD-Cl bound per molecule of CF_1 caused complete inhibition, and a second molecule of NBD-Cl reacted more slowly (Cantley and Hammes, 1975b). The residues specifically modified by NBD-Cl were located on the β subunit (Deters *et al.*, 1975; Nelson *et al.*, 1974; Mukohata *et al.*, 1978). However, in the case of EF_1, Verheijen *et al.* (1978) observed predominant labeling of the α subunit during short-term incubation (0.8 mol NBD-Cl/α and 0.4 mol NBD-Cl/β), although β was labeled predominantly during prolonged incubation, which is the condition used by Nelson *et al.* (1974). Evidence has also been obtained for a single essential tyrosine residue in mitochondrial F_1 (Ferguson *et al.*, 1974). Modification with NBD-Cl affected the conformation of the CF_1 molecule, as shown by change in the reactivity of sulfhydryls of CF_1, change of the circular dichroism spectrum (Holowska and Hammes, 1977), and changes in the nucleotide binding properties of the enzyme (Cantley and Hammes, 1975a). The NBD-Cl sites have been suggested to be between the β subunits and to be near the catalytic site. As reviewed extensively (Baird and Hammes, 1979), Hammes and collaborators estimated the distances between different sites in CF_1 by measurement of fluorescence energy transfer. They mapped the sites for NBD-Cl and quercetin (an inhibitor of ATPase), nucleotide regulatory sites, sulfhydryl groups in the γ subunit and a sulfhydryl group in the ϵ subunit. The distances in the map that they constructed on the basis of results on energy transfer are consistent with the spatial arrangement of subunits deduced from their cross-linking experiments (Baird and Hammes, 1977).

The essential amino acid residues in catalysis of F_1 have also been studied using other reagents. Treatment of mitochondrial F_1 from beef heart or rat liver with the arginine reagents 2,3-butanedione and phenylglyoxal resulted in enzyme inactivation (Marcus *et al.*, 1976). The kinetics of inactivation with both compounds indicated that the reaction of 1 arginyl residue per active site is required for the inactivation. The modification reaction was slowed down significantly by the addition of ATP. Kinetic data are consistent with a role of the modified residue at the active site of F_1, although other interpretations are possible. Frigeri *et al.* (1977) proposed the equimolar interaction of inhibitor and enzyme for inhibitions of the F_1-ATPase, oligomycin-sensitive ATPase, and ATP–P_i exchange activities of the complex V. Correlations between the binding and inhibitions of ATPase and ATP–P_i exchange activities have been obtained (Frigeri *et al.*, 1978). Spinach CF_1 also has an essential arginyl residue in the catalytic site; photophosphorylation, ATP–P_i exchange and Mg^{2+}-ATPase activities were inhibited by phenylglyoxal and butanedione (Andreo and Vallejos, 1977; Vallejos *et al.*, 1977b; Schmid *et al.*, 1977). Essentially the same results were obtained on F_1 of *Rhodospirillum rubrum* chromatophores (Vallejos *et al.*, 1978).

Pyridoxal phosphate inactivated CF_1, forming a Schiff base with lysine residues (Sugiyama and Mukohata, 1978, 1979). At 50% inactivation, about 0.5 mol of radioactive pyridoxal phosphate was found in each the α and β subunit per mole of CF_1. ATP and ADP protected CF_1 from this inactivation, and their half-effective concentrations were similar to the K_m of Ca^{2+} ATPase, suggesting that at least one of the lysine residues was at the active site of the enzyme. The presence of a functional tryptophan residue in F_1 from *Micrococcus* sp. ATCC398 has also been suggested (Risi *et al.*, 1978); from the correlation between inactivation and modification with *N*-bromosuccinimide, destruction of only about one tryptophan residue seemed to inactivate the enzyme completely. Recently Vignais and co-workers (Pougeois *et al.*, 1979; Satre *et al.*, 1979) have shown that mitochondrial F_1 or EF_1 can be modified with DCCD, which is known to react with a hydrophobic protein in F_0 portion as discussed in Section IV,B. Although F_1 portion is about ten times less sensitive to DCCD than F_0 portion, complete inactivation of mitochondrial F_1-ATPase was observed by the binding of 2 mol of ^{14}C-labeled DCCD to β subunit.

Differential modification of sulfhydryl groups in CF_1 was observed depending on the energy state of the chloroplasts. *N*-Ethylmaleimide reacts with a sulfhydryl group in the γ subunit, causing inhibition of photophosphorylation, and this group is exposed only during illumination (McCarty and Fagan, 1973). Other sulfhydryl reagents, 2,2'-dithiobis(5-nitropyridine) (Andreo and Vallejos, 1976) and iodosobenzoate (Vallejos and Andreo, 1976; Vallejos *et al.*, 1977a,b), inhibited photophosphorylation in the same manner as *N*-ethylmaleimide (Andreo and Vallejos, 1976). The sulfhydryl group exposed in the light can be cross-linked to another sulfhydryl group in the γ subunit (Weiss and McCarty, 1977). The bifunctional maleimide *O*-phenylenedimaleimide cross-links within the γ subunit in CF_1, and this cross-linking alters the conformation in such a way that rapid efflux of H^+ from the thylakoids occurs, resulting in inhibition of photophosphorylation. These results are very interesting in view of the role of the γ subunit in photophosphorylation. Conceivably modification of the sulfhydryl residue caused rapid passage of protons because the residue is involved in an essential conformational change during proton translocation.

2. Affinity Labeling of Subunits

Nucleotide binding sites in F_1 are of interest for elucidation of the mechanism of action of the enzyme complex as already reviewed (Harris, 1977; McCarty, 1978; Baird and Hammes, 1979). Although the catalytic site(s) of F_1 has not been clearly identified by nucleotide binding studies, the use of adenine nucleotide analogs, which inactivate F_1-ATPase by covalent reactions, have demonstrated that nucleotide binding sites on the enzyme are restricted to the α and β subunits.

Dose and collaborators (Hulla et al., 1978; Höckel et al., 1978) used 6-[3-carboxy-3-nitrophenyl)thio]-9-β-D-ribofuranosylpurine 5'-triphosphate to label F_1 from Micrococcus sp.. The analog was not hydrolyzed by F_1-ATPase, but it inhibited the enzyme competitively on short-term incubation and inactivated the enzyme on long-term incubation. The constant analogous to the K_m on long-time inactivation was identical with the K_i value of the competitive inhibition. Tight binding of 6 ± 1 mol of this compound per F_1 was observed, and of these nucleotides about 2 mol were found covalently bound to the β subunit. The two binding sites for 8-azidoadenosine 5'-triphosphate were also found in the β subunit of mitochondrial F_1 (Wagenvoord et al., 1977). On the other hand, Scheurich et al. (1978) found only a single binding site for this analog in Micrococcus sp. F_1 (in one of the β subunits). In both F_1 preparations, labeling and inactivation were decreased in the presence of ADP, ATP, or AMPPNHP. 9-Azidoadenoside 5'-triphosphate predominatly labeled the α subunit of EF_1, although significant label was also found in the β subunit (70% of the radioactivity in α and 30% in β) (Verheijen et al., 1978). N-4-Azido-2-nitrophenylaminobutyryl-2'-ADP labeled both the α and β subunit of mitochondrial F_1, causing inactivation (Lunardi et al., 1977). This nucleotide could photolabel only α subunit, provided that β subunit is protected against photolabeling by the previous modification with NBD-Cl (Lunardi and Vignais, 1979). Full inactivation of ATPase was observed from the binding of the nucleotide by only one α subunit. N-4-Azido-2-nitrophenylaminopropyl 2'-ATP also inactivated ATPase irreversibly (Russel et al., 1976). A correlation between nucleotide binding sites and subunits in CF_1 was also obtained using (azidonitrophenylaminopropionyl adenosine) triphosphate and diphosphate (Carlier, and Hames, 1980). The disphosphate specifically labeled the site from which ADP readily dissociates, identified in the α and β subunits, whereas the triphosphate labeled the site to which ADP bound tightly, identified in the β subunit.

Klein et al. (1977) pointed out that the geometry of the compound used for photolabeling should be carefully considered in interpretation of the results. They pointed out that, for instance, in azidonitrophenylaminobutyryl ADP, the azido group is linked to ADP by an arm of several carbon atoms, and thus the ADP moiety of this compound may bind only to the β subunit of F_1, whereas the azido group at the other end can interact not only with the β subunit, but also with the α subunit; upon photoactivation this would result in covalent photolabeling of both subunits. 8-Azido ATP is less likely to show similar binding, because the azido group is directly linked to the purine ring. Esch and Allison (1978) also concluded that analogs with an azido group may be unsuitable for use in characterization of nucleotide binding sites in primary structural studies. Photoaffinity analogs of ATP may not react with a single amino acid chain, because the aromatic nitrenes generated during illumination of these compounds have a finite lifetime and can react with virtually any amino acid side chain in their vicinity, thus making identification of modified amino acid residues impossible. For identification of the nucleotide binding site Esch and Allison (1978) used ^{14}C-labeled-p-fluorosulfonylbenzoyl-5'-adenosine, which reacts with nucleophilic amino acid side chains. This reagent inactivated mitochondrial F_1-ATPase irreversibly, and the inactivation was partially prevented by adenine nucleotides. After 90% inactivation of F_1-ATPase, the α subunit contained 0.45 mol of the label per mole, and the β subunit contained 0.88 mol. The degree of inactivation of ATPase was well correlated with the number of molecules of reagent incorporated into the β subunit, suggesting that the catalytic site is on this subunit. Only one tryptic peptide (16 amino acid residues) had radioactivity, and tyrosine in this peptide was found to be labeled, in agreement with the results of other studies (Senior, 1973a; Deters et al., 1975; Nelson et al., 1974; Ferguson et al., 1974). Pietro et al. (1979) also studied the kinetics of inactivation of mitochondrial F_1-ATPase by the nucleotide. These and other results show that the β subunit is a catalytic subunit in F_1, although this conclusion requires confirmation.

III. Isolation of Individual Subunits and Reconstitution of F_1

A. SUBUNITS REQUIRED FOR BINDING OF THE ATPASE PORTION OF F_1 TO F_2: δ AND ϵ SUBUNITS

Evidence of the role of the δ subunit was first obtained from study of EF_1. Bragg and Hou (1972) reported that EF_1 has five different subunits with molecular weights essentially similar to those of the subunits of other coupling factors. However, Kobayashi and Anraku (1972, 1974), Hanson and Kennedy (1973), and Nelson et al. (1974) have isolated a soluble enzyme composed of only 4 subunits with no δ subunit. Bragg et al. (1973) reported that the δ subunit was lost when the five-subunit enzyme was subjected to electrophoresis and then reisolated. They showed that the four-subunit enzyme (without δ) was unable to reconstitute ATP-driven transhydrogenase activity in membranes previously depleted of F_1. Futai *et al.* (1974) confirmed that the procedure of Nelson *et al.* (1974) gives a complex of four polypeptides and modified the procedure to obtain a complex consisting of five polypeptides. The four-subunit enzyme and the five-subunit enzyme had the same specific ATPase activity, but they suggested that the complex without the δ subunit cannot bind to membranes depleted of F_1 and is thus unable to reconstitute ATP-dependent transhydrogenase.

Smith and Sternweis (1975, 1977) purified the δ and ε subunits from the five-subunit enzyme after pyridine treatment, a procedure used to isolate subunits from CF_1 (Nelson *et al.*, 1972). In the presence of the purified δ subunit, the four-subunit enzyme could bind to F_0 in membranes previously depleted of F_1. Thus energy-driven reactions (oxidative phosphorylation and ATP-driven transhydrogenase) were restored in the membranes (Smith and Sternweis, 1975). These results suggest that the δ subunit attaches to the four-subunit enzyme, forming a five-subunit enzyme that can restore energy-driven reactions in membranes. The purified δ is a rather elongated molecule (Sternweis and Smith, 1977); its circular dichroism spectrum indicates that it contains 55–70% α-helical structure. The subunit has a molecular weight of about 18,500, as measured by SDS-gel electrophoresis and by sedimentation equilibrium with or without 6 *M* guanidine hydrochloride. The Stoke's radius estimated by gel filtration is about 25Å, whereas the radius calculated assuming that δ is a perfectly spherical molecule is about 18 Å. The elongated shape of the subunit was confirmed by small-angle X-ray scattering (C. H. H. Paradies, private communication).

Essentially similar observations were recently made on CF_1. Younis *et al.* (1977) obtained four-subunit CF_1 by passing five-subunit CF_1 through a DEAE-Sephadex column, and showed that the four-subunit enzyme could not bind to the membrane unless partially purified δ subunit was added. When CF_1 preparations containing various amounts of δ subunits were prepared from the chloroplasts of spinach, pea, and lettuce and their coupling abilities were tested in the presence and absence of pure subunit δ, the results were consistent with the interpretation that subunit δ plays a role in attaching CF_1 to membranes (Nelson and Karny, 1976). The molecular shape of the δ subunit of CF_1 is similar to that of the δ subunit of EF_1 (Schmidt and Paradies, 1977b); physical procedures, including small-angle X-ray scattering, indicated that it is an elongated molecule with a molecular weight of 22,000. On the other hand, the purified ε subunit was shown to be a spherical molecule with a diameter of 32 Å and a molecular weight of 11,900 (Schmidt and Paradies, 1977a).

The following results suggest that the ε subunit, together with the δ subunit, forms a connecting bridge between the active site of F_1 and F_0.

1. Subunits δ and ϵ from a TF_1 could both bind directly to the F_0 portion in liposomes, and both subunits were required for binding of a complex of the major subunits (α, β, γ) that had ATPase activity (Yoshida *et al.*, 1977a,b). The permeability of protons through F_0 was not affected by binding of the δ and ϵ subunits. However, addition of the γ subunit together with δ and ϵ blocked passive proton movement through F_0. From these observations Kagawa proposed that δ and ϵ form a channel for protons and that the γ subunit acts as a gate regulating the passage of protons to the catalytic portion (Kagawa, 1978). Further experiments are required on this interesting model.

2. Both subunits were also required for the binding of the major subunit complex (α, β, γ) from *E. coli* (Sternweis, 1978a; Dunn and Futai, 1979), which can be prepared by passing δ-deficient F_1 through an affinity column containing immobilized antibody against the ϵ subunit (Sternweis, 1978a) or by reconstitution from isolated α, β, and γ subunits (Futai, 1977; Dunn and Futai, 1980). In contrast to the δ and ϵ subunits of TF_1, those of EF_1 bind only poorly to depleted membranes, although they readily associated with the three subunits complex. A sequence of about 20 amino acids from the N terminal of the α subunit is necessary for the binding of the δ subunit to the major subunit assembly, as discussed in Section IIA, suggesting that this sequence interacts with the δ subunit in native F_1.

These results are consistent with the models of F_1 proposed for thermophilic bacteria (Yoshida *et al.*, 1977a) and *E. coli* (Sternweis, 1978b). A modified version of these models is shown in Fig. 1. In these models the δ and ϵ subunits are placed next to the F_0 portion as a connecting bridge for the major subunit assembly.

The function of the δ subunit is similar to that of nectin (Baron and Abrams, 1971), which is required for the attachment of F_1 of *S. faecalis* to the F_0 portion. Nectin appeared to be linked to the enzyme by Mg^{2+} ion, and it was released from the enzyme during gel filtration or DEAE-cellulose chromatography. The weight of nectin (37,000 daltons determined by gel filtration) was about twice that of the δ subunit of this F_1 (20,000 daltons by SDS–gel electrophoresis) (Abrams *et al.*, 1976b), possibly owing to dimerization of the δ subunit in nondissociating conditions. The δ subunit of this bacteria may be an elongated molecule like the δ subunit of EF_1 or CF_1. Because of its elongated shape, δ may have a longer Stoke's radius than expected.

The two minor subunits discussed in this section readily dissociate from F_1. Complexes of two (α, β) or three (α, β, γ) subunits of F_1 can be obtained from *S. faecalis* by a conventional procedure (Abrams, 1976). The ϵ polypeptide was released from five-subunit F_1 of *Microccocus* sp. by electrophoresis on 5% polyacrylamide (Risi *et al.*, 1977), and a complex of three subunits (α, β, γ) could be prepared from the resulting four-subunit F_1 by changing the ionic strength of the buffer and then electrophoresis. The three-subunit complex has also been obtained from yeast F_1 (Douglas et al., 1977) and CF_1 (Nelson et al., 1972).

The ϵ subunit prepared from CF_1 inhibited the ATPase activity of heat-activated CF_1 (Nelson et al., 1972), but not that of the two-subunit (α, β) complex obtained by trypsinization of CF_1 (Deters et al., 1975). These results suggest that the ϵ subunit acts as an inhibitor protein when the three minor subunits (γ, δ, ϵ) are present in CF_1. In chloroplasts, CF_1-catalyzed reactions are not reversible, possibly owing to the tight interaction of CF_1 and the inhibitor protein. It must be noted that more than the stoichiometric amount of the inhibitor is required to obtain more than 80% inhibition: about 2 μg of ϵ caused 80% inhibition of 1.5 μg of CF_1. Smith and Sternweis (1975) isolated the ϵ subunit of EF_1 and confirmed that it inhibited F_1 ATPase. On the other hand, purified ϵ and δ subunits from TF_1 had no inhibitor activity (Yoshida et al., 1977a).

A protein inhibitor of mitochondrial F_1-ATPase has been found in bovine heart (Pullman and Monroy, 1963; Horstman and Racker, 1970), yeast (Landry and Goffean, 1975; Satre et al., 1975; Ebner and Maier, 1977), and rat liver (Pedersen et al., 1974; Chan and Barbour, 1976). Binding of this inhibitor to mitochondrial F_1 is regulated by the ratio of ATP to ADP, the internal pH, and the electron flow (Horstman and Racker, 1970; van de Stadt et al., 1973). Contradictory results have been reported on whether the inhibitor protein is identical with subunit ϵ (Knowles and Penefsky, 1972a,b; Senior and Brooks, 1971). Cintron and Pedersen (1979) purified the inhibitor to homogeneity from rat liver and obtained values for its molecular weight of 12,300 and 14,500 by gel filtration and polyacrylamide gel electrophoresis, respectively. Since these values are significantly higher than that of the smallest polypeptide (ϵ, 7500) obtained from F_1 of this organism (Catterall et al., 1973), the inhibitor may be different from the ϵ subunit.

B. Isolation and Properties of the Major Subunits (α, β, γ) and Reconstitution of F_1

1. Isolation of the Major Subunits (α, β, γ) and Reconstitution of F_1

The three major subunits of F_1 from thermophilic bacteria and E. coli have been isolated in reconstitutively active forms (Yoshida et al., 1977a,b; Futai, 1977; Dunn and Futai, 1980). TF_1 was dissociated with 8 M guanidine-HCl, and pure subunits were obtained by column chromatography on CM- and DEAE-cellulose in the presence of $8 M$ urea (Yoshida *et al.*, 1977b). None of the isolated subunits alone had ATPase activity, but activity was reconstituted by mixing them as discussed below. This isolation procedure is probably applicable only to the very stable enzyme from a thermophilic bacterium, which could be reconstituted even after treatment with 0.7% SDS (Yoshida *et al.*, 1975). We found that this procedure was not suitable for EF_1, mainly because the enzyme dissociated irreversibly in $8 M$ guanidine-HCl (M. Futai, unpublished result).

EF_1 could be dissociated by freeze-thawing in slightly acidic buffer containing a high concentration of salt (Vogel and Steinhart, 1976; Larson and Smith, 1977). The dissociated materials were then partially fractionated. Vogel and Steinhart (1976) obtained three fractions; IA, containing α, γ, and ϵ subunits; IB, containing α, β, γ, and ϵ subunits; and II, containing the β subunit. Larson and Smith (1977) obtained two fractions: an $\alpha\beta$ fraction and a four-subunit fraction (containing threefold excess of γ). Both groups found that the F_1-ATPase activity could be reconstituted by mixing these fractions. These results suggest that at least part of EF_1 can be reversibly dissociated. Futai (1977) dialyzed F_1 overnight in the cold against buffer containing 0.1 M KNO_3 and 1 M KCl, to ensure its complete dissociation into subunits, and then rapidly froze the dialyzate and stored it at $-80°C$. The thawed fraction seemed to be completely dissociated, and practically pure preparations of the major subunits could be obtained by passing batches of the fraction through two different resins: α and β subunits were obtained using a phenyl agarose column, and γ subunits using butyl agarose. For this procedure two batches of dissociated material were required. An alternative procedure was developed using hydroxyapatite and DEAE-cellulose column (Dunn and Futai, 1980). This procedure had the advantages that it was applicable to a single batch of dissociated F_1, and that the chromatographic materials required are available in more standardized forms than the newer hydrophobic resins. The procedure could be used for EF_1, because the dissociated materials did not aggregate during fractionation. Attempts to fractionate cold-dissociated mitochondrial F_1 or CF_1, on a hydrophobic column were unsuccessful (U. Pick and M. Futai, unpublished observation). Conceivably this was due in part to aggregation of the dissociated subunits, because we have detected formation of a visible precipitate even after storage of dissociated material in the cold for a few hours.

Single subunits of either TF_1 or EF_1 had no ATPase activity, but in both cases ATPase could be reconstituted by mixing the subunits. There are some interesting differences between the reconstitutions of TF_1 and EF_1 (Yoshida *et al.*, 1977a,b; Futai, 1977).

1. Mg^{2+} and ATP are required for reconstitution of EF_1, whereas ATP

has no effect on reconstitution of TF_1. Studies on the role of ATP in the reconstitution are in progress. ATP is known to stabilize mesophilic F_1. However, it is not required for the stabilization of the thermophilic F_1 (Yoshida *et al.*, 1975), although conformations of α and β subunits of TF_1 were stabilized with ATP (Ohta *et al.*, 1978). It must be noted that EF_1 has 3 mol of tightly bound nucleotide that cannot be released during purification (Maeda *et al.*, 1976), whereas TF_1 has no nucleotide (Yoshida *et al.*, 1975). The triphosphate moiety of ATP was essential for the reconstitution (Dunn and Futai, 1980). ADP was about 10% as effective as ATP, and AMP was ineffective. Slight activity was obtained with AMPPNHP, whereas α,β- and β,γ-methylene ATP were ineffective. The pyridine nucleoside triphosphate CTP was ineffective, although the purine nucleoside triphosphate ITP was about 70% as effective as ATP.

2. A mixture of the α, β, and γ subunits of EF_1 had high ATPase activity. A mixture of $\beta + \gamma$ and $\alpha + \beta + \delta$ of TF_1 had significant activity, but a similar mixture of subunits of EF_1 had no activity. This result on EF_1 subunits is in apparent disagreement with the finding that the two-subunit complex ($\alpha + \beta$) obtained by trypsin treatment had full ATPase activity (Nelson *et al.*, 1974), but results obtained with specific antiserum indicated that a fragment of the γ polypeptide remained in the two-subunit complex (Smith and Wilkowski, 1978), and so the γ subunit may be required for the correct assembly of the α and β subunits. The requirement of the three subunits for reconstitution enables us to assay these subunits in mutant F_1 as discussed later.

The specific activity of reconstituted *E. coli* ATPase was 30–40 units per milligram protein using the major subunits prepared on hydrophobic columns (Futai, 1977) and 70–100 units per milligram of protein using subunits prepared on hydroxyapatite-DEAE (Dunn and Futai, 1980). The specific activity of the latter preparation was about 170 units per milligram of protein after gel filtration, which is slightly higher than that of native F_1 (90–150 units per milligram of protein) (Nelson *et al.*, 1974; Futai *et al.*, 1974). The reconstituted three-subunit ATPase, supplemented with the δ and ϵ subunits, could restore energy-driven reaction (ATP-dependent transhydrogenase and oxidative phosphorylation) in membranes previously depleted of F_1 (Dunn and Futai, 1980). These results suggest that the native F_1 molecule was formed when the subunits were reconstituted in this way.

The β subunit has been purified in active form from other organisms. Vershoor *et al.* (1977) dissociated mitochondrial F_1 from beef heart by treatment with 0.85 M LiCl at 20°C and fractionated it into β subunits, δ subunits, and a fraction of polypeptides. Douglas *et al.* (1977) found that the crude preparation from yeast contained an excess of apparently unassembled β subunits, presumably formed by degradation of F_1 by endogenous protease, and they purified the β subunit from this fraction. Only the β subunit could be released from chromatophores of *Rhodospirillum rubrum* by washing with 2 M LiCl in the presence of ATP (Philisoph *et al.*, 1977). The LiCl-treated vesicles were not leaky to protons, but showed no ATP synthesis or hydrolysis activities. The released subunit was purified by ammonium sulfate fractionation and gel filtration. Although the pure β had no ATPase activity, it could bind to LiCl-treated vesicles in the presence of Mg^{2+} and ATP. Vesicles reconstituted in this way had ATPase and photophosphorylation activities. The intact F_1 molecule (five subunits) of this organism could be purified from an acetone powder of chromatophores (Melandri and Baccarini-Melandri, 1971).

2. Properties of Isolated Major Subunits

Tightly bound nucleotides have been found in most F_1 preparations studied (Harris, 1977 for review). EF_1 isolated from cells grown in the presence of ^{32}P-labeled phosphate contains about 2 mol of ATP and 1 mol of ADP per enzyme (Maeda *et al.*, 1976). The ability of the isolated subunits of Ef_1 to bind nucleotide was examined by equilibrium dialysis. The α subunit isolated by either of the two methods described in Section III,B,1 bound ATP and ADP (approximately 0.9 mol per mole of α subunit) with K_D values of 0.1 μM and 0.9 μM, respectively (Dunn and Futai, 1980). Each of these nucleotides competed with the binding of the other, and AMPPNHP also inhibited the binding of both ADP and ATP in an apparently competitive manner. These results indicate that the α subunit has a single nucleotide binding site. Binding of nucleotides was optimal at pH 7.0. As EF_1 contains 3 mol of tightly bouhd nucleotide per mole (Maeda *et al.*, 1976), our findings suggest that the three sites on F_1 may all be in α subunits. Because the K_m of the catalytic site is relatively high (200–400 μM: Kobayashi and Anraku, 1972; Hanson and Kennedy, 1973; Futai *et al.*, 1974), it is unlikely that this site could be detected by equilibrium dialysis. Binidng of nucleotides to other subunits could not be detected by equilibrium dialysis. Dunn and Heppel (1980) found that the $s_{20,w}$ of the α subunit changed on addition of 20 μM ATP; the $s_{20,w}$ values of α in the presence and in the absence of ATP were 3.9 and 3.4, respectively. Since ATP does not change the molecular weight of the subunit more than 5%, as determined by sedimentation equilibrium analysis, it presumably changes the conformation of the α subunit.

Binding of nucleotide to isolated subunits of TF_1 has been studied by analyzing the change of the circular dichroism spectrum of nucleotides on binding (Kagawa *et al.*, 1980). The α and β subunits bound both ATP and ADP with approximate K_D values of 10^{-5} M. ITP did not bind to α, but it bound to β with an approximate K_D of 10^{-4} M. The interaction of α, β, and nucleotides have also been studied by examining the deutrium exchange reaction (Ohta *et al.*, 1978). The results suggest that the interaction between α and β subunits influences the nucleotide binding site and conformation of the α subunit. The conformation of the β subunit is also influenced by the α subunit.

Isolated β subunits of F_1 from beef heart (Vershoor *et al.*, 1977), yeast (Douglas *et al.*, 1977), and *E. coli* (Dunn and Futai, 1980) have an aurovertin binding site. Kinetic results are consistent with the presence of one binding site per subunit. The β subunit from an aurovertin-resistant mutant of yeast did not show this capacity (Douglas *et al.*, 1977). An aurovertin-resistant mutant of *E. coli* has been isolated (Satre *et al.*, 1978), although binding of aurovertin to the β subunit of this strain has not yet been studied.

IV. Subunits of the F_0 Portion and Other Factors of the Proton-Translocating ATPase

As discussed in Section I, the entire complex of proton-translocating ATPase consists of two main portions, F_1 and F_0. This section briefly describes recent developments in studies on subunit structure of F_0 and other factors, and leaves details to be described in a future article by R. H. Fillingame in this series.

A. THE ENTIRE PROTON-TRANSLOCATING ATPASE

The complete proton-translocating ATPase complex has been referred to as the oligomycin-sensitive ATPase DCCD-sensitive ATPase, or F_0-F_1. The purification of this complex has been studied for more than 10 years (Kagawa and Racker, 1966; Tzagoloff *et al.*, 1968; Tzagoloff and Meagher, 1971), but reconstitution of vesicles capable of energy transduction from purified components has only recently become possible (Kagawa and Racker, 1971). The first purified preparation of F_1-F_0 capable of reconstituting energy-transducing vesicles was obtained by Kagawa and his collaborators from a thermophilic bacterium PS3 (Sone *et al.*, 1975). Their preparation, called TF_1-TF_0 consisted of eight polypeptides, judging by SDS−polyacrylamide gel electrophoresis—five subunits of F_1 and three polypeptides of F_0. Later it was shown that two polypeptides are sufficient to form functional F_0 (Sone *et al.*, 1978). They suggested that a third protein (19,000 daltons) in F_0 may be similar to oligomycin sensitivity-conferring protein (OSCP) obtained from mitochondria (MacLennan and Tzagoloff, 1968; Senior, 1971). Membrane vesicles formed by dialyzing a mixture of TF_0-TF_1 and phospholipids are capable of synthesizing ATP from ADP and inorganic phosphate with energy from an artificial proton gradient ($\Delta\bar{\mu}H^+$) and an electrical potential (Sone *et al.*, 1977). The reverse gradient is formed by ATP hydrolysis by the vesicles. These studies, together with other results, clearly demonstrate that F_0-F_1 is a reversible H^+-translocating ATPase of oxidative phosphorylation. The TF_0 portion essentially free from TF_1 was separated by treating TF_0-TF_1 with urea (Okamoto *et al.*, 1977). Kagawa and his collaborators concluded that TF_0 carries out the proton translocation in the ATPase.

The TF_0 portion was further purified and found to contain only two polypeptides, band 6 and 8 proteins, identified as TF_1-binding protein (13,500 daltons) and DCCD-binding protein (5400 daltons), respectively. These two proteins were able to form a proton pathway in liposomes, suggesting that they are functionally sufficient as F_0 subunits. Recently an F_0-F_1 complex has been reconstituted from *E. coli* F_0 and F_1 (Fillingame, 1979; Foster and Fillingame, 1979). The preparation gave 8 bands on SDS–polyacrylamide gel electrophoresis.

Rutamycin (or oligomycin)-sensitive ATPase containing only 0–3% contamination with respiratory components was purified from bovine heart mitochondria (Serrano *et al.*, 1976). Vesicles with the function of a reversible ATP-driven proton pump were reconstituted from the purified enzyme, F_1, OSCP, and phospholipids. The ATPase and phospholipids together could also reconstitute vesicles with lower activity. On SDS–polyacrylamide gel electrophoresis the ATPase preparation showed the subunits of F_1, OSCP, three other light bands. The requirements of F_1 and OSCP for reconstitution of the activity may be due to loss of these components during fractionation. The OSCP has been purified as a single protein (18,000 daltons) conferring oligomycin sensitivity on F_1-ATPase (Mac-Lennan and Tzagoloff, 1968; Senior, 1971). Alfonzo and Racker (1979) purified F_0 further and concluded that the minimal composition of mitochondrial proton-translocating ATPase is F_1, OSCP, F_6 (a 9500-dalton membrane protein), DCCD-reactive proteolipid, and a 28,000-dalton subunit. Using a general fractionation procedure for the isolation of respiratory chain complexes I to IV from mitochondria, Hatefi and colleagues obtained a preparation (complex V) capable of the ATP–P_i exchange reaction that was sensitive to DCCD, rutamycin, and uncouplers (Hatefi *et al.*, 1974a,b; Stiggall *et al.*, 1978). Complex V contains five F_1 subunits, OSCP, DCCD-binding protein, and five other major proteins. The F_0 portion was prepared by treating complex V with 3.5 *M* NaBr (Glaser *et al.*, 1977). It consisted of five major polypeptides, including OSCP, F_6, and the DCCD-binding protein. Oligomycin-sensitive ATPase (Glaser *et al.*, 1977) and $P_i \rightleftharpoons HOH$ exchange (Ernster *et al.*, 1977) were reconstituted by incubating the F_1 and F_0 portions together. These studies suggest that mitochondrial proton-translocating ATPase may be more complex in subunit structure than TF_0-TF_1.

B. DCCD-BINDING PROTEINS

DCCD is a relatively specific probe for the F_0 portion. The F_1-ATPase activity is inhibited by DCCD only when F_1 is associated with F_0. Removal of F_1 from F_0 or modification of the interaction of these two portions results in enhanced proton permeability of the membranes. This enhanced flux is blocked by incubation of the membrane with DCCD. DCCD-reactive protein has been detected in a chloroform–methanol extract of mitochondrial membranes (Stekhoven et al., 1972; Cattell et al., 1971). The correlation of this extremely hydrophobic protein with the action on DCCD on the ATPase complex was established by studies in E. coli. The protein was labeled covalently with [^{14}C]DCCD in membranes of wild-type E. coli, but not in those of a mutant that is resistant to the effect of DCCD (Fillingame, 1975). The DCCD-binding protein has been purified to homogeneity in an unmodified or DCCD-bound form from E. coli (Fillingame, 1976), from TF_1-TF_0 (Sone et al., 1979), and from mitochondria of bovine heart (Graf and Sebald, 1978) and Neurospora crassa (Sebald et al., 1979). The polarity of DCCD binding proteins was calculated by the formulation of Capaldi and Venderkooi (1972); the values for preparations from a thermophilic bacterium, E. coli, N. Crassa, and Saccharomyces cerevisiae were 0.29, 0.23, 0.28, and 0.22, respectively, suggesting that these proteins are all extremely hydrophobic (Sone et al., 1979). The DCCD-binding protein is the smallest subunit, with a molecular weight of 6000–9,000 daltons, depending on the sources of the F_0-F_1 complex.

Recently Sebald and collaborators determined the amino acid sequence of the DCCD binding proteins from N. crassa, S. cerevisiae, E. coli, and beef heart (Sebald et al. 1977, 1979; Sebald and Wachter, 1978). From comparison of the primary structures of preparations from N. crassa, S. cerevisiae, and E. coli, Sebald and Wachter (1978) summarized the common features of DCCD-binding proteins as follows: (a) two hydrophobic sequences of about 25 residues; (b) one acidic residue in the center of the second hydrophobic sequences; (c) a central polar loop including two basic and three neutral hydrophilic residues; and (d) a polar N-terminal sequence. The residue to which DCCD binds is in the center of the second hydrophobic sequence; it has been shown to be glutamic acid in the proteins from N. crassa and S. cerevisiae, but aspartic acid in an identical position in E. coli protein. It would be extremely interesting to know how the polypeptide chain is arranged in the membrane.

Recent evidence suggests that the isolated DCCD-binding protein constitutes the proton pathway linking ATP synthesis to proton translocation when reconstituted into membranes. Nelson *et al.* (1977) obtained a homogeneous DCCD-binding protein from lettuce chloroplasts by butanol extraction and precipitation with ether. When reconstituted into liposomes this protein formed a DCCD-sensitive proton channel. A similar protein isolated from proton-translocating ATPase of yeast mitochondria by chloroform–methanol extraction is the oligomycin-sensitive ionophoric component (Criddle *et al.*, 1977). When this protein was prepared from an oligomycin-resistant mutant that has DCCD-binding proteins with altered amino acid sequences (Sone *et al.*, 1977), its ionophoric activity was insensitive to oligomycin.

The isolated proteolipid fraction extracted from TF_0 (Sone *et al.*, 1979) or *E. coli* (Criddle *et al.*, 1977) with chloroform–methanol, however, was inactive in proton translocation in an artificial system. In the thermophilic bacterium, it is highly likely that the proton channel is formed by the DCCD-binding protein in close interaction with an F_1-binding protein (Sone *et al.*, 1978). Modifying reagents, such as acetic anhydride or protease, destroyed the TF_1-binding activity of F_0 but had no effect on H^+ conductivity, suggesting that they had no effect on the DCCD-binding protein. On the other hand, binding of F_1 to the F_1-binding subunit sealed the proton pathway of untreated F_0 vesicles. Probably on oligomer of DCCD-binding proteins forms a pathway. Binding of one-third of the stoichiometric amount of DCCD to the proteolipid was enough to seal the proton pathway of TF_0 (Sone *et al.*, 1979), suggesting that three molecules of the protein constitute one functional proton pathway sensitive to DCCD. Similar results were obtained for other proteolipids (Fillingame, 1976; Altendorf, 1977; Sebald and Wachter, 1978).

V. Genetic Studies on Proton-Translocating ATPase

A. Mutants of *Escherichia coli* with Defects in F_0–F_1

The use of mutants has many advantages in studies on the F_1–F_0 complex. One of the most obvious advantages is that mutants contain polypeptide in which a single amino acid residue is modified. However, careful analysis of the mutation is always required, because in a multicomponent system alteration of a single polypeptide may affect the interactions of other subunits, resulting in a large change of the entire complex. Butlin *et al.* (1971) were the first to report mutants with defects in F_0–F_1. Their mutant AN120 showed no ATPase activity, and they named it *uncA*. They introduced *unc* genes, because the defects in the genes caused uncoupled oxidative phosphorylation. Subsequently, they isolated a series of uncoupled mutants, and in this way identified seven separate genes for F_0-F_1: the genes for the F_1 portion were *uncA* (Butlin *et al.*, 1971), *uncD* (Cox *et al.*, 1978), and *uncG* (Gibson *et al.*, 1979); those for the F_0 portion were *uncB* (Butlin *et al.*, 1973) and *uncE* (Downie *et al.*, 1979), and those unidentified were *uncC* (Gibson *et al.*, 1977) and *uncF* (Gibson *et al.*, 1979). Mutants of F_0-F_1 have also been isolated in other laboratories (Simoni and Schallenberger, 1972; Schairer and Haddock, 1972; Kanner and Gutnick, 1972; Gutnick *et al.*, 1972; Rosen, 1973; Schairer and Gruber, 1973; Yamamoto *et al.*, 1973; Thipayathasana, 1975). These mutants are able to grow on primary fermentable carbon sources, such as glucose or glycerol, but not on carbon sources that yield ATP via oxidative phosphorylation, such as succinate, malate, or lactate. These mutants all have little or no activity of oxidative phosphorylation. Initial findings by this approach have been reviewed (Cox and Gibson, 1974; Simoni and Postma, 1975).

Mutants resistant to inhibitors of the F_1 and F_0 portions have been isolated. Strains whose growth is resistant to DCCD were isolated (Fillingame, 1975; Friedle *et al.*, 1977), and their mutations were found to be closely linked to the *uncA* gene. Mutant RF7 (*dcc*-1) is resistant to DCCD because the reactivity of the DCCD binding protein is decreased, although ATPase coupled to energy transduction is normal (Fillingame, 1975). The mutant cells can derive energy from oxidative phosphorylation in the presence of 5 m*M* DCCD. Mutant DC-1 seems to have a similar defect, because it can carry out the $^{32}P_i$–ATP exchange reaction, but this shows reduced sensitivity to DCCD (Friedle *et al.*, 1977). An aurovertin-resistant mutant of *E. coli* was isolated recently (Satre *et al.*, 1978). Aurovertin inhibits *E. coli* F_1 ATPase as well as photophosphorylation (Lardy *et al.*, 1964; Gromet-Elhanan, 1975) and ATPase (Bertina *et al.*, 1973) in other systems, and thus it prevents the growth of *E. coli* on a nonfermentable carbon source. In aurovertin-resistant mutants energy coupling of ATPase is normal, but the activity is no longer inhibited by aurovertin. Recently Dunn and Futai (1980) showed that the β subunit isolated from wild-type cells can bind aurovertin, suggesting that the aurovertin-resistant mutant has a defect in β subunit.

Assignment of a certain mutation to a specific polypeptide is not an easy problem because F_0-F_1 is a multipolypeptide complex. It is especially difficult to detect a missense mutation in a subunit, but there are three possible methods for this type of analysis. The first is to isolate a nonsense or deletion mutation. Bragg *et al.* (1973) demonstrated that the *etc15* strain (Hong and Kaback, 1972) derived from *E. coli* ML308–225 has a defective γ subunit with an abnormally low molecular weight. Presumably this strain has a deletion or nonsense mutation. A mutant with a similar nonsense or deletion mutation in the F_0 portion has also been obtained (Simoni and Shandell, 1975). The second approach is to use a complementation type assay. As discussed in Section III, ATPase activity of EF_1 can be reconstituted by mixing the α, β, and γ subunits and the entire F_1 molecule can be reconstituted by adding δ and ϵ to the assembly of the three major subunits. Thus *in vitro* complementation assay for mutant F_1 can be established by mixing mutant F_1 (dissociated) and one of the isolated individual subunits from wild-type F_1. This approach was applied to strain AN120 (*uncA401*) (Dunn, 1978; Kanazawa *et al.*, 1978). Reconstitution of ATPase activity was observed when the α subunit from wild-type F_1 was added to the dissociated inactive F_1 and the mixture was dialyzed against buffer containing ATP and Mg^{2+}. The results indicated that the mutant is defective in the α subunit, and that this polypeptide plays an essential role in ATPase activity in the F_1 molecule. Using the same approach, mutation of the β subunit was also identified recently (Kanazawa *et al.*, 1980a). Furthermore, the apparent absence of F_1 in membranes of an uncoupled mutant NR70 (Rosen, 1973) was also confirmed by this method (Kanazawa *et al.*, 1978; Futai and Kanazawa, 1979b). The third approach is to analyze mutant membrane protein by two-dimensional polyacylamide gel electrophoresis (O'Farrell, 1975) to detect alterations in the mobility of subunits. By this approach AN463 (*uncD409*) was shown to have an altered β subunit (Fayle *et al.*, 1978), and results on the *uncA* mutant were confirmed (Senior *et al.*, 1979). However, only mutants with an altered molecular weight or isoelectric point can be detected by this procedure.

Mutation of a single subunit seems to change the assembly properties of the entire F_1 molecule, probably because alteration of a single polypeptide affects its interactions with other subunits. Such alteration is of interest in studying the assembly of this complex molecule. Several examples of this type of alteration have been reported recently. In the *uncD* mutant, the altered β subunit is tightly bound to the membranes (Fayle *et al.*, 1978), while the α subunit was found in the cytoplasm (D. R. H. Fayle, unpublished, but cited in Fayle *et al.*, 1978). Only the α subunit was released from the membrane of DL54 (Simoni and Schallenberger, 1972) by washing with dilute buffer, which releases the entire F_1 complex from wild-type membrane (Futai and Kanazawa, 1979b; Kanazawa and Futai, 1980); other components (β,γ, and ϵ subunits) were demonstrated immunochemically in SDS extract of the membranes, although they could not be released by milder procedures. Recently we found that F_1 from a mutant KF11 (with a defect in the β subunit) dissociates much more easily than wild-type F_1, and that methanol and Mg^{2+} had to be added to stabilize the mutant F_1 (Kanazawa *et al.*, 1980a). Analyses of these mutants are of interest in understanding F_1 and its interaction with F_0.

B. Organization of F_0–F_1 Genes in *Escherichia coli*

As discussed above, Gibson and his collaborators identified seven genes for F_0–F_1. These genes were shown to be independent by *in vivo* genetic complementation using plasmids carrying each *unc* allele of the mutants or wild type. Using a series of mutant *unc* alleles, which were isolated by Mu (mutator) phage mutagenesis, these genes were shown to be components of a single operon (Gibson *et al.*, 1978, 1979; Downie *et al.*, 1979). The Mu phage is inserted randomly into the *E. coli* chromosome and confers strong polarity on distal genes of any operon into which it is inserted (Howe and Bade, 1975). On the basis of this fact, Gibson *et al.* (1979) concluded that *unc* genes are transcribed in the order *unc-BEAFGDC*.

Use of transducing phages has been very helpful in these studies. The approximate position of F_0–F_1 genes in *E. coli* DNA could be determined definitely by this method (Kanazawa *et al.*, 1979), but not by the classic genetic approach alone. It was shown that all the genes of F_0–F_1 are located between *glmS* and *oriC* in *E. coli* DNA, and that the λ*asn* (c*I*857*S*7)

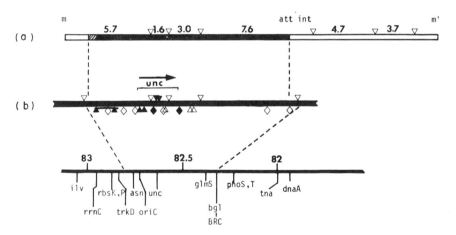

FIG. 2. *Escherichia coli* DNA segment carrying F_0–F_1 genes. (a) λ*asn* DNA. The transducing phage λ*asn-5* carries *E. coli* chromosomal DNA (solid bar) between *asn* and *bglR, C* (Kanazawa *et al.*, 1979). DNA of λ phage is shown by an open bar. The uncertain region of λ phage and *E. coli* DNA is shown by a hatched bar. (b) Segment of *E. Coli* DNA carrying the F_0–F_1 genes. F_0–F_1 (*unc*) genes are shown between *glmS* and *oriC*, and the direction of transcription is shown by an arrow. The approximate positions of other genes are also shown: *tna*, tryptophanase; *bglC*, β-glucoside transporter; *bglR*, regulatory gene for *bgl* operon; *glmS*, L-glutamine:D-fructose-6-phosphate aminotransferase; *oriC*, origin of replication of DNA; *asn*, asparagine synthetase; *ilv*, isoleucine valine operon. The cleavage sites of restriction endonucleases are shown: EcoR1, ▽; BamHI, ▲; Hind III, ◇; Bgl 1, ◆; Hpa 1, ▼; Pst 1, △. The sites for Bgl 1, Hpa 1, and Pst 1 were determined only in fragments of 1.6×10^6 and 3.0×10^6 daltons. Numbers show weights of EcoR1 fragments in 10^6 daltons.

phage carrying this portion (Fig. 2) could complement all the mutations tested [14 strains isolated in our laboratory; AN120 (*uncA*; Butlin *et al.*, 1971), AN382 (*uncB*; Butlin *et al.*, 1973)]. Furthermore, when a logarithmic phase culture of the lysogen of this phage grown at 30°C was shifted to 42°C to induce phage replication by inactivating the temperature-sensitive repressor, F_1-ATPase in the membranes, F_1 binding sites, and DCCD-sensitive proton pathway increased in propotion to increase in DNA of the F_0–F_1 portion. We have isolated a series of λ phages carrying different portions of chromosomal DNA from *glmS* to *asn*. From genetic and biochemical analyses of these phages we concluded that F_0–F_1 genes are in the region shown in Fig. 2 (Kanazawa *et al.*, 1980b). The lysogens of λ phage carrying this region showed essentially the same properties as λ*asn* lysogen. From our results and those of Gibson's laboratory, we conclude that the direction of transcription is from the *asn* side of the *unc* gene to the *glmS* side of the genes, as shown by an arrow in Fig. 2b. These studies suggest that it will now possible to determine the nucleotide sequence of DNA of the F_0–F_1 genes. Recent improvements in the method for nucleotide sequencing (Maxam and Gilbert, 1977) have made it possible to determine the sequence of DNA much more easily than that of amino acids in proteins. In a few years we may be able to discuss the function of F_0–F_1 depending on the amino acid sequence derived from the DNA sequence. It may also be possible to study the synthesis and assembly of F_0–F_1 *in vitro* using this DNA.

This review does not cover studies on mutants of eukaryotes, such as yeast or *Neurospora crassa*, which are discussed in recent review articles (Kovač, 1974; Sebald, 1977).

VI. Conclusion

This review covers studies on the role of subunits of the F_0–F_1 complex and their *in vitro* assembly into functional proton-translocating ATPase. The essential features of the complexes found in the inner membranes of mitochondria and in the plasma membranes of bacteria are similar. From the reports discussed in the review, it is possible to draw the following conclusions on the function(s) of each subunit and the structure of the entire F_0–F_1 complex. Subunit β is the catalytic site of F_1. The α subunit may be a regulatory polypeptide because it binds ATP or ADP tightly. The correct interaction of the α and β seems to be essential for formation of the catalytic site. Both subunits are located in the spherical head position of F_1 (Fig. 1). The γ polypeptide binds to the $\alpha + \beta$ structure or assembles with the two subunits in the head portion. This head portion is connected to F_0 by the two low molecular weight polypeptides, δ and ϵ. Protons come from F_0, possibly passing through the space between the δ and ϵ subunits. The γ subunit somehow regulates the proton flow, as shown from studies on TF_1 and CF_1, and γ, δ, and ϵ together may form a gate for protons, as suggested by Kagawa (1978). Details of the F_0 portion are still unknown, but we already know that two functional proteins exist in this portion, DCCD-binding protein and F_1-binding protein. In more recently initiated studies on *E. coli,* mutations in α, β, and γ subunits of F_1 and DCCD-binding protein of F_0 have been identified by reconstitution assay, inhibitor binding, and other procedures. The segment of DNA carrying the F_0–F_1 genes has been identified. Further studies on this organism by techniques of molecular biology should contribute greatly to our understanding of the function and assembly of F_0–F_1.

The central question, How, at the molecular level, does proton-translocating ATPase utilize a proton gradient for ATP synthesis?, has not yet been fully answered. In this connection we have regretfully to admit that a sentence on the last page of a stimulating review article by F. Harold still holds true: "In bioenergetics, as in other fields of science, problems are not solved so much as transformed" (Harold, 1977).

ACKNOWLEDGMENTS

We are grateful to all who sent preprints and useful suggestions, in particular to Drs. A. Abrams, P. D. Bragg, K. Dose, R. D. Fillingame, F. Gibson, Y. Hatefi, G. Hammes, A. T. Jagendorf, R. McCarty, P. L. Pedersen, and W. Sebald. We also wish to thank Drs. L. A. Heppel, S. D. Dunn, and Y. Kagawa for critical reading of the manuscript and for allowing us to cite their unpublished results. We wish to thank Ms. Elizabeth Ichihara for correcting the English and Ms. Michiko Ohtaki for patient typing. The work in authors' laboratory cited in this review was supported by grants from the Ministry of Education, Science, and Culture of Japan and the Naito Foundation.

REFERENCES

Abrams, A. (1976). *In* "The Enzymes of Biological Membranes" (A. Martonosi, ed.), Vol. 3, pp. 57–73. Plenum, New York.

Abrams, A., Morris, D., and Jensen, C. (1976a). *Biochemistry* **15,** 5560–5566.

Abrams, A., Jensen, C., and Morris, D. (1976b). *Biochem. Biophys. Res. Commun.* **69,** 804–811.

Alfonzo, M., and Racker, E. (1979). *Fed. Proc., Fed. Am. Soc. Exp. Biol.* **38,** 455.

Altendorf, K. (1977). *FEBS Lett.* **73,** 271–275.

Amzel, M., and Pedersen, P. L. (1978). *J. Biol. Chem.* **253,** 2057–2069.

Andreo, C. S., and Vallejos, R. H. (1976). *Biochim. Biophys. Acta* **423,** 590–601.

Andreo, C. S., and Vallejos, R. H. (1977). *FEBS Lett.* **78,** 207–210.

Baird, B. A., and Hammes, G. G. (1976). *J. Biol. Chem.* **251,** 6953–6962.

Baird, B. A., and Hammes, G. G. (1977). *J. Biol. Chem.* **252,** 4743–4748.

Baird, B. A., and Hammes, G. G. (1979). *Biochim. Biophys. Acta* **549,** 31–53.

Baird, B. A., Pick, U., and Hammes, G. G. (1979). *J. Biol. Chem.* **254**, 3818–3825.
Baron, C., and Abrams, A. (1971). *J. Biol. Chem.* **246**, 1542–1544.
Bertina, R. M., Schrier, P. I., and Slater, E. C. (1973). *Biochim. Biophys. Acta* **305**, 503–518.
Binder, A., Jagendorf, A. T., and Ngo, E. (1978). *J. Biol. Chem.* **253**, 3094–3100.
Boyer, P. D., Chance, B., Ernster, S., Mitchell, P., Racker, E., and Slater, E. C. (1977). *Annu. Rev. Biochem.* **46**, 955–1026.
Bragg, P. D., and Hou, C. (1972). *FEBS Lett.* **28**, 309–312.
Bragg, P. D., and Hou, C. (1975). *Arch. Biochem. Biophys.* **167**, 311–321.
Bragg, P. D., Davies, P. L., and Hou, C. (1973). *Arch. Biochem. Biophys.* **159**, 664–670.
Butlin, J. D., Cox, G. B., and Gibson, F. (1971). *Biochem. J.* **124**, 75–81.
Butlin, J. D., Cox, G. B., and Gibson, F. (1973). *Biochim. Biophys. Acta* **292**, 366–375.
Cantley, L. C., Jr., and Hammes, G. G. (1975a). *Biochemistry* **14**, 2968–2975.
Cantley, L. C., Jr., and Hammes, G. G. (1975b). *Biochemistry* **14**, 2976–2981.
Capaldi, R. A., and Vanderkooi, G. (1972). *Proc. Natl. Acad. Sci. U.S.A.* **69**, 930–932.
Carlier, M. F., and Hammes, G. G. (1980). In preparation (cited in Baird and Hammes, 1979).
Cattell, K. J., Lindop, C. R., Knight, I. G., and Beechey, R. B. (1971). *Biochem. J.* **125**, 169–177.
Catterall, W. A., Coty, W. A., and Pedersen, P. L. (1973). *J. Biol. Chem.* **248**, 7427–7431.
Chan, S. H. P., and Barbour, R. L. (1976). *J. Supramol. Struct.* **8**, 111–117.
Cintron, B. M., and Pedersen, P. L. (1979). *J. Biol. Chem.* **254**, 3439–3443.
Cox, G. B., and Gibson, F. (1974). *Biochim. Biophys. Acta* **346**, 1–26.
Cox, G. B., Downie, J. A., Gibson, F., and Radik, J. (1978). *Biochem. J.* **170**, 593–598.
Criddle, R. S., Packer, L., and Smith, P. (1977). *Proc. Natl. Acad. Sci. U.S.A.* **74**, 4306–4310.
Deters, D. W., Racker, E., Nelson, N., and Nelson, H. (1975). *J. Biol. Chem.* **250**, 1041–1047.
Douglas, M. G., Koh, Y., Dockter, M. E., and Schatz, G. (1977). *J. Biol. Chem.* **252**, 8333–8335.
Downie, J. A., Senior, A. E., Gibson, F., and Cox, G. B. (1979). *J. Bacteriol.* **137**, 711–718.
Dunn, S. D. (1978). *Biochem. Biophys. Res. Commun.* **82**, 596–602.
Dunn, S. D., and Futai, M. (1980). *J. Biol. Chem.* **255**, 113–118.
Dunn, S. D., and Heppel, L. A. (1979). *Fed. Proc., Fed. Am. Soc. Exp. Biol.* **38**, 455.
Dunn, S. D., and Heppel, L. A. (1980). In preparation.
Ebner, E., and Maier, K. L. (1977). *J. Biol. Chem.* **252**, 671–676.
Ernster, L., Carlsson, C., and Boyer, P. D. (1977). *FEBS Lett.* **84**, 283–286.
Esch, F. S., and Allison, W. S. (1978). *J. Biol. Chem.* **253**, 6100–6106.
Fayle, D. R. H., Donwnie, J. A., Cox, G. B., Gibson, F., and Radik, J. (1978). *Biochem. J.* **172**, 523–531.
Ferguson, S. J., Lloyd, W. J., and Radda, G. K. (1974). *FEBS Lett.* **38**, 234–236.
Fillingame, R. H. (1975). *J. Bacteriol.* **124**, 870–883.
Fillingame, R. H. (1976). *J. Biol. Chem.* **251**, 6630–6637.
Fillingame, R. H. (1979). *Fed. Proc., Fed. Am. Soc. Exp. Biol.* **38**, 455.
Fillingame, R. H. (1980). *Curr. Top. Bioenerg.* **11** (in preparation).
Foster, D. L., and Fillingame, R. H. (1979). *J. Biol. Chem.* **254**, 8230–8236.
Friedle, P., Schmid, B. I., and Schairer, H. U. (1977). *Eur. J. Biochem.* **23**, 3461–3468.
Frigeri, L., Galante, Y. M., Hanstein, W. G., and Hatefi, Y. (1977). *J. Biol. Chem.* **252**, 3147–3152.
Frigeri, L., Galante, Y. M., and Hatefi, Y. (1978). *J. Biol. Chem.* **253**, 8935–8940.
Futai, M. (1977). *Biochem. Biophys. Res. Commun.* **79**, 1231–1237.

Futai, M., and Kanazawa, H. (1979a). *Fed. Proc., Fed. Am. Soc. Exp. Biol.* **38**, 455.

Futai, M., and Kanazawa, H. (1979b). *In* "Cation Flux Across Biomembranes" (L. Packer and Y. Mukohata, eds.), pp. 291–298. Academic Press, New York.

Futai, M., Sternweis, P. C., and Heppel, L. A. (1974). *Proc. Natl. Acad. Sci. U.S.A.* **71**, 2725–2729.

Garber, M. P., and Steponkus, P. L. (1974). *J. Cell Biol.* **63**, 24–34.

Gibson, F., Cox, G. B., Downie, J. A., and Radik, J. (1977). *Biochem. J.* **164**, 193–198.

Gibson, F., Downie, J. A., Cox, G. B., and Radik, J. (1978). *J. Bacteriol.* **134**, 724–736.

Gibson, F., Cox, G. B., Downie, J. A., and Senior, A. E. (1979). *Fed. Proc., Fed. Am. Soc. Exp. Biol.* **38**, 455.

Glaser, E., Norling, B., and Ernster, L. (1977). *In* "Bioenergetics of Membranes" (L. Packer, ed.), pp. 513–526. Elsevier/North-Holland Biomedical Press, Amsterdam.

Graf, T., and Sebald, W. (1978). *FEBS Lett.* **94**, 218–222.

Gregory, P., and Racker, E. (1973). *Abstr. Int. Congr. Biochem. 9th, 1973,* Abstract, p. 238.

Gromet-Elhanan, Z. (1975). *Proc. Congr. Photosynth. Res., 3rd, 1974* pp. 791–794.

Gutnick, D. C., Kanner, B. I., and Postma, P. W. (1972). *Biochim. Biophys. Acta* **283**, 217–222.

Haddock, B. A., and Jones, C. W. (1977). *Bacteriol. Rev.* **41**, 47–99.

Hanson, R. L., and Kennedy, E. P. (1973). *J. Bacteriol.* **114**, 772–781.

Harold, F. M. (1977). *Curr. Top. Bioenerg.* **6**, 83–149.

Harris, D. A. (1978). *Biochim. Biophys. Acta* **463**, 245–273.

Hatefi, Y., Stiggall, D. L., Galante, Y., and Hanstein, W. G. (1974a). *Biochem. Biophys. Res. Commun.* **61**, 313–321.

Hatefi, Y., Hanstein, W. G., Galante, Y., and Stiggall, D. (1974b). *Fed. Proc., Fed. Am. Soc. Exp. Biol.* **34**, 1699–1706.

Hinkle, P. C., and McCarty, R. E. (1978). *Sci. Am.* **238**, 104–123.

Höckel, M., Hulla, F. W., Risi, S., and Dose, K. (1976). *Biochim. Biophys. Acta* **429**, 1020–1080.

Höckel, M., Hulla, F. W., Risi, S., and Dose, K. (1978). *J. Biol. Chem.* **253**, 4292–4296.

Holowska, D. A., and Hammes, G. G. (1977). *Biochemistry* **16**, 5538–5545.

Hong, J. S., and Kaback, H. R. (1972). *Proc. Natl. Acad. Sci. U.S.A.* **69**, 3336–3340.

Horstman, L. L., and Racker, E. (1970). *J. Biol. Chem.* **245**, 1336–1344.

Howe, M. M., and Bade, E. G. (1975). *Science* **190**, 624–632.

Howell, S. H., and Moudrianakis, E. M. (1967). *Proc. Natl. Acad. Sci. U.S.A.* **58**, 1261–1268.

Hulla, F. W., Hockel, M., Rack, M., Risi, S., and Dose, K. (1978). *Biochemistry* **17**, 823–828.

Kagawa, Y. (1978). *Biochim. Biophys. Acta* **505**, 45–93.

Kagawa, Y., and Racker, E. (1966). *J. Biol. Chem.* **241**, 2475–2482.

Kagawa, Y., and Racker, E. (1971). *J. Biol. Chem.* **246**, 5477–5487.

Kagawa, Y., Sone, N., Yoshida, M., Hirata, H., and Okamoto, H. (1976). *J. Biochem. (Tokyo)* **80**, 141–151.

Kagawa, Y., Sone, N., Hirata, H., and Yoshida, M. (1979). *Trends Biochem. Sci.* **4**, 31–33.

Kagawa, Y., Ohta, S., Yoshida, M. K., and Sone, N. (1980). *Ann. N.Y. Acad. Sci.* (in press).

Kanazawa, H., and Futai, M. (1980). *FEBS Lett.* **109**, 104–106.

Kanazawa, H., Saito, S., and Futai, M. (1978). *J. Biochem. (Tokyo)* **84**, 1513–1517.

Kanazawa, H., Miki, T., Tamura, F., Yura, T., and Futai, M. (1979). *Proc. Natl. Acad. Sci. U.S.A.* **76**, 1126–1130.

Kanazawa, H., Horiuchi, M., Takagi, M., Ishino, Y., and Futai, M. (1980a). *J. Biochem. (Tokyo)* (in press).

Kanazawa, H., Tamura, F., Mabuchi, K., Miki, T., and Futai, M. (1980b). In preparation.
Kanner, B. I., and Gutnick, D. L. (1972). *J. Bacteriol.* **111**, 287–289.
Klein, G., Sunardi, J., Satre, M., Lauguin, G. J. M., and Vignais, P. V. (1977). *In* "Structure and Function of Energy-Transducing Membranes" (K. Van Dam and B. F. van Gelder, eds.), pp. 283–294. Elsevier/North-Holland Biomedical Press, Amsterdam.
Knowles, A. F., and Penefsky, H. S. (1972a). *J. Biol. Chem.* **247**, 6617–6623.
Knowles, A. F., and Penefsky, H. S. (1972b). *J. Biol. Chem.* **247**, 6624–6630.
Kobayashi, H., and Anraku, Y. (1972). *J. Biochem. (Tokyo)* **71**, 387–399.
Kobayashi, H., and Anraku, Y. (1974). *J. Biochem. (Tokyo)* **76**, 1175–1182.
Kovač, L. (1974). *Biochim. Biophys. Acta* **346**, 101–135.
Kozlov, I. A., and Mikelsaar, H. N. (1974). *FEBS Lett.* **43**, 212–214.
Kozlov, I. A., and Skulachev, V. P. (1977). *Biochim. Biophys. Acta* **563**, 29–89.
Landry, Y., and Goffean, A. (1975). *Biochim. Biophys. Acta* **376**, 470–484.
Lardy, H. A., Connelly, J. L., and Johnson, D. (1964). *Biochemistry* **3**, 1961–1968.
Larson, R. J., and Smith, J. B. (1977). *Biochemistry* **16**, 4266–4270.
Lien, S., and Racker, E. (1971). *J. Biol. Chem.* **246**, 4298–4307.
Lunardi, J., and Vignais, P. V. (1979). *FEBS Lett.* **102**, 23–28.
Lunardi, J., Lauguin, G. J. M., and Vignais, P. V. (1977). *FEBS Lett.* **80**, 317–323.
McCarty, R. E. (1978). *Curr. Top. Bioenerg.* **7**, 245–278.
McCarty, R. E., and Fagan, J. (1973). *Biochemistry* **12**, 1503–1507.
MacLennan, D. H., and Tzagoloff, A. (1968). *Biochemistry* **7**, 1603–1610.
Maeda, M., Kobayashi, H., Futai, M., and Anraku, Y. (1976). *Biochem. Biophys. Res. Commun.* **70**, 228–234.
Marcus, F., Schuster, S. M., and Lardy, H. A. (1976). *J. Biol. Chem.* **251**, 1775–1780.
Maxam, A. M., and Gilbert, W. (1977). *Proc. Natl. Acad. Sci. U.S.A.* **74**, 560–564.
Melandri, B. A., and Baccarini-Melandri, A. (1971). *In* "Methods in Enzymology" (A. S. Pietro, ed.), Vol. 23, Part A, pp. 556–561. Academic Press, New York.
Miller, K. R., and Staehelin, L. A. (1976). *J. Cell Biol.* **68**, 30–47.
Mirsky, R., and Barlow, V. (1973). *Biochim. Biophys. Acta* **291**, 480–488.
Mitchell, P. (1961). *Nature (London)* **191**, 144–149.
Mukohata, Y., Nakabayashi, S., and Higashida, M. (1978). *FEBS Lett.* **85**, 215–218.
Nelson, N. (1976). *Biochim. Biophys. Acta* **456**, 314–338.
Nelson, N., and Karny, O. (1976). *FEBS Lett.* **70**, 249–253.
Nelson, N., Nelson, H., and Racker, E. (1972). *J. Biol. Chem.* **247**, 7657–7662.
Nelson, N., Deters, D. W., Nelson, H., and Racker, E. (1973). *J. Biol. Chem.* **248**, 1049–2055.
Nelson, N., Kanner, B. I., and Gutnick, D. L. (1974). *Proc. Natl. Acad. Sci. U.S.A.* **71**, 2720–2724.
Nelson, N., Eytan, E., Notsani, B., Sigrist, H., Sigrist-Nelson, K., and Gitler, C. (1977). *Proc. Natl. Acad. Sci. U.S.A.* **74**, 2375–2378.
O'Farrell, P. H. (1975). *J. Biol. Chem.* **250**, 4007–4021.
Ohta, S., Nakanishi, M., Tuboi, M., Yoshida, M., and Kagawa, Y. (1978). *Biochem. Biophys. Res. Commun.* **80**, 929–935.
Okamoto, H., Sone, N., Hirata, H., Yoshida, M., and Kagawa, Y. (1977). *J. Biol. Chem.* **252**, 6125–6131.
Oleszko, S., and Moudrianakis, E. N. (1974). *J. Cell Biol.* **63**, 936–943.
Panet, R. P., and Sanadi, D. R. (1976). *Curr. Top. Membr. Transp.* **8**, 99–160.
Pedersen, P. L. (1975). *Bioenergetics* **6**, 243–275.
Pedersen, P. L., Levine, H., and Cintron, N. M. (1974). *In* "Membrane Proteins in Trans-

port and Phosphorylation'' (G. F. Azzone, M. Klingenberg, E. Quagliariello, and N. Siliprandi, eds.), pp. 43–54. Elsevier, Amsterdam.

Philosoph, S., Binder, A., and Gromet-Elhanan, Z. (1977). *J. Biol. Chem.* **252**, 8747–8752.

Pietro, A. D., Godinot, C., Martin, J., and Gautheron, D. C. (1979). *Biochemistry* **18**, 1738–1745.

Pougeois, R., Satre, M., and Vignais, P. V. (1979). *Biochemistry* **18**, 1408–1413.

Pullman, M. E., and Monroy, G. C. (1963). *J. Biol. Chem.* **238**, 3762–3769.

Racker, E. (1969). *J. Gen. Physiol.* **54**, 385–495.

Racker, E. (1976). ''A New Look at Mechanisms in Bioenergetics.'' Academic Press, New York.

Risi, S., Höckel, M., Hulla, F. W., and Dose, K. (1977). *Eur. J. Biochem.* **81**, 103–109.

Risi, S., Schröder, C., Kraiser, H.-J., Carreira, J., and Dose, K. (1978). *Hoppe-Seyler's Z. Physiol. Chem.* **359**, 37–45.

Rosen, B. P. (1973). *J. Bacteriol.* **116**, 1124–1129.

Russel, J., Jeng, S. J., and Guillory, R. J. (1976). *Biochem. Biophys. Res. Commun.* **70**, 1225–1234.

Ryrie, I. J., and Jagendorf, A. T. (1971). *J. Biol. Chem.* **246**, 3771–3774.

Ryrie, I. J., and Jagendorf, A. T. (1972). *J. Biol. Chem.* **247**, 4453–4459.

Salton, M. R. J., and Schor, M. T. (1974). *Biochim. Biophys. Acta* **345**, 74–82.

Satre, M., de Jerphanion, M. B., Huet, J., and Vignais, P. V. (1975). *Biochim. Biophys. Acta* **387**, 241–255.

Satre, M., Klein, G., and Vignais, P. V. (1978). *J. Bacteriol.* **134**, 17–34.

Satre, M., Lunardi, J., Pougeois, R., and Vignais, P. V. (1979). *Biochemistry* **18**, 3134–3140.

Schairer, H. U., and Gruber, D. (1973). *Eur. J. Biochem.* **37**, 282–286.

Schairer, H. U., and Haddock, B. A. (1972). *Biochem. Biophys. Res. Commun.* **48**, 544–551.

Scheurich, P., Schäfer, H.-J., and Dose, K. (1978). *Eur. J. Biochem.* **88**, 253–257.

Schmid, R., Jagendorf, A. T., and Hulkower, S. (1977). *Biochim. Biophys. Acta* **462**, 177–186.

Schmidt, U. D., and Paradies, H. H. (1977a). *Biochem. Biophys. Res. Commun.* **78**, 383–390.

Schmidt, U. D., and Paradies, H. H. (1977b). *Biochem. Biophys. Res. Commun.* **78**, 1043–1052.

Sebald, W. (1977). *Biochim. Biophys. Acta* **463**, 1–27.

Sebald, W., Hoppe, J., and Wachter, E. (1979). In ''Function and Molecular Aspects of Biomembrane Transport'' (E. Quagliaviello ed.), pp. 63–74. Elsevier/North-Holland, Amsterdam and New York.

Sebald, W., and Wachter, E. (1978). *In* ''Energy Conservation in Biological Membranes'' (G. Schäfer and M. Klingenberg, eds.), 29th Mosbacher Colloq., pp. 228–236. Spring-Verlag, Berlin and New York.

Sebald, W., Sebald-Althaus, M., and Wachter, E. (1977). *In* ''Genetics and Bioenergetics of Mitochondria'' (W. Bandlow, R. J. Schweyen, K. Wolf, and F. Kaudewitz, eds), pp. 433–440. de Gruyter, Berlin.

Sebald, W., Graf, T., and Lukins, H. B. (1979). *Eur. J. Biochem.* **93**, 587–599.

Senior, A. E. (1971). *J. Bioenerg.* **2**, 141–150.

Senior, A. E. (1973a). *Biochemistry* **12**, 3622–3627.

Senior, A. E. (1973b). *Biochim. Biophys. Acta* **301**, 249–277.

Senior, A. E. (1975). *Biochemistry* **14**, 660–664.

Senior, A. E., and Brooks, J. C. (1971). *FEBS Lett.* **17**, 327–329.

Senior, A. E., Downie, J. A., Cox, G. B., Gibson, F., Langman, L., and Fayle, D. R. H. (1979). *Biochem. J.* **180**, 103–109.

Serrano, R., Kanner, B. I., and Racker, E. (1976). *J. Biol. Chem.* **251**, 2453–2461.

Simoni, R. D., and Schallenberger, M. K. (1972). *Proc. Natl. Acad. Sci. U.S.A.* **68**, 2663–2667.

Simoni, R. E., and Postma, P. W. (1975). *Annu. Rev. Biochem.* **44**, 523–554.

Simoni, R. E., and Shandell, A. (1975). *J. Biol. Chem.* **250**, 9421–9427.

Smith, J. B., and Sternweis, P. C. (1975). *Biochem. Biophys. Res. Commun.* **62**, 764–771.

Smith, J. B., and Sternweis, P. C. (1977). *Biochemistry* **16**, 306–311.

Smith, J. B., and Wilkowski, C. (1978). *Fed. Proc., Fed. Am. Soc. Exp. Biol.* **37**, 1521.

Sone, N., Yoshida, M., Hirata, H., and Kagawa, Y. (1975). *J. Biol. Chem.* **250**, 7917–7923.

Sone, N., Yoshida, M., Hirata, H., and Kagawa, Y. (1977). *J. Biol. Chem.* **252**, 2959–2960.

Sone, N., Yoshida, M., Hirata, H., and Kagawa, Y. (1978). *Proc. Natl. Acad. Sci. U.S.A.* **75**, 4219–4223.

Sone, N., Yoshida, M., Hirata, H., and Kagawa, Y. (1979). *J. Biochem. (Tokyo)* **85**, 503–509.

Spitsberg, V., and Haworth, R. (1977). *Biochim. Biophys. Acta* **492**, 237–240.

Stekhoven, F. S., Waitkus, R. F., and van Moerkerk, H. T. B. (1972). *Biochemistry* **11**, 1144–1150.

Sternweis, P. C. and Smith, J. B. (1977). *Biochemistry* **16**, 4030–4025.

Sternweis, P. C. (1978a). *J. Biol. Chem.* **253**, 3123–3128.

Sternweis, P. C. (1978b). Ph.D. Thesis, Section of Biochemistry, Molecular and Cell Biology, Cornell University, Ithaca, New York.

Stiggall, D. L., Galante, Y. M., and Hatefi, Y. (1978). *J. Biol. Chem.* **253**, 956–964.

Sugiyama, Y., and Mukohata, Y. (1978). *FEBS Lett.* **85**, 211–214.

Sugiyama, Y., and Mukohata, Y. (1979). *FEBS Lett.* **98**, 276–280.

Telford, J. N., and Racker, E. (1973). *J. Cell Biol.* **57**, 580–586.

Thipayathasana, P. (1975). *Biochim. Biophys. Acta* **408**, 47–57.

Tzagoloff, A., and Meagher, P. (1971). *J. Biol. Chem.* **246**, 7328–7336.

Tzagoloff, A., Byington, K. H., and MacLennan, D. H. (1968). *J. Biol. Chem.* **243**, 2405–2412.

Vallejos, R. H., and Andreo, C. S. (1976). *FEBS Lett.* **61**, 95–99.

Vallejos, R. H., Ravizzini, R. A., and Andreo, C. S. (1977a). *Biochim. Biophys. Acta* **459**, 20–26.

Vallejos, R. H., Viale, A., and Andreo, C. S. (1977b). *FEBS Lett.* **84**, 304–308.

Vallejos, R. H., Lescano, W. I. M., and Lucero, J. A. (1978). *Arch. Biochem. Biophys.* **190**, 578–584.

van de Stadt, R. J., DeBoer, B. L., and Van Dam, K. (1973). *Biochim. Biophys. Acta* **292**, 338–349.

Verheijen, J. H., Postma, P. W., and Van Dam, K. (1978). *Biochim. Biophys. Acta* **502**, 345–353.

Vershoor, G. J., van der Sluis, P. R., and Slater, E. C. (1977). *Biochim. Biophys. Acta* **462**, 438–449.

Vogel, G., and Steinhart, R. (1976). *Biochemistry* **15**, 208–216.

Wagenvoord, R. J., van der Kraan, I., and Kemp, A. (1977). *Biochim. Biophys. Acta* **460**, 17–24.

Wakabayashi, T., Kubota, M., Yoshida, M., and Kagawa, Y. (1977). *J. Mol. Biol.* **117**, 515–519.

Weiss, M. A., and McCarty, R. E. (1977). *J. Biol. Chem.* **252**, 8007–8012.

Wilson, D. B., and Smith, J. B. (1978). *In* "Bacterial Transport" (B. P. Rosen, ed.), pp. 495–557. Dekker, New York.

Yamamoto, T. H., Mevel-Ninio, M., and Valentine, R. C. (1973). *Biochim. Biophys. Acta* **314,** 267–275.

Yamato, I., Futai, M., Anraku, Y., and Nonomura, Y. (1978). *J. Biochem. (Tokyo)* **83,** 117–128.

Yoshida, M., Sone, N., Hirata, H., and Kagawa, Y. (1975). *J. Biol. Chem.* **250,** 7910–7916.

Yoshida, M., Okamoto, H., Sone, N., Hirata, H., and Kagawa, Y. (1977a). *Proc. Natl. Acad. Sci. U. S. A.* **74,** 936–940.

Yoshida, M., Sone, N. Hirata, H., and Kagawa, Y. (1977b). *J. Biol. Chem.* **252,** 3480–3485.

Yoshida, M., Sone, N., Hirata, H., and Kagawa, Y. (1978). *Biochem. Biophys. Res. Commun.* **84,** 117–122.

Yoshida, M., Sone, N., Hirata, H., Kagawa, Y., and Ui, N. (1979). *J. Biol. Chem.* **254,** 9525–9533.

Younis, H., Winget, G. D., and Racker, E. (1977). *J. Biol. Chem.* **252,** 1814–1818.

Control of Mitochondrial Substrate Oxidation

RICHARD G. HANSFORD

Laboratory of Molecular Aging
Gerontology Research Center
National Institute on Aging
National Institutes of Health
Baltimore City Hospitals
Baltimore, Maryland

I. Introduction

This review is mainly concerned with the control of dehydrogenase activity. The enzymes chosen for discussion include the pyruvate dehydrogenase complex and some of the enzymes of the tricarboxylate cycle. As far as this review is concerned their most important characteristics are that they catalyze nonequilibrium reactions, and thus exert a dominant influence over the flux through pathways central to catabolic metabolism, and that they are mitochondrial. This localization means that the supply of substrate, and dissipation of product, may be limited by the permeability properties of the inner mitochondrial membrane. It also means, since these enzymes are dehydrogenases, that the final arbiter of their activity is the respiratory chain, with its normally obligatory coupling to the phosphorylation of ADP. Because of the overriding importance of oxidative phosphorylation to the activity of mitochondrial dehydrogenases, a brief discussion of ideas on the rate control of this process will be attempted first; it will be concerned mainly with the consequences of an increased availability of ADP to the mitochondria. This discussion will then be followed by sections that describe the control of the tricarboxylate cycle and of pyruvate dehydrogenase in their mitochondrial context. Most of the work described will involve isolated mitochondria or perfused organs and attempts to correlate flux through these reactions with measured or calculated concentrations of mitochondrial substrates and effectors. Information gathered from work with purified enzymes is often, but not always, informative in view of the generally much higher enzyme concentration in the mitochondrion than in the cuvette and in view of other aspects of the intramitochondrial milieu, which it is hard to reconstruct, including the free concentrations of Ca^{2+} and Mg^{2+} ions and the possible existence of functional enzyme–enzyme or enzyme–carrier complexes (see, e.g., Srere, 1972; Duszynski et al., 1978). The tricarboxylate cycle and pyruvate dehydrogenase are merely taken as examples in illustrating the interaction of dehydrogenases and the respiratory chain, and no attempt is made to present the whole of catabolic metabolism.

For an excellent recent review of somewhat similar scope, the reader is referred to Williamson (1979).

II.   Respiratory Control—Control of Hydrogen Transfer by the Phosphorylation Potential

An increased flux through energy-utilizing reactions, whether biosynthetic processes, the active transport of solutes, or muscle contraction, usually results in the increased uptake of oxygen. The change may be dramatic; for instance, the rate of O_2 consumption by a blow fly increases more than 60-fold when the insect takes to flight (Davis and Fraenkel, 1940). The O_2 uptake reflects the activity of the mitochondrial respiratory chain, and the signal for enhanced activity is a decrease in phosphorylation potential of the adenine nucleotides of the cytosol.

Phosphorylation potential (cytosol) = ΔG ATP(c) = $\Delta G^{0'}$ ATP + RT ln $\dfrac{[\text{ATP}]}{[\text{ADP}][\text{P}_i](c)}$ (1)

Although an expected consequence of increased ATP-hydrolytic activity, the demonstration of such a decrease in phosphorylation potential has been elusive. In muscle, where changes in power output, and hence ATP consumption, are easy to impose, a decreased phosphorylation potential was observed, for instance, on the onset of flight in the blow fly (Sacktor and Hurlbut, 1966), but was not at first detected in the perfused heart on increasing the work load (Neely *et al.*, 1972a). More recent work with isolated perfused heart shows that a substantial decrease in phosphate potential is seen on increased pressure development, provided that the ADP concentration used in Eq. (1) is calculated from measured ATP, creatine, and creatine phosphate concentrations (Illingworth *et al.*, 1975; Nishiki *et al.*, 1978). This gives an answer for free cytosolic [ADP], owing to the maintenance of near equilibrium by the creatine kinase enzyme and to its exclusive localization in the cytosol. Measured muscle ADP contents are much higher and reflect the contribution of ADP bound to actin (Hiltunen and Hassinen, 1976) and an elevated mitochondrial content (see later). Changes in ATP and ADP concentration with increased work performance by muscle tend to be minimized by the existence of the creatine kinase reaction, but the increase in P_i content may be quite large (Illingworth *et al.*, 1975; Nishiki *et al.*, 1978). Granted that such a change in phosphorylation potential occurs, the question arises of how it elicits increased O_2 uptake and, therefore, increased ATP production. This is tantamount to questioning the nature of respiratory control. This in turn hinges on the mechanism of energy transduction and demands some description of current thinking on this problem. This section is intended only as a background to the discussion of respiratory control. It is necessarily quite incomplete, and the reviewer asks indulgence for omitting much, or most, relevant work. Discussion is mainly from the perspective of the chemiosmotic theory of energy transduction (Mitchell, 1966; for reviews, see Greville, 1969; Mitchell, 1979), which the reviewer finds most plausible. However, many of the experimental findings discussed are neutral with respect to the different theories of the mechanism of oxidative phosphorylation.

A. Oxidative Phosphorylation and Controlled Respiration

Experimentally it is found that most of the free energy released by the oxidation of substrates ($\Delta G_{\text{ox/red}}$) is conserved in the form of the phosphorylation potential of ATP [ΔG ATP(c)], where $\Delta G_{\text{ox/red}}$ is given by

$$\Delta G_{\text{ox/red}} = -nF\Delta Eh \qquad (2)$$

where n is the number of electrons transferred, F is the Faraday, and ΔEh is the difference in observed reduction potential between donor and acceptor couples. The observed reduction potential of each couple is given by

$$Eh = E^{0\prime} + \frac{RT}{nF} \ln \frac{[\text{acceptor}]}{[\text{donor}]} \qquad (3)$$

where $E^{0\prime}$ is the half-reduction or midpoint potential under standard conditions. In state 4 respiration (controlled respiration after the completion of ADP phosphorylation, in the nomenclature of Chance and Williams, 1956), ΔG ATP(c) is approximately 90% of $\Delta G_{\text{ox/red}}$, when electron transfer from substrate to O_2 is considered (Slater *et al.*, 1973).

The components of the respiratory chain fall into three groups, each group containing components with very similar observed reduction potentials, separated by potential differences of approximately 300 mV (Erecińska *et al.*, 1974). The three sites of potential drop correspond to the three sites of phosphorylation. Thus: site I between $NAD^+/NADH$ (-320 mV) and cytochrome b Fe^{3+}/Fe^{2+}, coenzyme $Q_{\text{ox/red}}$ (-20 mV); site II between coenzyme $Q_{\text{ox/red}}$ and cytochrome c Fe^{3+}/Fe^{2+}, cytochrome a Fe^{3+}/Fe^{2+} (270 mV); site III between cytochrome a Fe^{3+}/Fe^{2+} and $\frac{1}{2}$ O_2/H_2O (820 mV). The potential drop in the site III region of the chain is considerably greater than 300 mV, but it is presumed that not all of this is available for energy transduction (Wilson *et al.*, 1974, 1977). This is in agreement with the long-understood equivalence of high-energy intermediate (or state, see later) generated at the three different sites and the difficulty or impossibility of reversing electron transfer from water by ATP hydrolysis. It thus seems likely that electron transfer from cytochrome a to a_3 is linked to phosphorylation, and in near equilibrium with the phosphorylation potential, and that electron transfer from cytochrome a_3 to O_2 is nonequilibrium and subject to control (Wilson *et al.*, 1974). Topographical studies show that the cytochrome oxidase complex ($a + a_3$) spans the mitochondrial membrane (see, e.g., Hackenbrock and Hammon, 1975), consistent with a site of energy transduction within the complex, on the chemiosmotic theory (see later). It is noted that Slater *et al.* (1973) locate site III between cytochrome a_3 and O_2 on the grounds of potential, but that this would be mutable if the midpoint potential of cytochrome a_3 shifts with energization (Wilson and Brocklehurst, 1973; Wilson *et al.*, 1977). Although there is a consensus that ΔG ATP(c) and $\Delta G_{\text{ox/red}}$ for sites I and II are in equilibrium in state 4, it is unclear whether this continues to be true in the state of high flux generated on adding ADP to mitochondria (state 3 of Chance and Williams, 1956) and the whole question of the relation between phosphorylation potential and mitochondrial respiratory rate will be examined in some detail below.

On the basis of the chemiosmotic hypothesis, $\Delta G_{ox/red}$ is transduced into ΔG ATP via a proton-motive force, Δp, existing across the inner mitochondrial membrane (Mitchell, 1961, 1966). This has a chemical component, the pH gradient ΔpH, and an electrical component, the membrane potential $\Delta \psi$, these being related as follows:

$$\Delta p = \Delta \psi - 2.3(RT/F) \, \Delta pH \qquad (4)$$

The proton-motive force is created by hydrogen transfer from substrate to O_2 by a respiratory chain consisting in alternating hydrogen and electron carriers and arranged to form loops in the inner mitochondrial membrane. This results in the expulsion of protons to the extramitochondrial phase. The proton-motive force so established opposes further hydrogen flow down the respiratory chain until the proton circuit is completed by allowing the reentry of protons via the proton-translocating ATPase (or ATP synthetase). This results in ATP synthesis (Mitchell, 1961, 1966). Alternatively, the induction of an electrogenic proton (or hydroxyl ion) permeability in the membrane, other than that due to the ATPase, results in continued respiration and the dissipation of $\Delta G_{ox/red}$ as heat. This occurs physiologically in brown adipose tissue mitochondria, which have a thermogenic role (Nicholls, 1974a) and, nonphysiologically, when proton ionophores like dinitrophenol are used to uncouple mitochondria. ADP generated in the cytosol has to enter the mitochondrion, mainly in exchange for ATP, on the adenine nucleotide translocase (for reviews, see Klingenberg, 1970, 1976). The entering nucleotide may not fully equilibrate with matrix nucleotide, but may react preferentially with the ATPase, reflecting some sort of functional microcompartmentation of the translocase and the ATPase (Vignais *et al.,* 1975; but, for a different view, see Heldt and Pfaff, 1969; Pfaff *et al.,* 1969). The translocation is thought to involve the species ATP^{4-} and ADP^{3-} and has recently been shown to be fully electrogenic (Klingenberg and Rottenberg, 1977; LaNoue *et al.,* 1978). Inorganic phosphate, the other substrate for phosphorylation, enters in antiport with a hydroxyl ion, or symport with a proton (Chappell, 1968; Palmieri *et al.,* 1970), this being electrically neutral. Thus, during phosphorylation the formal equivalent of one proton enters the mitochondrion via the entry of one ADP and one phosphate ion. The consequence of this is that the phosphorylation potential is greater in the fluid surrounding the mitochondrion than within the mitochondrial matrix. This has been amply documented in studies with isolated mitochondria (Heldt *et al.,* 1972; Slater *et al.,* 1973; Davis and Lumeng, 1975) and recently shown to be true also in intact hepatocytes (Akerboom *et al.,* 1978) and perfused liver (Soboll *et al.*, 1978). The difference in phosphorylation potential between the two compartments has been variously estimated as 2–4 kcal/mol, but cannot be determined with precision owing to uncertainty about the activity coefficients of the various species in the matrix and the relevant value of $\Delta G^{0\prime}$ for ATP synthesis.

The question of the stoichiometry of protons entering via the ATPase per ATP molecule synthesized is a vexed one, but it does not bear directly on the nature of respiratory control and will be mentioned only in passing. The original suggestion of $2H^+$ per loop of the respiratory chain and per ATP synthesized (Mitchell, 1966; Mitchell and Moyle, 1968) has been amended upward following recent kinetic experiments in which proton extrusions have been measured in the absence of the proton reentry catalyzed by inorganic phosphate transport (Brand *et al.*, 1976; Reynafarje *et al.*, 1976; Vercesi *et al.*, 1978; Reynafarje and Lehninger, 1978). A stoichiometry of 3 would seem to be a reasonable, if somewhat arbitrary, choice and consistent with a finding of $2H^+$/ATP-hydrolyzed in experiments with submitochondrial particles, in which membrane transport is not involved (Thayer and Hinkle, 1973) and the entry of one proton via adenine nucleotide and phosphate transport, as mentioned above. The total of three protons per molecule of ATP then demands an equal number to be expelled by each of the three spans of the respiratory chain, for there is no net proton flux across the membrane during steady-state respiration. A stoichiometry of 3 would also be consistent with thermodynamic data mentioned below. However, the direct kinetic evidence suggesting a stoichiometry of 4 (Vercesi *et al.*, 1978; Reynafarje and Lehninger, 1978) is also compelling. The whole matter has become more complex with the very recent finding that the number of protons may differ from site to site (Brand *et al.*, 1978), and is reviewed in detail by Wikström and Krab elsewhere in this volume.

If proton-motive force indeed mediates between redox events and phosphorylation, its magnitude has to be sufficient that

$$2\Delta Eh = n\Delta p = [\Delta G \text{ ATP(c)}]/F \tag{5}$$

where n is the number of protons expelled as two electrons traverse each loop of the respiratory chain and per molecule of ATP generated and exported to the cytosol. During state 4 respiration, Δp values of approximately 230 mV (Mitchell and Moyle, 1969; Nicholls, 1974a,b) or somewhat less (approximately 180 mV, Wiechmann *et al.*, 1975; Johnson and Hansford, 1977) have been measured. Corresponding values of $[\Delta G$ ATP(c)]/F are 530–600 mV, requiring that n be 3 in Eq. (5) for proton-motive force to poise phosphate potential. A value of between 2.5 and 3 was obtained by Nicholls and Bernson (1977) and is probably particularly reliable in that it was obtained from the slope of the relationship between ΔG ATP(c) and Δp, varied by adding different amounts of uncoupling agent, and thus avoided error in the assumption of values of $\Delta G^{0'}$ ATP. Thus, n values obtained from the comparison of thermodynamic parameters during state 4 oxidation at least fall within the range of more recent experimental values obtained in direct, kinetic measurements of proton extrusion (Brand *et al.*, 1976). State 4 respiration may therefore be said to be characterized by near-equilibrium relations between the energy of oxidoreductions ($\Delta G_{ox/red}$) and the extramitochondrial phosphorylation potential [ΔG ATP(c)], and the proton-motive force may be taken to be quantitatively adequate to mediate between these two parameters, given n values of 3, or possibly more. The question of concern for this review is the mechanism whereby rates of substrate oxidation are controlled, and this requires the comparison of state 4 with states associated with higher fluxes of oxidoreductions.

B. Transition to Active Respiration

Addition of ADP to mitochondria elicits high rates of O_2 uptake (state 3 respiration, Chance and Williams, 1956). Throughout most of the stimulated phase of O_2 uptake it is clear that $\Delta G_{ox/red}$ and ΔG ATP(c) are far from equilibrium, the latter parameter changing continually until the attainment of state 4. Correspondingly, state 3 respiration has classically been said to be under kinetic control, by [ADP] in the theory of Chance and Williams (1956) and by the [ATP]/[ADP] ratio according to Davis and Lumeng (1975), Davis and Davis-van Thienen (1978), and Küster *et al.* (1976). It is noted, however, that Owen and Wilson (1974) and Wilson *et al.* (1977) consider that the entire concentration term of the phosphorylation potential, [ATP]/[ADP] [P_i], is involved in the kinetic control of respiration, at least in the region of near-physiological phosphorylation potentials, and this will be discussed later.

A chemiosmotic description of the state 4 to 3 transition might be as follows. The potential that drives hydrogen transfer from substrate to O_2 is the difference between $2\Delta Eh$ and $n\Delta p$. Facilitation of proton reentry into the mitochondrion via the proton-translocating ATPase results in a diminished Δp term, on the initiation of state 3 respiration. In the simplest case, ΔEh from the substrate couple to the $\frac{1}{2} O_2/H_2O$ couple remains the same and the respiratory rate increases, reflecting the increased difference $2\Delta Eh - n\Delta p$. (Less simply, Eh for the $NAD^+/NADH$ couple, the immediate substrate for the respiratory chain, may change, depending on the degree of equilibrium achieved by the dehydrogenases, as will be discussed further.) To what extent are these changes observed to occur in practice? The original determination was by Mitchell and Moyle (1969) and showed a Δp in state 3 diminished by 30 mV relative to the state 4 value. Subsequently, Nicholls (1974b) observed a decrease of 50 mV in Δp on initiating state 3 respiration in rat liver mitochondria. Further, he showed that the rate of glycerol 3-phosphate oxidation by brown adipose tissue mitochondria was linearly related to the proton-motive force when the latter was manipulated over the range from 217 to 166 mV, either by adding uncoupling agents or GDP, which reduces the intrinsic proton (hydroxyl) permeability of the membrane (Nicholls, 1974a). Diminution of Δp below 166 mV led to no further increment in respiratory rate, presumably because of limitation by the dehydrogenase rather than the respiratory chain. In a related study, Nicholls and Bernson (1977) established quite clearly that the rate of glycerol 3-phosphate oxidation, again by brown adipose tissue mitochondria, was linearly related to Δp and that a given respiratory rate was associated with a certain value of Δp, regardless of whether the latter was varied with uncoupling agents or with added hexokinase. An increased addition of hexokinase generated a decreased extramitochondrial steady-state [ATP]/[ADP] ratio and, within limits, increased respiration. However, respiration could not be stimulated as much as with uncoupling agent, because of a relatively inactive mitochondrial ATPase or adenine nucleotide translocase, or both, in mitochondria from this tissue. Clearly, respiration is more intimately related to Δp than to ΔG ATP(c) in these experiments. They are reproduced as Fig. 1, as the reviewer believes them to be very revealing.

It must be admitted, however, that there are other reports in the literature that do not support the concept of respiratory control primarily by Δp (strictly by $2\Delta Eh - n\Delta p$). For instance, Padan and Rottenberg (1973) demonstrated that although an uncoupling agent and varying K^+ ion concentrations in the presence of the ionophore valinomycin produced changes in respiration that had the same linear dependence on Δp, the phosphorylation of ADP led to an equal rate of respiration at a substantially greater Δp value. Otherwise, this paper produced good evidence that the $\Delta \psi$ and $- 2.3 \, RT/F \, \Delta pH$ components of Δp do indeed summate in their effect on respiratory rate, as predicted by the chemiosmotic hypothesis. The apparently very slight drop in Δp during ADP phosphorylation (Padan and Rottenberg, 1973) does not accord with later work (Nicholls, 1974b; Nicholls and Bernson, 1977; Johnson and Hansford, 1977), and the reason for this is not clear. Possibly it relates to the relaxation of ion gradients during the termination of the reaction by centrifugation. Azzone et al. (1978a) also queried a primary coupling role for Δp in experiments suggesting that the rate of respiration was sensitive to the technique used in varying Δp. In experiments made the more solid by the

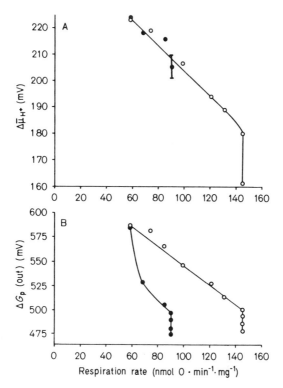

FIG. 1. The dependence of the rate of respiration upon the proton-motive force (plotted as $\Delta\bar\mu H^+$) or the phosphorylation potential of extramitochondrial adenine nucleotide (ΔGp). $\Delta\bar\mu H^+$ and ΔGp were varied by the use of different concentrations of carbonyl cyanide p-trifluoromethoxyphenylhydrazone (○) or activities of hexokinase (●). The vertical bar in panel A represents the standard deviation of 14 determinations made in the presence of excess hexokinase. From Nicholls and Bernson (1977), by permission of the copyright holder.

simultaneous use of three different penetrant cations to measure $\Delta\psi$ (Ca^{2+}, K^+ plus valinomycin and triphenylmethylphosphonium), they showed that the dependence of respiratory rate upon Δp was steeper with A23187 (a divalent cation ionophore) than with nigericin plus valinomycin (which permit K^+ ion cycling), which in turn gave a slope steeper than that with the proton ionophore carbonylcyanide p-trifluoromethoxyphenylhydrazone. In addition, they corroborated the results of Padan and Rottenberg (1973) showing that Δp is greater at a given respiratory rate during ADP phosphorylation than during uncoupler-stimulated respiration. Thus there is a lack of agreement on this very central question.

It is noted that Padan and Rottenberg (1973), Nicholls (1974a,b), Nicholls and Bernson (1977), and Azzone *et al.* (1978a) relate respiration to Δp, rather than to $2\Delta Eh - n\Delta p$; this treatment assumes that ΔEh is invariant between states 3 and 4. This is potentially an explanation of the discrepancies between these pieces of work, with ΔEh possibly less during uncoupled respiration than during state 3 respiration. However, it is not clear how large such a difference could be, as the $NAD^+/NADH$ couple would be highly oxidized under both conditions, with succinate as substrate. That ΔEh need not necessarily be the same in states 3 and 4 was implicit in the original work of Chance and Williams (1956), where it was greater in state 4. This was confirmed recently by Rich and Williamson (1978), who used the perfused interventricular septum of rabbit heart and studied the response to low-Ca^{2+} or high-K^+ media. For the span $NAD^+/NADH$ to cytochrome c Fe^{3+}/Fe^{2+}, ΔEh was found to increase with the inhibition of contraction and to decrease with more frequent electrical stimulation of the muscle. That the converse may be true and that in fact ΔEh may be greater in the state of high flux was shown in a study by Johnson and Hansford (1977) using flight-muscle mitochondria from the blow fly. In these mitochondria, which are capable of very great intensities of energy transduction, the complete oxidation of pyruvate via the tricarboxylate cycle is greatly stimulated by a decrease in the intramitochondrial [ATP]/[ADP] ratio, which has a direct effect at the level of substrate dehydrogenation. The mechanism of this will be discussed in Section III, on the tricarboxylate cycle. The consequence of this stimulation is that the $NAD^+/NADH$ couple becomes more reduced during the state 4 to 3 transition, the converse of the classical finding of Chance and Williams (1956). This simply reflects increased dehydrogenase activity. At the same time, the cytochrome c Fe^{3+}/Fe^{2+} couple also becomes more reduced, but to a lesser extent. The consequence of this is that ΔEh for the span from $NAD^+/NADH$ to cytochrome c Fe^{3+}/Fe^{2+} actually increases slightly from state 4 to state 3.

These results are presented in Table I, together with data relating to the oxidation of glycerol 3-phosphate, which is not subject to control by the [ATP]/[ADP] ratio at the dehydrogenase level. In the latter case, the ΔEh for the span $NAD^+/NADH$ to cytochrome c Fe^{3+}/Fe^{2+} decreases from state 4 to state 3, reflecting the much diminished reduction of NAD^+ by reversed electron transfer (Chance and Hollunger, 1961; Klingenberg and Bücher, 1961) on adding ADP. Measurements of Δp under the same conditions are presented in Fig. 2, and the values are included in Table I for comparison with the other thermodynamic parameters. With each of the two substrates Δp falls by 30 mV when respiration is stimulated by ADP. It then fully returns to state 4 values with the cessation of phosphorylation. Thus, by dint of dehydrogenase level activation by ADP, the state 3

TABLE I

COMPARISON OF THE MAGNITUDE OF REDOX SPAN, PHOSPHORYLATION POTENTIAL, AND PROTON-MOTIVE FORCE DURING THE STATE 3 AND STATE 4 OXIDATION OF PYRUVATE OR GLYCEROL 3-PHOSPHATE BY BLOW FLY FLIGHT MUSCLE MITOCHONDRIA[a]

Substrate (state)	ΔEh[b] (mV/site)	ΔG ATP(c)[c] (mV)	Δp (mV)	$\Delta\Delta p$[d] (mV)
Pyruvate (4)	287 ± 3 (4)	264 ± 2 (6)	180 ± 6 (7)	30 ± 3 (3)
Pyruvate (3)	299 ± 3 (4)	—	159 ± 13 (3)	
Glycerol 3-phosphate (4)	292 ± 2 (4)	286 ± 1 (6)	169 ± 3 (6)	31 ± 2 (4)
Glycerol 3-phosphate (3)	271 ± 2 (4)	—	140 ± 4 (4)	

[a] From Johnson and Hansford (1977), by permission of the copyright holder.

[b] ΔEh is the redox span NAD–cytochrome c divided by 2.

[c] ΔG ATP(c), the extramitochondrial adenine nucleotide phosphorylation potential, is expressed in millivolts by dividing the value in kilocalories per mole by $2F$.

[d] $\Delta\Delta p$ is the mean of the differences obtained by subtraction of state 3 from state 4 values for each individual mitochondrial preparation.

oxidation of pyruvate by fly flight muscle mitochondria can maintain both a value of Δp large enough to give phosphorylation and a large $2\Delta Eh - n\Delta p$ difference, to allow rapid respiration. The dehydrogenase level control also ensures a very oxidized state for cytochrome c (and by inference cytochrome a_3) during resting respiration, giving a very low flux through the nonequilibrium electron transfer step from cytochrome a_3 to O_2, as will be discussed further.

The thermodynamic sufficiency of the proton-motive force, previously discussed in relation to state 4 respiration, is not so clear in the high-flux states. Thus, Van Dam et al. (1977) showed that parallel measurements of Δp and ΔG ATP(c) in the presence of various concentrations of uncoupling agent (dinitrophenol) resulted in ΔG ATP(c)/Δp quotients that increased from 2.35 to 2.99 with increasing uncoupler concentration. These quotients represent thermodynamic measurements of H^+ translocated per ATP hydrolyzed (or synthesized), as mentioned above. Similarly, Azzone et al. (1978b) found ΔG ATP(c)/Δp quotients of approximately 3 at high values of Δp but approaching infinity when Δp was diminished sufficiently by classical uncoupling agents (proton ionophores). By contrast, ΔG ATP(c)/Δp remained constant near 3 when Δp was diminished by K^+ ion cycling in the presence of valinomycin and nigericin. These results either require a H^+/ATP stoichiometry that is flexible, depending on Δp, which is not attractive aesthetically and hard to envisage mechanistically, or they require that Δp be seriously and systematically underestimated in the high-flux states. The latter is the view taken by Van

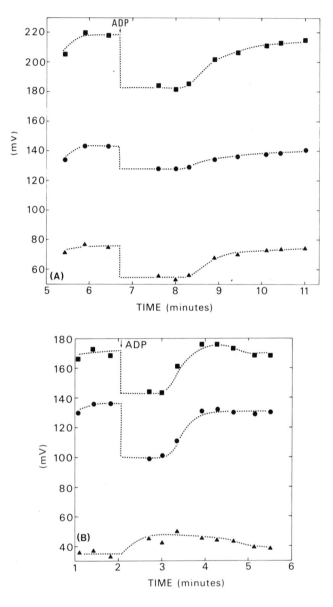

FIG. 2. The response of proton-motive force, and of its components, to state $4 \rightarrow 3 \rightarrow 4$ transitions. Blow fly flight muscle mitochondria were used, with either pyruvate (panel A) or glycerol 3-phosphate (panel B) as substrate. Presented are $\Delta\psi$ (●), $-59\Delta pH$ (▲) and Δp (■). From Johnson and Hansford (1977), by permission of the copyright holder.

Dam *et al.* (1977), who envisage a zone of limited mixing surrounding the energy-transducing proteins of the inner mitochondrial membrane, such that the activity of the proton is not the same in this milieu as in the bulk matrix phase, and such that the difference in activity becomes greater the greater the flux through the system. By this suggestion, determinations of Δp by bulk-phase ion gradients are inappropriate, especially in high-flux states.

C. OTHER MODELS OF RESPIRATORY CONTROL

Leaving the chemiosmotic hypothesis aside for a moment, a different interpretation of the nature of respiratory control has been made by Wilson and colleagues. They emphasize that electron transfer from the $NAD^+/NADH$ couple to the cytochrome c Fe^{3+}/Fe^{2+} couple (and by inference to cytochrome a_3, too) remains at equilibrium with ΔG ATP(c) not only in state 4 (Erecińska *et al.*, 1974), but also in states of higher flux (Owen and Wilson, 1974; Holian *et al.*, 1977). These do not include state 3, with values of $[ATP]/[ADP][P_i]_c$, the concentration term of ΔG ATP(c), that are initially extremely low and nonphysiological, but do include those states, referred to as the "region of dynamic control," where O_2 uptake begins to decrease progressively with the increase in $[ATP]/[ADP][P_i]_c$. These are states of great physiological interest. They were investigated (Holian *et al.*, 1977) by making simultaneous measurements of $[ATP]/[ADP][P_i]_c$ and the rate of O_2 uptake at several points during the transition from state 3 to state 4. It was found that respiratory rate was proportional to the log $[ATP]/[ADP][P_i]_c$, and a model was advanced (Owen and Wilson, 1974) in which respiratory rate was considered to be proportional to the content of reduced cytochrome a_3, the latter determined by the mitochondrial $NAD^+/NADH$ ratio and the $[ATP]/[ADP]$ $[P_i]_c$ ratio, because of equilibrium at sites I through III. It is noted that $[P_i]$ was found to be as important a determinant of respiratory rate as $[ATP]/[ADP]$, and this is relevant to the discussion of the role of the adenine nucleotide translocase (below).

Subsequently, a model was developed taking into account the participation of "invisible" copper in the reaction of cytochrome oxidase with O_2 (Wilson *et al.*, 1977; Erecińska *et al.*, 1978). This model relates respiration (expressed as cytochrome c turnover) to the $[ATP]/[ADP][P_i]_c$ ratio and to the mitochondrial $NADH/NAD^+$ ratio, and provides a good fit to experimental data obtained with a variety of cells and organisms. This is shown in Fig. 3. The points represent experimental determinations of cytochrome c turnover plotted versus either the measured mitochondrial $NADH/NAD^+$ ratio, as $NAD^+/NADH$ (A) or the measured $[ATP][ADP]$

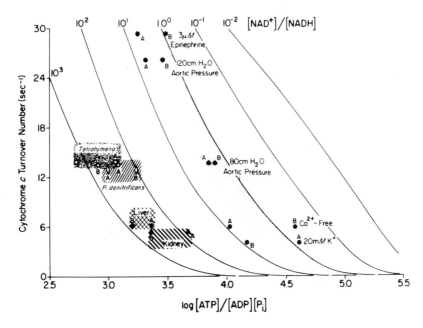

FIG. 3. Fit of experimental points to a mathematical model of oxidative phosphorylation. The lines represent the calculated relationship between the variables displayed as ordinate and abscissa, at each of a series of values of [NAD$^+$]/[NADH] ratio. The experimental data points marked A show intramitochondrial [NAD$^+$]/[NADH] ratio plotted versus respiratory rate (as turnover number for cytochrome c); points marked B show cytosolic (heart) or cellular (other data) [ATP]/[ADP][P$_i$] plotted versus turnover number for cytochrome c. From Erecińska *et al.* (1978), by permission of the copyright holder.

[P$_i$]$_c$ ratio (B). Superposition of points A and B would indicate a perfect fit to the model. It is seen that in general there is good agreement, especially in light of the wide variation in absolute magnitude of the parameters in different tissues and organisms. Possible experimental problems tending to minimize the agreement are the lack of active NAD-linked dehydrogenases to provide an accurate measure of free mitochondrial NADH/NAD$^+$ in all tissues and the use of total cellular ATP, ADP, and P$_i$ contents, instead of calculated cytosolic values, for some tissues (Erecińska *et al.*, 1978). An interesting aspect of the model is the increase in respiratory rate to be expected if NADH/NAD$^+$ (or cytochrome c Fe^{2+}/Fe^{3+}) is increased, at a constant phosphorylation potential. This was in fact achieved in an experiment in which cytochrome c reduction was varied, using different amounts of mediator dye, at constant levels of imposed phosphorylation potential (Wilson *et al.*, 1977). Conversely, respiratory rate will increase with decreased phosphorylation potential, in the absence of changes in NADH/NAD$^+$ ratio, this being what appears to happen with increased work load in the heart in some studies (Nishiki *et al.*, 1978), although it is possible that glutamate dehydrogenase is not active enough to give an equilibrium measure of mitochondrial NADH/NAD$^+$ ratio in this tissue. The role of dehydrogenase-level activation in preventing a decrease in NADH/NAD$^+$ ratio on transition to high-flux states (in distinction to the classical results of Chance and Williams, 1956) was mentioned above in connection with fly flight muscle mitochondria. On this model (Erecińska *et al.*, 1978), also, the advantages of maintaining a high NADH/NAD$^+$ ratio are apparent in terms of allowing rapid respiration without large decreases in [ATP]/[ADP] [P$_i$]$_c$.

A kinetic expression has also been derived by van der Meer *et al.* (1978), using nonequilibrium thermodynamics, relating the rate of O$_2$ uptake to an affinity term that incorporates

$$\log \left(\frac{\text{NADH}}{\text{NAD}} \right)_m \times \left(\frac{\text{ADP P}_i}{\text{ATP}} \right)_c^3 \times O_2^{1/2}$$

Experiments with perifused hepatocytes, in which the [ATP]/[ADP] [P$_i$]$_c$ ratio was derived from the glyceraldehyde phosphate dehydrogenase and 3-phosphoglycerate kinase equilibria, were in good accord with this relationship.

D. ROLE OF THE ADENINE NUCLEOTIDE TRANSLOCASE IN THE CONTROL OF RESPIRATION

Regardless of the mechanism of coupling of redox events and ADP phosphorylation, the mitochondrial response to a decreased cytosolic phosphorylation potential, which is the main interest of this section, involves the entry of ADP into the mitochondrion and the exit of ATP. This is catalyzed by the adenine nucleotide translocase (for reviews, see Klingenberg, 1970, 1976; Vignais, 1976), which is implicated increasingly as a site at which control is exerted over oxidative phosphorylation. There are four main lines of evidence.

First, direct measurement has established that the phosphorylation of intramitochondrial ADP is more rapid than that of extramitochondrial ADP (Heldt and Klingenberg, 1968). The difference was most marked at low temperatures (0–6°C) and was abolished at 14°C, thus strictly leaving open the question of limitation under physiological conditions. However, rates of phosphorylation of endogenous nucleotide may have been suboptimal, owing to the limitation of entry of the substrate succinate in a medium of low ionic strength (Meisner *et al.*, 1972); this is suggested by higher rates of phosphorylation with ascorbate as substrate (Heldt and

Klingenberg, 1968). This leaves open the possibility that nucleotide trans-location could limit phosphorylation at temperatures above 14°C, under more optimal conditions. Indeed, Kemp *et al.* (1969) showed such a limi-tation at all temperatures up to 23°C in a system that allowed much higher rates of endogenous phosphorylation. In addition, translocation limits the rate of uncoupler-stimulated hydrolysis of exogenous ATP up to 25°C, the highest temperature studied (Heldt and Klingenberg, 1968).

Second, a comparison can be made between measured rates of translo-cation and rates of state 3 substrate oxidation, in an attempt to comment on the control role of the adenine nucleotide translocase. Translocation can be measured only at low temperatures using conventional sampling techniques, and such an approach has therefore usually involved extrapo-lation of transport activity to higher temperatures. When this was done (Pfaff *et al.,* 1969), a rate of 340 nmol/min per milligram of mitochondrial protein was obtained for 25°C. This compares with a state 3 rate of suc-cinate oxidation of approximately 200 ng atoms of O_2/min per milligram, which requires a rate of phosphorylation of 400 nmol/min per milligram assuming a P/O ratio of 2. More recent work using the quench-flow tech-nique (Nohl and Klingenberg, 1978) to measure translocation has ex-tended the experimental range to 30°C, tending to confirm the earlier, ex-trapolated, results (Klingenberg, 1976). Thus, translocation of ADP into the mitochondrion has approximately the same maximal activity as oxida-tive phosphorylation of exogenous nucleotide, and could limit the latter process. It might be mentioned at this point that there are tissue dif-ferences in relative activities of adenine nucleotide translocation and phosphorylation, the difference in rate of phosphorylation of endogenous and exogenous ADP being less marked in heart mitochondria, which have a very active translocase, than in liver (Heldt and Klingenberg, 1968).

Third, the question can be approached by a titration with the specific translocase inhibitor atractyloside (see Heldt, 1969, for a review) to see whether there is any excess capacity of translocase activity or whether the lowest inhibitor concentration causes reduced flux through the pathway. This was done very recently by Lemasters and Sowers (1979) using liver mitochondria, with the conclusion that there was significant in-hibition of the phosphorylation of ADP when atractyloside-binding sites were in 3.8-fold excess over the atractyloside concentration, indicating that there is very little, if any, spare capacity. A similar approach had pre-viously been followed by Akerboom *et al.* (1977), who used the ratio of (lactate production)/(glucose production) as an index of (glycolytically derived ATP)/(ATP formed by oxidative phosphorylation), in isolated liver cells incubated with dihydroxyacetone. They found an increase in this ratio, indicative of diminished oxidative phosphorylation, at the lowest atractyloside concentration used (2 μM) and a linear increase in inhibition with increased atractyloside concentration thereafter. This was interpreted in terms of a rate-limiting role for adenine nucleotide translocation, an interpretation that was challenged by Stubbs *et al.* (1978) on the grounds that the introduction of the inhibitor introduces a rate limitation. This is a reasonable criticism and one that Akerboom *et al.* (1977) attempted to confront by emphasizing inhibition at the lowest inhibitor concentration. Stubbs *et al.* (1978) also investigated the effects of atractyloside on the metabolism of isolated hepatocytes and found a constant percentage of inhibition of oxidative phosphorylation, at a given inhibitor concentration, regardless of the absolute flux through the pathway. The latter was measured from the formation of glucose and urea. The authors found this paradoxical in the light of a (presumed) excess of translocase activity. It seems to the reviewer that this experimental finding is more consistent with a model in which translocase activity is controlled by competition between cytosolic ATP and ADP for entry into the mitochondrion, the important parameters being $[ADP^{3-}]/K_{m_{ADP^{3-}}}$ and $[ATP^{4-}]/K_{i_{ATP^{4-}}}$. Thus, the finding that the concentration of ADP is much greater than the K_m for ADP does not guarantee V_{max} (*pace* Stubbs *et al.*, 1978), in the absence of knowledge of the concentration of ATP. Further, if flux through the translocase is adjusted by changes in cytosolic [ATP]/[ADP], to meet changing demands for cytosolic ATP, there being no excess catalytic capacity, then the introduction of an essentially uncompetitive inhibitor like carboxyatractyloside (Scherer *et al.*, 1973) might give the pattern of inhibition observed.

Finally, there are some experiments that indicate that respiration responds to the $[ATP]/[ADP]_c$ ratio, not to $[ATP]/[ADP][P_i]$ and this has been cited as being consistent with rate-limitation by the translocase. Thus, apart from the state 4 experiments of Slater *et al.* (1973) already mentioned, Davis and Lumeng (1975) used the elegant technique of stimulating respiration with limiting amounts of added ATPase, thus generating a series of steady states intermediate between states 3 and 4. It is noted that this is the "region of dynamic control" of Owen and Wilson (1974) and Holian *et al.* (1977), but with the convenience and precision of measurement possible in a steady state. Davis and Lumeng (1975) demonstrated a dependence of respiratory rate on the $[ATP]/[ADP]_c$ ratio and went on to establish a K_m value for ADP and K_i for ATP through the determination of the steady-state concentration of ADP necessary to stimulate respiration 50% at various concentrations of ATP. Their thesis is that net phosphorylation ceases when $[ATP]/[ADP]_c$ exceeds $K_{i_{ATP}}/K_{m_{ADP}}$. These values were found to be 725 μM and 13 μM, giving a predicted state 4 ratio of $[ATP]/[ADP]_c$ of 57, which agrees closely with that actually found. It should be noted, however, that direct determinations of adenine nucleotide transport have given substantially lower values for $K_{m_{ADP}}$ and $K_{m_{ATP}}$ and somewhat complex kinetics (Pfaff *et al.*, 1969; Klingenberg, 1976). However, in energized mitochondria $K_{m_{ATP}}$ is always larger than $K_{m_{ADP}}$, a consequence of the membrane potential and electrogenic nature of the ATP^{4-}/ADP^{3-} exchange (Klingenberg and Rottenberg, 1977; LaNoue *et al.*, 1978). In addition, Mg^{2+} ions, present in the study by Davis and Lumeng (1975), raise the K_m values determined owing to chelation of the free nucleotides, the substrate for the translocase (Pfaff *et al.*, 1969; Klingenberg, 1976). Thus, the indirect measurements of K_m and K_i (Davis and Lumeng, 1975) are plausible, though high. In a later paper, Davis and Davis-van Thienen (1978) used the ATPase technique described above at different P_i concentrations and showed that respiratory rate correlates much better with $[ATP]/[ADP]_c$ ratio than with $[ATP]/[ADP][P_i]_c$ ratio. It is noted that there is a small effect of P_i concentration at high respiratory rates and low $[P_i]$, which may represent kinetic control by the P_i^-/OH^- antiport responsible for net P_i entry (Chappell, 1968; Palmieri *et al.*, 1970) under these conditions. Thus, these authors concluded that respiratory rate is regulated by $[ATP]/[ADP]_c$ in states intermediate between 3 and 4 and this is consistent with a limiting role for the translocase. The underlying reason for the discrepancy with the results of Holian *et al.* (1977) is not clear. However, a dependence of respiration on the $[P_i]$ term of the $[ATP]/[ADP][P_i]_c$ ratio does not rule out the exertion of respiratory control by the translocase (*pace*, Holian *et al.*, 1977). This is because, as also pointed out by Lemasters and Sowers (1979), increased P_i concentration tends to diminish the ΔpH component of Δp owing to P_i^-/OH^- exchange and increase the $\Delta\psi$ component (see, e.g., Nicholls, 1974b). The latter will enhance the entry of ADP into the mitochondrion in exchange for ATP because of the electrogenic nature of the exchange alluded to earlier.

E. CONCLUDING REMARKS

In the organism the rate of oxidative phosphorylation is determined by the rate of hydrolysis of ATP in primarily extramitochondrial reactions; *in vitro* this is well mimicked by the addition of ATPase (Davis and Lumeng, 1975) or hexokinase (Hansford and Johnson, 1975; Küster *et al.*, 1976) to respiring mitochondria, with the generation of respiratory states intermediate between state 3 and state 4. On any model of energy coupling, mediation between usage of extramitochondrial ATP and the process of respiration involves the adenine nucleotide translocase and the mitochondrial (proton-translocating) ATPase. To what extent each of these exerts control over flux remains an open question. To provide an answer one must determine the degree of disequilibrium at each reaction, which is difficult in the case of the translocase because it involves the determination of the ratio of free $[ATP^{4-}]/[ADP^{3-}]$ in the mitochondrial matrix, where activity coefficients are unknown. In the limit it may also be uninformative, in the light of a possible functional complex between translocase and ATPase (Vignais *et al.*, 1975). In the case of the ATPase it is also difficult to measure the degree of disequilibrium in respiratory states more active than state 4, if one accepts the proton gradient Δp as a reactant in ATP synthesis (Mitchell, 1961, 1966), as Δp may be improperly measured in higher flux states (Van Dam *et al.*, 1977). The manner in which the overall disequilibrium between $\Delta G_{ox/red}$ and ΔG ATP(c) is partitioned between the respiratory chain, the ATPase and the adenine nucleotide translocase may be, in truth, somewhat tissue specific. Thus, in brown adipose tissue mitochondria (Nicholls and Bernson, 1977) the ATPase and translocase are rather inactive and the disequilibrium between ΔG ATP(c) and $nF\Delta p$ is large and increases with increasing flux. In heart mitochondria, the ATPase and translocase (Heldt and Klingenberg, 1968) are highly active, and less disequilibrium at these two steps is to be expected. This in turn implies a proportionately greater disequilibrium in heart between $2\Delta Eh$ and $n\Delta p$. The reviewer would like to believe that it is this difference $(2\Delta Eh - n\Delta p)$ that drives respiration (Mitchell, 1961, 1966) and points out that this disequilibrium can be enhanced by activation at the level of the dehydrogenases, via increase in the $NADH/NAD^+$ ratio (Johnson and Hansford, 1977). Finally, in state 3 respiration, with excess ADP available to the mitochondria, in contrast to the more physiological states discussed above, substrate permeability into the mitochondrion or dehydrogenase activity may become limiting (see Nicholls and Bernson, 1977), and these topics are discussed below.

III.   Control of the Tricarboxylate Cycle

This section will examine the mechanism whereby the increased availability of ADP within a tissue leads to an increased rate of substrate dehydrogenation and a consequently increased provision of hydrogen as substrate for the phosphorylating electron transport chain. The preceding section explored the phenomenon of respiratory control at the level of the mitochondrial membrane; this section aims to go on and look at control at the level of the dehydrogenases and the way in which flux through the dehydrogenases is matched to flux through oxidative phosphorylation. The starting point is the observation by Chance and Williams (1956) that adding ADP to a suspension of mitochondria results in a shift toward more oxidized values in the steady-state level of reduction of mitochondrial NAD and flavins. This finding is almost universal, although it may in truth be a special case if the near-equilibrium description of oxidative phosphorylation discussed in Section II is correct. Thus, the parameter that one would expect to change in response to a change in the phosphorylation potential is actually the redox span (ΔEh) between the $NAD^+/NADH$ couple and cytochrome oxidase (or the cytochrome c coupled if only the first two sites are considered). Thus, the decrease in phosphorylation potential on adding ADP could be satisfied by no change, or even an increase, in the $NADH/NAD^+$ ratio, provided that the cytochrome couple became sufficiently reduced. An extreme case is that of insect flight muscle, where the state of high flux is indeed associated with increased $NADH/NAD^+$ ratios, as previously discussed. Nevertheless, the most usual result is that a decreased adenine nucleotide phosphorylation potential is associated with a decreased $NADH/NAD^+$ ratio and that this is a major contributor to the decrease in ΔEh for the span NAD–cytochrome c. The decreased $NADH/NAD^+$ ratio is in turn responsible for enhanced activity of NAD-linked dehydrogenases. Other factors are also involved in determining dehydrogenase activity, including the concentration of the oxidizable substrate, the concentration of end-product inhibitors and of allosteric effectors, and, possibly, the partition by covalent modification of the enzyme between active and inactive forms. Together these factors determine the effectiveness with which individual dehydrogenases compete for the pool of mitochondrial flavin and coenzyme Q. This competition has been discussed recently by Gutman (1977) and will feature later in this review in connection with the competition between pyruvate dehydrogenase and the enzymes of β-oxidation.

In order to answer the question of what respiratory control—the starting point of this review—means at the level of the dehydrogenases, an examination will be made of the way in which flux through the tricarboxylate cycle is adjusted to meet the metabolic needs of the tissue. The tricarboxylate cycle is chosen for its overriding importance in catabolic metabolism, as the sequence in which the greatest proportion of the free energy of foodstuff substrates is released. It is also chosen because it includes enzymes that respond directly to the ATP/ADP ratio, the original signal to the mitochondrion, and to the $NADH/NAD^+$ ratio, with which it is intimately related by oxidative phosphorylation. The first part of this section will discuss the mechanisms by which the tricarboxylate cycle adjusts to changes in the availability of ADP. The main approach will be to focus on those reactions known to be far from equilibrium, and therefore known to exert control on the flux through the cycle, identifying substrates and other effectors, and then examine changes in flux in the light of changes in the concentration of these effectors. Studies of the molecular properties of isolated enzymes will be mentioned only briefly, in the context of identifying which potentially regulatory substances to measure in intact tissue or mitochondria; it is felt that such in cuvette studies of isolated enzymes cannot identify sites of regulation in intact tissues. The nonequilibrium reactions to be discussed are those catalyzed by citrate synthase (EC 4.1.3.7), NAD-isocitrate dehydrogenase (EC 1.1.1.41), and 2-oxoglutarate dehydrogenase (EC 1.2.4.2).

For each enzyme, the work described first involves the use of isolated mitochondria, which offer the advantage that respiration can be stimulated by the simple addition of ADP, in the presence of a wide range of added substrates. Fluxes can be easily measured by the depletion of substrates and accumulation of products, but a disadvantage is that mitochondrial metabolites tend to wash out into a near-infinite external space. Subsequently, work done with intact tissues will be described. This involves mainly the isolated perfused heart, in which ADP availability to the mitochondrion can be manipulated by the amount of mechanical work imposed. An advantage of this system is the preservation of the cytsol as the milieu surrounding the mitochondria; a disadvantage is that intermediates measured in whole tissue extracts cannot authoritatively be assigned to mitochondrial or cytosolic compartments.

A.   Control of Citrate Synthase Activity

Citrate synthase commits acetyl groups to the formation of citrate as opposed to the alternative fates of acetylcarnitine formation or, in liver, of ketogenesis. It is usually assumed to be a nonequilibrium reaction, although this is hard to establish with certainty owing to the problem of estimating the concentration of free oxaloacetate, which is extremely low. Certainly Williamson *et al.* (1972) showed that the combined reactions catalyzed by malate dehydrogenase and citrate synthase (thereby avoiding the measurement of free oxaloacetate concentration) where two orders of magnitude displaced from equilibrium, provided that the β-hydroxybutyrate dehydrogenase is active enough in heart to give a measure of the free $NADH/NAD^+$ ratio in the mitochondrion. Randle *et al.* (1970) failed to show any incorporation of isotope from citrate into acetyl-CoA, which would also be consistent with nonequilibrium at this reaction. The activity of citrate synthase has been suggested to be regulated by the concentration of its substrates oxaloacetate and acetyl-CoA and by the putative effectors ATP, ADP, AMP, and palmitoyl-CoA (see Srere, 1974, for a review). Inhibition of purified citrate synthase by an elevated ratio of [ATP]/[ADP][AMP] was shown by Shepherd and Garland

(1969) and appeared to offer a mechanism of direct control by the adenine nucleotide phosphorylation potential of the mitochondrial matrix (Shepherd et al., 1965). However, other experiments revealed that the Mg^{2+} chelates of the adenine nucleotides, almost certainly the form existing in the matrix, were not effectors of the enzyme (Kosicki and Lee, 1966). In addition, the dependency of the rate of citrate formation on the coupled or uncoupled status of liver mitochondria, taken as indicative of direct control by the matrix [ATP]/[ADP] [AMP] ratio (Garland et al., 1967), was later shown to be an artifact of the use of malonate. This competes with malate for entry into the mitochondrion, and thus deprives citrate synthase of oxaloacetate, more effectively in coupled than uncoupled mitochondria (Olson and Williamson, 1971) and had been included in the earlier studies as an inhibitor of flux through succinate dehydrogenase (Garland et al., 1967). The significance of citrate synthase inhibition by long-chain acyl-CoA compounds (Wieland and Weiss, 1963) is difficult to assess because of the high degree of binding of these compounds by intramitochondrial proteins which is to be expected.

By contrast, the regulation of citrate synthase by its substrates is on a surer footing. The control of activity by the concentration of oxaloacetate was first suggested by Lehninger (1946). More recently, Olson and Williamson (1971) demonstrated that citrate synthesis by rat liver mitochondria oxidizing palmitoylcarnitine was stimulated by malate in a concentration-dependent fashion and by respiratory states associated with a highly oxidized nicotinamide nucleotide. Both conditions will lead to an increased oxaloacetate concentration, by enhancing the forward velocity of the malate dehydrogenase reaction. Whether this enzyme actually maintains equilibrium or not is a moot point. Opie and Owen (1975) advanced the view that it may. On the other hand, Williamson et al. (1972), in a study of heart mitochondria, calculated a free mitochondrial oxaloacetate concentration of 0.35 μM based on the assumption of equilibrium at malate dehydrogenase compared to a value of 10 μM calculated on the aspartate aminotransferase equilibrium. One explanation of the discrepancy would be nonequilibrium at malate dehydrogenase. This is consistent with recent findings on the mitochondrial malate dehydrogenase reaction in isolated hepatocytes (Tischler et al., 1977). However, free oxaloacetate will presumably increase with malate concentration and decrease with $NADH/NAD^+$ ratio, even if the mass action ratio does not equal the K_{equ} for the malate dehydrogenase reaction. Olson and Williamson (1971) found no difference in the rate of citrate synthesis between state 3 respiration and the uncoupled state, suggesting that matrix ATP/ADP ratios were unimportant (in distinction to the results of Shepherd et al., 1965; Garland et al., 1967). A similar conclusion was made from an experiment in which mitochondrial NADH/NAD$^+$ and phosphorylation potential were divorced by the use of oligomycin and uncoupling agent and O$_2$ uptake was varied by addition of ATP. Citrate synthesis and O$_2$ uptake declined in parallel, indicating no preferential shift to ketogenesis at high ATP concentration; however, the mechanism of the decline in both parameters with increasing ATP concentration was not addressed. Malate concentration and nicotinamide nucleotide redox state were the two controlling parameters emphasized in this study. Similar conclusions were reached by Lopes-Cardozo and Van den Bergh (1972), in a study of rat liver mitochondria. In an important experiment they stimulated respiration progressively with increasing amounts of hexokinase and showed a linear relation between the fraction of acetyl groups directed into ketogenesis (as opposed to citrate formation) and the percentage reduction of mitochondrial NAD, as measured by the β-hydroxybutyrate/acetoacetate ratio. The dependence was shifted by a change in the concentration of added malate, consistent with regulation of citrate synthase by oxaloacetate concentration. Independent manipulation of the mitochondrial phosphorylation potential and NADH/NAD$^+$ ratio by the use of uncoupling agent, oligomycin, and rotenone failed to show any effect of the ATP/ADP ratio on the partition of acetyl groups between ketogenesis and citrate formation.

Studies with heart mitochondria, however, have been interpreted somewhat differently. Thus, although LaNoue et al. (1970, 1972) discussed regulation of citrate synthase activity by oxaloacetate availability in state 4 respiration and in another state of low flux associated with highly reduced nicotinamide nucleotide (i.e., plus oligomycin plus ADP), they also emphasized a control role of the ATP/ADP ratio, exerted indirectly via the ratio acetyl-CoA/succinyl-CoA. The suggested relationship here is that a high mitochondrial ATP/ADP ratio is associated with a high succinyl-CoA/CoA ratio, via the near equilibrium maintained at the succinic thiokinase step (LaNoue et al., 1972) and that succinyl-CoA inhibits citrate synthase, competitively with respect to acetyl-CoA (Smith and Williamson, 1971). LaNoue et al. (1972) did in fact demonstrate a diminished flux through citrate synthase in the presence of oligomycin plus uncoupling agent compared to uncoupling agent alone. The former state is associated with a high ATP/ADP ratio, owing to substrate level phosphorylation, and a correspondingly low acetyl-CoA/succinyl-CoA ratio. The diminution in flux through citrate synthase was more dramatic when acetylcarnitine rather than pyruvate was the acetyl group donor, as the former maintains a lower steady state concentration of acetyl-CoA. It is noted that this control mechanism was demonstrated only in the presence of uncoupling agent, with highly oxidized nicotinamide nucleotide and therefore no limitation by the concentration of oxaloacetate. In the transition from state 4 to state 3, the analog of the low-work-to-high-work transition in the intact tissue, there is a decrease in mitochondrial $NADH/NAD^+$ ratio. Under these circumstances LaNoue *et al.* (1970, 1972) invoked a control of citrate synthase by oxaloacetate concentration. The intramitochondrial malate concentration was found to be only marginally elevated (LaNoue *et al.*, 1972) or not at all (Williamson *et al.*, 1972) in state 3 compared to state 4, so that any such control rests largely on the well documented nicotinamide nucleotide oxidation in state 3 (Chance and Williams, 1956; LaNoue *et al.*, 1970). It is noted that McElroy *et al.* (1968) did demonstrate an elevated intramitochondrial malate content in state 3 compared to state 4, using heart mitochondria. This may well be correct, although there is the real concern that the filtration technique used may have led to anaerobiosis of the mitochondria before quenching, and a consequent formation of malate, this being more of a threat at the higher rates of O_2 uptake.

It is clear that the uncoupler-generated states of low mitochondrial $NADH/NAD^+$ but high ATP/ADP in which control by succinyl-CoA was demonstrated (LaNoue *et al.*, 1972), though informative, are not physiologically appropriate. With this in mind Hansford and Johnson (1975) measured the mitochondrial content of CoA thioesters, including succinyl-CoA, and the flux through citrate synthase under a variety of conditions of substrate and ADP availability to see whether any correlation could be made between flux and acetyl CoA/succinyl CoA ratio in experiments involving neither uncoupling agent nor oligomycin. It was found that the straightforward state 4 to 3 transition was associated with a marked decrease in acetyl-CoA content and an increase in succinyl-CoA content, regardless of whether the substrate of the rabbit heart mitochondria was pyruvate plus malate or palmitoylcarnitine plus malate. This is shown in Fig. 4. These changes are the converse of those needed to explain the increased flux through citrate synthase in state 3, which is presumed to reflect instead the oxaloacetate concentration. Parenthetically, the decreased acetyl-CoA/CoA ratio in state 3 shown in Fig. 4 will lead to increased flux through pyruvate dehydrogenase, as discussed in a later section. Conditions of relatively low $NADH/NAD^+$ but less than maximal flux through citrate synthase should reveal control by the acetyl-CoA/succinyl-CoA ratio, if indeed it exists in any quasi-physiological state. Some such conditions were as follows (Hansford and Johnson, 1975).

1. When pyruvate concentration was raised from 0.16 to 2.4 mM, in the presence of nonlimiting concentrations of ADP, flux increased from 66

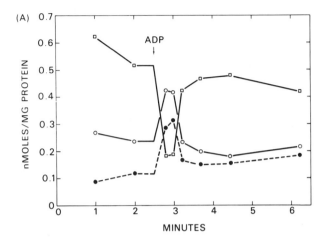

FIG. 4. The response of mitochondrial CoA and CoA thioester content to state $4 \rightarrow 3 \rightarrow 4$ transitions. The mitochondria were from heart, and the substrate was 0.25 mM pyruvate plus 0.5 mM L-malate. Symbols: ○, CoA; □, acetyl-CoA; ●, succinyl-CoA. From Hansford and Johnson (1975), by permission of the copyright holder.

to 76 nmol/min per milligram of protein and the acetyl-CoA/succinyl-CoA ratio increased from 0.49 to 1.1. NADH/NAD$^+$ was not measured but probably increased, and malate was present at 0.5 mM, so that an increased mitochondrial oxaloacetate concentration is unlikely.

2. When respiration was increased progressively by additions of hexokinase via the generation of decreased ATP/ADP ratios, states intermediate between 3 and 4 were found to be associated with very high succinyl-CoA contents and correspondingly low values of the acetyl-CoA/succinyl-CoA ratio. This is shown in Table II. Further stimulation by increased ADP concentration resulted in an increased acetyl-CoA/succinyl-CoA ratio and an increased flux (lines 4 and 5). However, the NADH/NAD$^+$ ratio also declined with this addition of hexokinase (lines 4 and 5), so that increased flux could reflect either an increased acetyl-CoA/succinyl-CoA ratio or an increased oxaloacetate concentration in this experiment. It is noted that the addition of excess ADP, as normally made to effect a state 4 to 3 transition, would have obscured the interesting changes in succinyl-CoA content seen in intermediate respiratory states (Table II).

3. When 2-oxoglutarate was available as a substrate as well as pyruvate and malate, mitochondrial succinyl-CoA contents were very high, apparently setting the stage for control by the acetyl-CoA/succinyl-CoA

TABLE II

RELATION BETWEEN FLUX THROUGH CITRATE SYNTHASE, OXIDATION-REDUCTION STATE OF NAD(P), AND MITOCHONDRIAL ACETYL-CoA/SUCCINYL-CoA RATIO, DURING ACETYLCARNITINE OXIDATION BY HEART MITOCHONDRIA IN STATE 3, STATE 4, AND INTERMEDIATE STATES[a]

Hexokinase present[b] (units/ml)	Ratio ATP/ADP	Rate of O_2 consumption[c] (μg-atoms O_2/min/mg protein)	CoA content	Acetyl-CoA content (% total CoA)	Succinyl-CoA content (% total CoA)	Ratio acetyl-CoA/succinyl-CoA	Reduction of NAD(P) (%)
—	128	0.034	5.2 ± 0.4	75 ± 1	20 ± 1	3.75	73 → 55
1.1	110	0.059	10 ± 1	66 ± 1	23 ± 0.05	2.84	47
2.2	103	0.086	21 ± 2	49 ± 1	31 ± 1	1.60	37
4.3	74	0.117	25 ± 2	23 ± 3	52 ± 1	0.45	21
8.6 + added ADP	0.53	0.162	51 ± 0.2	24 ± 0.4	26 ± 0.2	0.91	15

[a] From Hansford and Johnson (1975), by permission of the copyright holder.

[b] Respiration was stimulated by addition of different amounts of hexokinase in the presence of ATP, Mg^{2+}, and glucose.

[c] The rate of O_2 consumption is proportional to the flux through citrate synthase, owing to the minimal accumulation of tricarboxylate cycle intermediates (see the original work).

ratio. However, an increase in this ratio from 0.48 to 0.81 on changing the ATP/ADP ratio from 22 to 4 was also associated with a decreased $NADH/NAD^+$ ratio, so that any increase in citrate synthase flux was hard to attribute (Hansford and Johnson, 1975).

Possibly the best proof of citrate synthase regulation by oxaloacetate in heart mitochondria comes from the work of Hull *et al.* (1973), who measured oxaloacetate directly in suspensions of mitochondria. Because of the very restricted permeability of the heart mitochondrial membrane to oxaloacetate at micromolar levels (Gimpel *et al.*, 1973; see also Passarella *et al.*, 1978) most of this intermediate was probably intramitochondrial, and one can assume that the concentration of free oxaloacetate was at least qualitatively related to the measured total. Hull *et al.* (1973) showed that addition of malate to mitochondria in state 4 caused a decrease in acetyl-CoA content but a large increase in measured oxaloacetate content, and an increased flux through citrate synthase. Addition of low concentrations of succinate had a similar effect whereas high concentrations of succinate gave a decreased oxaloacetate content, through elevation of the $NADH/NAD^+$ ratio, and a decreased flux through citrate synthase. As the acetyl-CoA content was greater in the last experiment than with malate, one can infer a predominant role for oxaloacetate in controlling citrate synthase under these experimental conditions.

Another dimension to the substrate control of citrate synthase was added by the finding that citrate inhibits the enzyme, competitively with respect to oxaloacetate (Smith and Williamson, 1971). The K_i of 1.6 mM is well within the range of experimentally determined matrix citrate concentrations when mitochondria are incubated with malate as well as an acetyl-group donor (LaNoue *et al.*, 1972; Hansford and Johnson, 1975). The ratio oxaloacetate/citrate thus becomes a determinant of oxaloacetate binding to citrate synthase and an important control parameter (Williamson *et al.*, 1972). It is noteworthy that the state 4 to 3 transition is associated with a large decrease in mitochondrial citrate content when the substrate is pyruvate plus malate, although not when it is pyruvate alone (LaNoue *et al.*, 1972). In the former case, the state 3 $NADH/NAD^+$ ratio is relatively high (LaNoue *et al.*, 1970) and the consequently low concentration of oxaloacetate would presumably severely limit oxaloacetate binding to citrate synthase, in the absence of such a decrease in citrate content.

A summary of this work at the mitochondrial level might be that control of citrate synthase by the oxaloacetate/citrate ratio appears predominant, certainly for the state 4 to 3 transition, which is the main interest of this review. However, a role for the ratio acetyl-CoA/succinyl-CoA in regulating flux in the range of activity between 70% and 100% of state 3 cannot be excluded. In addition, acetyl-CoA availability may mediate the response of flux through citrate synthase to different acetyl-donor activity, as mentioned above in connection with varying pyruvate concentrations, and as discussed below for substrate transitions in intact organs.

Many studies with perfused heart suggest a rise in mitochondrial free oxaloacetate concentration with increased work load. Thus, Neely et al. (1972a) measured an increased whole-tissue oxaloacetate content, either with glucose as substrate or glucose plus palmitate. Malate content was elevated with increased work in the presence of palmitate, but not with glucose alone. It is noted parenthetically that the whole-tissue malate content is often used in the calculation of mitochondrial free oxaloacetate concentration, but that this is not strictly correct owing to the distribution of malate across the mitochondrial membrane in response to the ΔpH (Palmieri et al., 1970). There was no index of the mitochondrial $NADH/NAD^+$ ratio in this study (Neely et al., 1972a) so that the free oxaloacetate concentration is not available. Subsequent work from the same group (Neely et al., 1976) also showed an elevated measured tissue oxaloacetate content with increased work, in the absence of an increased malate content. Opie and Owen (1975) calculated mitochondrial free oxaloacetate concentration from (whole-tissue) malate content and calculations of mitochondrial $NADH/NAD^+$ ratio based on assumption of equilibrium at glutamate dehydrogenase and β-hydroxybutyrate dehydrogenase. They estimated a threefold rise in oxaloacetate concentration to be associated with the threefold increase in O_2 uptake caused by increased work load. Neither glutamate dehydrogenase nor β-hydroxybutyrate dehydrogenase is very active in heart, but the values for mitochondrial $NADH/NAD^+$ ratio calculated on the basis of these equilibria actually agreed very well, provided that the total ketone concentration in the system was low. The mitochondrial $NADH/NAD^+$ ratio fell with increased flux. This corroborated the results of an earlier study (Moravec et al., 1974) in which increased work load gave an oxidation of mitochondrial NADH, measured by fluorometry. Mitochondrial and cytosolic changes could be separated when β-hydroxybutyrate was used as the substrate, because under these conditions change in work load caused no change in the cytosolic $NADH/NAD^+$ ratio, as evidenced by an unchanged lactate/pyruvate ratio. The fluorescence changes could not be so easily assigned when the substrate was glucose, and there was no clear mitochondrial redox change. Similarly, Illingworth et al. (1975) showed a rapid decrease in tissue nicotinamide nucleotide fluorescence on increasing external work performance, which they reasonably attribute to a decreased mitochondrial $NADH/NAD^+$ ratio, on the grounds that it closely parallels the fluorescence change of (predominantly mitochondrial) flavins. In addition, a minimal contribution from cytosolic NADH would be expected, as the substrate used was pyruvate, which would lead to extensive oxidation in this compartment.

Illingworth *et al.* (1975) also showed a large transient rise in malate concentration on increasing the work load and a sustained fall in citrate content. This work is reproduced as Fig. 5, as increased malate concentration, decreased $NADH/NAD^+$ ratio, and decreased citrate concentration will all tend to increase the degree of saturation of citrate synthase with oxaloacetate and explain increased flux through that step. It is noted that Neely *et al.* (1972b) have also shown a decrease in citrate content with increased work load, in that case with glucose plus palmitate as substrate. Similar findings with respect to $NADH/NAD^+$ ratio emerged from studies in which hearts were arrested by exposure to high K^+ concentrations: this led to an increased $NADH/NAD^+$ ratio measured by fluorometry, with glucose plus octanoate as substrate (Hassinen and Hiltunen, 1975), and an increased mitochondrial $NADH/NAD^+$ ratio calculated from the glutamate dehydrogenase equilibrium, with glucose as substrate (Hiltunen and Hassinen, 1976). At the same time there was a decreased flux through citrate synthase. Although results on redox change are fairly consistent and agree with the changes seen in isolated mitochondria during the analogous

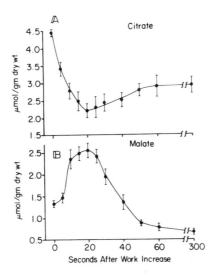

FIG. 5. The response of the whole-tissue content of citrate and malate to a sudden increase in cardiac output. Hearts were perfused with Krebs bicarbonate buffer containing 1 m*M* pyruvate. From Illingworth *et al.* (1975), with permission of the copyright holder.

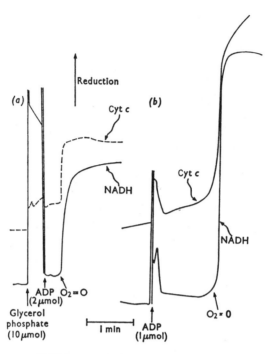

FIG. 6. The response of NAD and cytochrome c to the addition of ADP to blow fly flight muscle mitochondria oxidizing (a) glycerol 3-phosphate and (b) pyruvate. Mitochondrial NADH was measured by fluorometry and reduced cytochrome c by dual-wavelength spectrophotometry. From Hansford (1972a), by permission of the copyright holder.

state 4 to state 3 transitions, there are large discrepancies in the response of malate and citrate contents to changes in work load. Thus, not all studies reproduce the changes shown in Fig. 6. In part this may reflect different responses to different substrates. For instance, Schaffer *et al.* (1978), studying hearts perfused with glucose plus insulin, found a higher steady-state malate content in the state of low work, and a higher measured tissue oxaloacetate content. Moreover, the ratio of oxaloacetate/citrate was only very marginally increased in the state of high work, giving scant explanation of the enhanced flux through citrate synthase on the grounds of oxaloacetate availability. However, the mitochondrial $NADH/NAD^+$ ratio decreased with increased work, and it is possible that the mitochondrial free oxaloacetate concentration and the cytosolic oxaloacetate concentration moved in opposite senses, with the latter dominating the whole-tissue measurement. Neely *et al.* (1972a) also presented data equivocal to a model of citrate synthase control by the oxaloacetate/citrate ratio in that an increased work load gave an unchanged malate content and a decreased citrate content when the substrate was glucose plus acetate, but a decreased malate and unchanged citrate content when the substrate was glucose alone. Clearly, under these conditions, a considerably decreased mitochondrial $NADH/NAD^+$ ratio (and this was not measured) would be necessary to give an increased mitochondrial oxaloacetate/citrate ratio in the state of high flux, under both substrate conditions. Indeed, such an oxidized tendency is probably the most crucial element in this suggested mechanism of control. In keeping with this would be, for instance, the fact that the heart malate content is much higher in the low work state with glucose plus acetate as substrate than in the high work state with glucose alone (Neely et al., 1972a), even though the citrate synthase flux is lower in the former state. Thus the increased $NADH/NAD^+$ ratio with acetate overrides the effect of increased malate, and presumably generates a lower mitochondrial oxaloacetate concentration.

Whereas there is a large body of evidence, much of it indirect, in favor of a control of citrate synthase activity by oxaloacetate availability, there is less evidence in favor of control by the availability of acetyl-CoA. The most likely condition in which this may occur is that of the extremely limited provision of acetyl-CoA seen when the heart is perfused with glucose alone (Neely et al., 1972a,b). In the state of low work the pyruvate dehydrogenase is inhibited by the high $NADH/NAD^+$ ratio by both covalent modification and by end-product inhibition, as discussed in a later section, severely limiting the production of acetyl-CoA. However, even under these conditions, it is not clear that flux through citrate synthase correlates with acetyl-CoA content, or acetyl-CoA/succinyl-CoA ratio. Thus, Neely et al. (1976) maintain that citrate synthase activity must be limited by acetyl-CoA concentration when hearts are perfused with glucose alone, because the absolute tissue content of acetyl-CoA is so low (less than 50 nmol/gm dry wt). However, the transition to high work is associated with, if any change, a decrease in acetyl-CoA content, meaning that this cannot be the explanation of the enhanced flux. Moreover, the general response of heart succinyl-CoA content is an increase with work load (Neely et al., 1972b), making the acetyl-CoA/succinyl-CoA ratio even less favorable. In other experiments, involving substrate transitions, there is, however, suggestive evidence for a control role for acetyl-CoA concentration. Thus, Randle et al. (1970) showed that the introduction of acetate into a heart oxidizing glucose gave a 66% increase in the steady-state flux through citrate synthase, owing to the lowered P/O ratio for acetate oxidation and the avoidance of the pyruvate dehydrogenase reaction. This increased flux was associated with an elevated acetyl-CoA content and an inferred decrease in mitochondrial oxaloacetate. The latter follows from a decreased tissue malate content and the likelihood from other work that the mitochondrial $NADH/NAD^+$ ratio would be raised by acetate oxidation. Furthermore, there was isotopic evidence for production of oxaloacetate from aspartate, which was presumably initiated by a fall in oxaloacetate concentration. At the same time, tissue citrate content increased markedly upon acetate introduction. Similar responses to a shift of substrate from glucose to glucose plus acetate were reported by Neely et al. (1972a), though here increased flux through citrate synthase was associated with an increased tissue malate content, as well as acetyl-CoA content, so that an increased mitochondrial oxaloacetate concentration cannot be excluded from contributing to increased flux through citrate synthase, depending on the magnitude of the change in $NADH/NAD^+$ ratio. In summary, either of the two substrates can probably be made rate-determining experimentally, but in the response of citrate synthase to an increased energy demand upon the tissue, increased oxaloacetate availability through an oxidation of nicotinamide nucleotide is the dominant factor.

B. Control of NAD-Isocitrate Dehydrogenase Activity

NAD–isocitrate dehydrogenase catalyzes a nonequilibrium reaction in the tricarboxylate cycle and has been shown to respond to NAD^+, NADH, ATP, ADP (Chen and Plaut, 1963; Goebell and Klingenberg, 1964; Plaut and Aogaichi, 1968; see Plaut, 1970, for a review), and Ca^{2+} ions (Denton et al., 1978) as allosteric effectors, in studies of the isolated enzyme from a variety of tissues. The increase in catalytic activity in response to a decrease in $NADH/NAD^+$ and ATP/ADP ratios led to the suggestion that NAD–isocitrate dehydrogenase might adjust flux through the tricarboxylate cycle to the energy status of the mitochondrion and the metabolic demands of the tissue (Chen and Plaut, 1963; Goebell and Klingenberg, 1964). The clearest proof of this role for the enzyme in the intact mitochondrion would be the demonstration of increased flux through the isocitrate dehydrogenase reaction in response to a decreased $NADH/NAD^+$ or ATP/ADP ratio and associated with a decreased intramitochondrial concentration of isocitrate. This was essentially shown for rat heart mitochondria by LaNoue et al. (1972), who demonstrated a decreased intramitochondrial citrate content in the state 3, relative to state 4, oxidation of pyruvate plus malate. The content of isocitrate was not measured, and so any extrapolation of these results to isocitrate dehydrogenase involves the assumption of equilibrium at aconitase. LaNoue et al. (1972) also showed that flux through isocitrate dehydrogenase was higher when mitochondria were treated with uncoupling agent plus oligomycin than during state 4 respiration. These states are both associated with high values for the intramitochondrial ATP/ADP ratio, but differ in that the $NADH/NAD^+$ ratio is much lower in the uncoupler plusy oligomycin state. This result suggests an important role for the $NADH/NAD^+$ ratio in regulating flux at this step: the increased flux in the presence of uncoupling agent plus oligomycin cannot be explained on the basis of the intramitochondrial citrate (and presumably isocitrate) content, which is higher in state 4 (LaNoue *et al.*, 1972).

Somewhat similar experiments were done by Hansford and Johnson (1975) with rabbit heart mitochondria. In this case, the intramitochondrial isocitrate content was measured and was shown to decline greatly on the state 4 to 3 transition. Taken with the increased flux through this reaction, the decrease in the term [isocitrate] $\times$ [NAD^+] defines an activation of isocitrate dehydrogenase by an effector other than the substrate. It is noted that this activation may be associated with an increased concentration of the products, 2-oxoglutarate (Hansford and Johnson, 1975; Johnson and Hansford, 1975) and NADH, but that such a "crossover" (see Chance and Williams, 1956) is not necessary for the demonstration of control, as the reaction is far enough from equilibrium for the reverse reaction to be inconsequential (see Rolleston, 1972, for a discussion). This work also showed that control of NAD–isocitrate dehydrogenase by the ratio $NADH/NAD^+$ predominates over control by the ratio ATP/ADP in mitochondria from heart muscle (Hansford and Johnson, 1975). Thus, as shown in Table III, addition of the uncoupling agent carbonyl cyanide *p*-trifluoromethoxyphenylhydrazone in the presence of oligomycin gave an enhanced flux (as approximated by O_2 uptake) and a decreased intramitochondrial isocitrate content, regardless of whether an addition of ADP had first been made. In contrast, addition of ADP in the presence of oligomycin gave no change in flux and little or no change in isocitrate content. The uncoupling agent generated an extremely low $NADH/NAD^+$ ratio; however, the intramitochondrial ATP/ADP ratio presumably remained high (see LaNoue *et al.*, 1972) until the addition of ADP to the suspension.

In heart, there is an obligatory linkage of flux through isocitrate dehydrogenase to flux through citrate synthase, in that mitochondrial permeability to citrate is very limited (England and Robinson, 1969; Sluse *et al.*, 1971; Hansford and Johnson, 1975). Thus active citrate synthesis could presumably lead to increased flux through the isocitrate dehydrogenase reaction, owing to an elevated citrate and isocitrate concentration within the mitochondrion, in the absence of a decrease in $NADH/NAD^+$ or ATP/ADP ratio. Such a control by substrate concentration seems to un-

TABLE III

RELATIVE IMPORTANCE OF ATP/ADP AND NADH/NAD$^+$ RATIONS IN THE
CONTROL OF ISOCITRATE DEHYDROGENASE IN HEART MITOCHONDRIA[a]

Time of sampling or addition (min)	Addition	Mitochondrial content of isocitrate (nmol/mg protein)	Rate of O$_2$ uptake (ng-atoms O$_2$/min/mg protein)	NADH/NAD$^+$ ratio[b]
A				
3		0.48		12
4	Oligomycin plus ADP		21	
5.4		0.39		18 → 5
6		0.44		
6.6	FCCP[c]			
7.5		0.15	98	Nil
8.3		0.15[d]		
B				
1.5	Oligomycin		13	4.2 → 3.1
3		0.30		
4	FCCP			
4.5		0.03	115	Nil
5		0.07		
5.5	ADP[e]			
6		0.04	140	0.08
6.8		0.11[f]		

[a] Redrawn from Hansford and Johnson (1975), by permission of the copyright holder.

[b] NADH/NAD$^+$ ratios were obtained by fluorometry: they are not exact and are used merely to identify very oxidized and very reduced states.

[c] FCCP, carbonyl cyanide p-trifluoromethoxyphenylhydrazone.

[d] $p < 0.005$ for FCCP versus oligomycin + ADP.

[e] ADP was added to give a concentration of 4 mM; prior to that, ATP was present at 0.5 mM.

[f] $p < 0.005$ for oligomycin + FCCP versus oligomycin.

derlie the increased tricarboxylate cycle flux seen on introducing acetate into the perfused heart (Randle *et al.*, 1970). In liver, by contrast, there are alternative fates for mitochondrial citrate—for instance, egress from the mitochondrion and cleavage by citrate cleavage enzyme. Under these circumstances, control of isocitrate dehydrogenase becomes particularly crucial. It was found that isocitrate oxidation by coupled rat liver mitochondria was inhibited by the oxidation of palmitoylcarnitine (Nicholls *et al.*, 1967) and that this effect was largely abolished by uncoupling agents. The mechanism of the inhibition was considered to be the elevation of the NADH/NAD$^+$ or ATP/ADP ratio. Addition of uncoupling agent lowers these ratios but also opens up another pathway of isocitrate oxidation, involving the NADP-linked isocitrate dehydrogenase (EC 1.1.1.42) and the energy-linked transhydrogenase. The latter activity is too low in the coupled mitochondrion, in the direction of oxidation of NADPH, for this pathway to contribute materially to total oxidation of isocitrate (Nicholls and Garland, 1969). However, flux in this direction is facilitated on uncoupling. Nicholls and Garland (1969) declined to attribute quantitative significance to either effector of the NAD-linked enzyme. However, Lenartowicz et al. (1976), in studying the effect of palmitoyl-CoA and palmitoylcarnitine on isocitrate oxidation by rat liver mitochondria, emphasized inhibition by the elevated $NADH/NAD^+$ ratio as much the more important effect quantitatively. Unlike the similar conclusion reached by Hansford and Johnson (1975) for heart isocitrate oxidation, this determination was based upon the kinetic properties of NAD-isocitrate dehydrogenase in a soluble fraction from liver mitochondria. It is hard to extrapolate such results to the enzymes in situ in the mitochondrion, where the protein concentration is much higher and the free Ca^{2+} and Mg^{2+} concentrations, for instance, are not known. However, their conclusion is in accord with the low K_i for NADH (16 μM) found for the purified liver enzyme by Plaut and Aogaichi (1968). Interestingly, palmitoyl-CoA and palmitoylcarnitine had the same effect upon isocitrate oxidation and the ratios ATP/ADP and $NADH/NAD^+$, but by different mechanisms, the former inhibiting the adenine nucleotide translocase (as described by Pande and Blanchaer, 1971; Lerner et al., 1972) and the latter acting as a second substrate, where substrate dehydrogenation was limiting (Lenartowicz et al., 1976).

At the level of the intact perfused heart there is now considerable evidence supporting the model that emerged from the mitochondrial work described above of a direct effect of energy status (ATP/ADP or $NADH/NAD^+$) upon the isocitrate dehydrogenase reaction. Thus isocitrate content fell with increased work load in the presence of glucose or glucose plus palmitate as substrate (Neely et al., 1972b) and increased markedly with cardiac arrest (Hiltunen and Hassinen, 1977). Furthermore, citrate content fell with increased work load when the substrate was pyruvate (Illingworth et al., 1975), isocitrate content not being measured in this latter study but probably being in near equilibrium. The reader is referred to Section III,A on citrate synthase for further discussion of the response of citrate content to changes in work load.

C. Control of the Tricarboxylate Cycle in Insect Flight Muscle

At this point it seems appropriate to describe experiments on the control of the tricarboxylate cycle in insect flight muscle, a tissue uniquely active in catabolism and which offers peculiar advantages in the study of metabolic control. A most pronounced characteristic is the degree of control exercised at the dehydrogenase level, such that the onset of flight in the blow fly is associated with an increased reduction of NAD in the flight muscles (Hansford, 1975). These results are the converse of those discussed so far in relation to the heart and the performance of work and are presented as Table IV. Studies with isolated flight muscle mitochondria (Hansford, 1968, 1972a; Johnson and Hansford, 1977) similarly showed increased reduction of NAD and of cytochrome c on transition from state 4 to state 3, provided the respiratory substrate was pyruvate. This is oxidized completely to CO_2 and H_2O via the operation of the tricarboxylate cycle in insect flight muscle, as mitochondrial tricarboxylate cycle intermediates are not free to leave the mitochondria (Van den Bergh and Slater, 1962). Figure 6 contrasts this increased reduction seen with pyruvate with the "classical" (see Chance and Williams, 1956) oxidation of mitochondrial NAD and cytochrome c seen with glycerolphosphate, the oxidation of which does not involve the tricarboxylate cycle. The site of interaction of ADP with the tricarboxylate cycle emerges quite clearly from the measurements of intramitochondrial intermediates shown in Fig. 7. Citrate and isocitrate contents fall on the state 4 to 3 transition, while

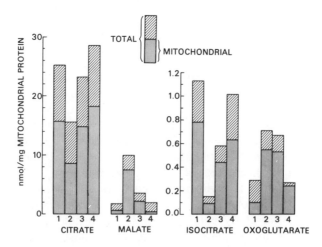

FIG. 7. The response of mitochondrial tricarboxylate cycle intermediates to the transition state 4 → 3 → 4. The mitochondria were derived from blow fly flight muscle. Both the total content of intermediate in the mitochondrial suspension and the intramitochondrial content are presented. The experiment was repeated with five mitochondrial preparations, and changes were significant at the $P < 0.005$ level for citrate and isocitrate, $p < 0.025$ for malate, and $p < 0.05$ for 2-oxoglutarate. Redrawn from Johnson and Hansford (1975), by permission of the copyright holder.

malate content rises markedly. When these intermediates are estimated in extracts of whole blow fly thoraces, analogous changes occur when the insect takes to flight, as shown in Table IV. These results clearly identify an activation at the isocitrate dehydrogenase reaction. Moreover, since the mitochondrial NADH/NAD$^+$ ratio rises in the state of increased flux, this cannot act as a signal to the enzyme for increased activity, as happens in the heart. Thus, the isocitrate dehydrogenase must be responding directly to the decreased mitochondrial ATP/ADP ratio. Experimental confirmation of this emerges from the results shown in Table V, where addition of oligomycin plus ADP resulted in a decreased mitochondrial citrate and isocitrate content, and a large increase in NADH/NAD$^+$ (the latter not shown; see Johnson and Hansford, 1975). Subsequent addition of carbonyl cyanide p-trifluoromethoxyphenylhydrazone enhanced flux (as measured by O_2 uptake) and decreased NADH/NAD$^+$, but gave rise to no further decrement in isocitrate content. These results are contrasted with those presented earlier for the heart.

The kinetics of the NAD–isocitrate dehydrogenase isolated from insect flight muscle mitochondria are in accord with this control role, the enzyme showing exquisite sensitivity to the ratio ATP/ADP (Hansford, 1968, 1972a). The increased mitochondrial NADH/NAD$^+$ ratio in the state of high flux has implications for the regulation of citrate synthase activity in the fly, as clearly redox changes cannot be relied upon to generate an increased oxaloacetate concentration as in the heart. The mechanism instead appears to be the generation of a much increased malate concentration in the presence of ADP (Fig. 8), the mitochondrial changes presumably being somewhat muted by an invariant cytosolic content in the

TABLE IV

Rresponse of Blow Fly Flight Muscle NAD$^+$, NADH, Citrate, Isocitrate, and Malate Content to the Initiation of Flight[a,b]

	NAD$^+$	NADH	Citrate	Isocitrate	Malate
Rest	645 ± 11 (5)	63 ± 4 (7)	1092 ± 57 (10)	30 ± 1 (8)	504 ± 54 (10)
Flight (30 sec)	*561 ± 8 (4)	*183 ± 17 (3)	**732 ± 73 (9)	†22 ± 2 (6)	*804 ± 21 (9)
Flight (120 sec)	589 ± 10 (4)	*153 ± 9 (4)	*686 ± 75 (8)	†22 ± 2 (7)	*834 ± 32 (8)

[a] From Hansford (1975) and Johnson and Hansford, (1975), by permission of the copyright holder.

[b] Values are expressed as nanomoles per gram net weight.

* $p < 0.001$ for the difference between rest and flight.

** $p < 0.005$ for the difference between rest and flight.

TABLE V

RELATIVE IMPORTANCE OF ATP/ADP AND NADH/NAD[+] RATIOS IN THE CONTROL
OF ISOCITRATE DEHYDROGENASE IN BLOW FLY FLIGHT MUSCLE MITOCHONDRIA[a]

Time of sampling or addition (min)	Addition	Mitochondrial content of citrate (nmol/mg protein)	Mitochondrial content of isocitrate (nmol/mg protein)	Rate of O_2 uptake (ng-atoms O_2/min/mg protein)	$\dfrac{NADH}{NAD^+}$ ratio[b]
5.5		7.7	0.41		
6.2	Oligomycin				
6.7	ADP[c]			128	
7.5		2.9	0.20		$\infty \to 2$
8.1		2.8	0.18		
8.7	FCCP[d]				
9.5		4.4	0.14	710	Nil
10.1		4.3	0.18		

[a] From Johnson and Hansford (1975), by permission of the copyright holder.
[b] NADH/NAD[+] ratios were obtained by fluorometry: they are not exact and are used merely to identify very oxidized and very reduced states.
[c] ADP was added to 3.5 mM: prior to that addition ATP was present at 0.5 mM.
[d] FCCP, carbonyl cyanide p-trifluoromethoxyphenylhydrazone.

whole-muscle studies (Table IV). This increase in turn reflects the activation of NAD–isocitrate dehydrogenase, which causes the redistribution of carbon around the cycle, favoring 2-oxoglutarate and subsequent intermediates at the expense of the tricarboxylates. Thus, the oxaloacetate concentration may rise despite the small increase in the NADH/NAD[+] ratio in the state of high flux. Furthermore, oxaloacetate binding to citrate synthase will be enhanced by the lowered citrate content (see Smith and Williamson, 1971). Thus, in this highly specialized catabolic tissue the primary site in the tricarboxylate cycle that is sensitive to the energy status of the mitochondrion is the NAD–isocitrate dehydrogenase, and the primary regulator is the ATP/ADP ratio. Redox changes are small compared to the enormous differences in flux between rest and flight, or state 4 and state 3, but are in the wrong direction to enhance dehydrogenase activity. Finally, pyruvate dehydrogenase in this tissue does not seem to be susceptible to covalent modification (R. G. Hansford, unpublished observation) and is presumably controlled by the acetyl-CoA/CoA ratio, which decreases on transition from state 4 to 3 (Hansford, 1974) in response to increased citrate synthase activity. These experiments with fly mitochondria are described in that the distinction between the effects of ATP/ADP and NADH/NAD[+] ratios is clearer in this tissue and the repercussions of

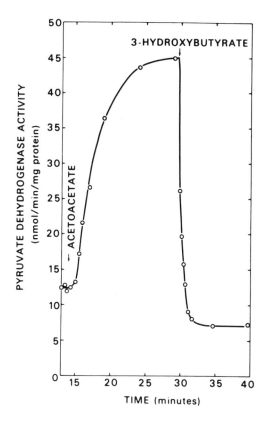

FIG. 8. The effect of changing the NADH/NAD$^+$ ratio on the active, nonphosphorylated pyruvate dehydrogenase (PDH$_a$) content of heart mitochondria. The NADH/NAD$^+$ ratio was measured to be 0.08 after the addition of acetoacetate and 0.14 after the addition of 3-hydroxybutyrate. The other effector ratios were stabilized during the course of the experiment; for details, see the original work. From Hansford (1976), by permission of the copyright holder.

control at the isocitrate dehydrogenase level for the control of citrate synthase activity are apparent. In addition, the control role of isocitrate dehydrogenase operating in the intact mitochondrion was first shown in flies (Hansford, 1968, 1972a; Johnson and Hansford, 1975) and later demonstrated in heart (Hiltunen and Hassinen, 1977).

Very recent experiments with locusts have revealed a somewhat similar pattern of control of the tricarboxylate cycle in flight muscle (Rowan and Newsholme, 1979). The whole-muscle content of citrate was found to fall, and that of malate to rise, with the onset of flight, but changes in isocitrate content were less clear than in the fly (Table IV). The mitochondrial free

NADH/NAD$^+$ ratio was calculated to fall on flight, on the basis of the glutamate dehydrogenase equilibrium, in distinction to the change measured by fluorometry for isolated fly mitochondria during the state 4 to 3 transition. Unfortunately, there is no NAD-linked enzyme of sufficient activity in fly flight muscle to allow the comparable calculation. However, if the reasonable assumption is made of equilibrium at the cytosolic glycerol 3-phosphate dehydrogenase reaction, there is a slight decrease in the cytosolic free NADH/NAD$^+$ ratio on flight (Hansford, 1978). Together with the increase in this ratio seen in whole-tissue extracts, this would tend to confirm that the mitochondrial NAD pool does indeed become more reduced on flight, in the fly. The balance of dehydrogenase and respiratory chain activity may not be the same in flight muscle from the fly and the locust, these two orders differing markedly, for instance, in their ability to use fatty acids.

D. CONTROL OF 2-OXOGLUTARATE DEHYDROGENASE ACTIVITY

2-Oxoglutarate dehydrogenase (EC 1.2.4.2) catalyzes a nonequilibrium reaction that commits 2-oxoglutarate to decarboxylation, as opposed to the alternative fates of transamination or egress from the mitochondria as required by the malate/aspartate cycle (Borst, 1963; Chappell, 1968). For this reason, it is a primary site of control for the segment of the tricarboxylate cycle from 2-oxoglutarate to malate (Randle et al., 1970; Smith et al., 1974), and measurement of 2-oxoglutarate dehydrogenase activity in tissue extracts is a possible yardstick of maximal tricarboxylate cycle activity. Product inhibition of the purified enzyme by NADH and succinyl-CoA was shown by Garland (1964) and later by Smith et al. (1974). It comes within the province of this review in the sense that the mitochondrial ATP/ADP ratio is linked to the succinyl-CoA/CoA ratio, an increase in the former giving an increase in the latter. Thus, high-energy states of the mitochondrion tend to give rise to diminished flux through 2-oxoglutarate dehydrogenase, owing to high succinyl CoA/CoA ratios (LaNoue et al., 1973; Smith et al., 1974). The mechanism involves the succinic thiokinase and nucleoside diphosphate kinase reactions. It is noted that although the measured ATP/ADP and succinyl-CoA/CoA ratios change in the expected sense, equilibration is not achieved, with the suggestion that the nucleoside diphosphate kinase reaction is not at equilibrium in liver mitochondria (Smith et al., 1974). If so, the regulation of this enzyme becomes of interest. Experiments in which NADH/NAD$^+$ and ATP/ADP ratios are divorced with oligomycin and uncoupling agent clearly show that flux through 2-oxoglutarate dehydrogenase is modulated by the succinyl-CoA/CoA ratio in both oxidized and reduced states

(LaNoue *et al.*, 1973; Smith *et al.*, 1974). It is the ratio inhibitor/substrate that is important, as the compounds are present at manyfold the K_i and K_m values, respectively. However, flux is also sensitive to changes in $NADH/NAD^+$ ratio, although the redox changes in these experiments are larger than those expected during physiological transitions. Furthermore, flux is quite dependent on mitochondrial 2-oxoglutarate content, as shown very clearly by LaNoue *et al.* (1973) for heart mitochondria. Comparison of flux through this reaction with measured intramitochondrial 2-oxoglutarate content gave an apparent K_m of 0.67 mM, when mitochondrial 2-oxoglutarate was varied by exchange with extramitochondrial malate, with a mitochondrial NADH content of 1 nmol per milligram of protein and a succinyl-CoA/CoA ratio of 0.4. This K_m value for 2-oxoglutarate is considerably higher than that determined for the purified enzyme (Hirashima *et al.*, 1967; Smith *et al.*, 1974), a finding that demonstrates the dangers of inferring control mechanisms from studies with dilute solutions of purified enzymes. The 2-oxoglutarate content of the mitochondria is a steady-state value, determined primarily by the activities of NAD–isocitrate dehydrogenase and 2-oxoglutarate dehydrogenase. It reaches near equilibrium with the other components of the aspartate aminotransferase reaction and with extramitochondrial 2-oxoglutarate, the distribution across the membrane being near equilibrium with the transmembrane ΔpH (Tischler *et al.*, 1977). Regulation of 2-oxoglutarate dehydrogenase is thus complex, with factors that affect citrate synthase and isocitrate dehydrogenase activity, and thus the supply of 2-oxoglutarate, affecting the susceptibility of the enzyme to inhibition by the succinyl-CoA/CoA ratio (LaNoue *et al.*, 1973).

It is noted that the relation between ATP/ADP and succinyl-CoA/CoA ratios obtained in oligomycin and uncoupler-treated mitochondria (LaNoue *et al.*, 1973; Smith *et al.*, 1974) does not always apply. Thus, although Smith *et al.* (1974) and Hansford and Johnson (1975) found the succinyl-CoA/CoA ratio to be lower in state 3 than in state 4 with 2-oxoglutarate as substrate, Hansford and Johnson (1975) and Hansford (1974) found the converse to be true with pyruvate as substrate, in heart and fly mitochondria, respectively. In the former case, the increased flux through 2-oxoglutarate dehydrogenase in state 3 may reflect the decreased $NADH/NAD^+$ ratio or an increased intramitochondrial concentration of 2-oxoglutarate. In the latter case, the change in the $NADH/NAD^+$ ratio is in the wrong sense to cause activiation, which instead has to be explained in terms of the increased content of 2-oxoglutarate found in state 3 (Johnson and Hansford, 1975) or in terms of a decreased mitochondrial ATP/ADP ratio, which will have a direct activatory effect on the flight muscle enzyme (Hansford, 1972b). Very recently, and after the writing of this section, a direct effect of the ATP/ADP ratio on purified mammalian (pig heart) 2-oxoglutarate dehydrogenase has also been shown (McCormack and Denton, 1979). An increase in this ratio leads to a decrease in enzyme activity, by a mechanism not involving protein phosphorylation. In the light of this finding, the role of the succinyl-CoA/CoA ratio in adjusting flux through 2-oxoglutarate dehydrogenase in accordance with the mitochondrial ATP/ADP ratio may not be as important as previously envisaged (LaNoue et al., 1973; Smith et al., 1974).

Regulation of 2-oxoglutarate dehydrogenase by the concentration of its substrate is a key factor in the adjustment of tricarboxylate cycle activity to changes in substrate availability. Thus, the addition of glucose plus insulin to hearts perfused in the absence of substrate leads to a transient excess in flux through citrate synthase over flux through 2-oxoglutarate dehydrogenase (Safer and Williamson, 1973). The mechanism is thought to be a decreased mitochondrial 2-oxoglutarate content, occasioned by rapid generation of malate in the cytosol and exchange of this malate for mitochondrial 2-oxoglutarate. In time mitochondrial 2-oxoglutarate is replenished by aspartate aminotransferase activity, which is limited at early time points by a slow entry of glutamate into the mitochondrion in exchange for aspartate. The enhanced entry of glutamate that occurs with time, as the cytosolic glutamate concentration rises, also allows mitochondrial aspartate aminotransferase to compete more effectively for oxaloacetate with citrate synthase, and adjusts the flux through the latter enzyme downward. This transient imbalance in activities in the oxaloacetate-to-2-oxoglutarate and the 2-oxoglutarate-to-malate segments of the cycle has been somewhat inelegantly dubbed "unspanning" by the authors (Safer and Williamson, 1973). For more details, the reader is referred to the original paper (Safer and Williamson, 1973) and to a more recent review (Williamson, 1979). The transition has also been simulated using computing techniques by Achs and Garfinkel (1977) with essentially similar conclusions. Achs and Garfinkel (1977), however, put somewhat more weight on the control of 2-oxoglutarate dehydrogenase by 2-oxoglutarate concentration and less on control by the succinyl-CoA/CoA ratio, than do Safer and Williamson (1973). Imbalances in flux, albeit somewhat smaller, on the introduction of acetate into hearts perfused with glucose have been noted by Randle et al. (1970).

E. CONTROL OF SUCCINIC THIOKINASE, SUCCINATE DEHYDROGENASE, AND FUMARASE ACTIVITIES

This topic must be dealt with briefly, for reasons of space. Succinic thiokinase activity in the steady state requires nucleoside diphosphate kinase activity to regenerate GDP, and these combined reactions appear to be significantly displaced from equilibrium in liver mitochondria (Smith *et al.*, 1974). In the absence of accurate measurements of intramitochondrial GDP content, it is hard to know which of the two reactions is non-equilibrium, although the authors consider this to be the nucleoside diphosphate kinase. For a kinetic treatment of purified succinic thiokinase the reader is referred to Cha and Parks (1964); and for nucleoside diphosphate kinase, to Parks and Agarwal (1973).

Succinate dehydrogenase is subject to complex control involving an inhibition by oxaloacetate (Wojtczak *et al.*, 1969), which is modulated by the redox poise of the coenzyme QH_2/coenzyme Q couple (Gutman and Silman, 1975) and an activation by ATP (Gutman *et al.*, 1971b) and by coenzyme QH_2 (Gutman *et al.*, 1971a). The activation by coenzyme QH_2 and by ATP appears paradoxical in that it will favor high enzyme activity in the state of low flux (state 4). For this reason it seems more likely that flux through succinate dehydrogenase is determined by the difference between the K_{equ} and the mass-action ratio of reactants and products. In this connection an increase in the mitochondrial succinate content has been inferred to occur on transition from state 4 to state 3 in heart mitochondria (LaNoue *et al.*, 1970), and a decreased $FADH_2$/FAD ratio has long been known to be a consequence of this transition (Chance and Williams, 1956). There is a very recent review by Gutman (1978) on the control of succinate dehydrogenase.

The reaction catalyzed by fumarase (EC 4.2.1.2) is generally presumed to be near equilibrium, but the author can find no measurements of mitochondrial fumarate content to furnish strict proof.

F. MODELING OF THE TRICARBOXYLATE CYCLE

The transition from low to high work load for isolated heart has been simulated very recently using computing techniques (Kohn *et al.*, 1979). The major source of data on fluxes and intermediate concentrations was the report by Illingworth *et al.* (1975) alluded to earlier; kinetic constants for the very large number of enzymes modeled were derived from elsewhere in the literature. The outcome, very interestingly, is a coordinated control of citrate synthase, aconitase, isocitrate dehydrogenase, succinic thiokinase, nucleoside diphosphate kinase, and fumarase by the intramitochondrial concentration of free Mg^{2+} ion. This is elevated in the state of high work, presumably reflecting exchange of mitochondrial ATP^{4-} by ADP^{3-}. The elevated free Mg^{2+} concentration relieves the inhibition of citrate synthase by citrate^{3-} (and possibly by unchelated adenine nucleotide) and activates NAD–isocitrate dehydrogenase by raising the concentration of the substrate Mg-isocitrate$^-$ and activator MgADP$^-$ and lowering the concentrations of the inhibitors isocitrate^{3-} and ATP^{4-}. Changes in mitochondrial ATP/ADP ratio are inevitably associated with changes in free Mg^{2+} concentration. It seems to the reviewer that the former have been stressed as a mechanism of metabolic control, somewhat at the expense of the latter. The article by Kohn et al. (1979) should help redress the balance. One experimental problem is the measurement of free Mg^{2+} concentration, and this is a strength of the model-building approach.

Other simulations of the tricarboxylate cycle emphasize the importance of the NADH/NAD$^+$ ratio in determining oxaloacetate availability to citrate synthase (McMinn and Ottaway, 1976), as do Kohn et al. (1979). However, there is disagreement about the role of NAD–isocitrate dehydrogenase—McMinn and Ottaway (1976) maintaining that it exerts no control over flux through the cycle in heart, whereas Dynnik and Temnov (1977) found evidence for the concerted control of NAD–isocitrate dehydrogenase by the ATP/ADP ratio and of citrate synthase by citrate concentration, which was advocated by Johnson and Hansford (1975).

IV. Control of Pyruvate Dehydrogenase Activity

The pyruvate dehydrogenase reaction is nonequilibrium and commits glycolytically derived pyruvate to the formation of acetyl groups, with the eventual fate of complete oxidation or lipogenesis. Reformation of glucose is not possible from acetyl groups, and so, to conserve glucose, flux through pyruvate dehydrogenase must be stringently controlled during starvation, the oxidation of fatty acids assuming a greater importance in the provision of acetyl groups for the tricarboxylate cycle and energy production. In addition, flux through pyruvate dehydrogenase must adjust to rates of cellular ATP consumption. In this latter regard, the pyruvate dehydrogenase complex is regulated not only by the ratio NADH/NAD$^+$ but also directly by the ratio ATP/ADP, which makes the enzyme very sensitive to feedback control by the activity of oxidative phosphorylation and an obvious choice of subject for the last part of this review. There are two entirely separate forms of regulation of the activity of the pyruvate dehydrogenase complex. One involves interconversion between an active and an inactive (phosphorylated) form of the enzyme and will be discussed first. The other involves the feedback inhibition of the active (nonphosphorylated) form of the enzyme by the products of the reaction, NADH and acetyl-CoA. This will be discussed later and some attempt made to assign quantitative importance to the two disparate forms of regulation in the overall adjustment of flux through this step. This section will not attempt a complete account of the control of pyruvate dehydrogenase, and in particular the response to hormonal status will not be considered. For recent reviews on this subject the reader is referred to Denton and Hughes (1978) and Denton *et al.* (1975).

A.   CONTROL OF PYRUVATE DEHYDROGENASE BY COVALENT MODIFICATION

The interconversion of pyruvate dehydrogenase between an active, nonphosphorylated, form (denoted PDH_a in this review) and an inactive, phosphorylated, form was first described by Linn *et al.* (1969a,b). Phosphorylation requires an ATP- and Mg^{2+}-dependent kinase, and inactivation is associated with the phosphorylation of one serine residue in the α-subunit of the pyruvate dehydrogenase (decarboxylase) component of the complex (Yeaman *et al.*, 1978). In addition to these studies with the purified enzyme, inactivation has also been shown to be associated with phosphorylation of pyruvate dehydrogenase in the intact mitochondrion (Schuster *et al.*, 1975; Hughes and Denton, 1976; Leiter *et al.*, 1978). Kinase activity is enhanced by increased $NADH/NAD^+$ and acetyl-CoA/CoA ratios (Pettit *et al.*, 1975; Cooper *et al.*, 1975; Kerbey *et al.*, 1976), and quite probably by citrate (Taylor and Halperin, 1973), and is diminished by pyruvate and other monocarboxylates and by ADP (Hucho *et al.*, 1972). Dephosphorylation requires a phosphatase having a low affinity for Mg^{2+} ions relative to the kinase and activated by micromolar concentrations of Ca^{2+} ions (Linn *et al.*, 1969a,b; Denton *et al.*, 1972; Severson *et al.*, 1974). Phosphatase activity, in addition, is diminished by an increase in the ratio of $NADH/NAD^+$ (Pettit *et al.*, 1975). The content of PDH_a at any moment will reflect the relative activities of kinase and phosphatase: the continuous "cycling" between the two forms of pyruvate dehydrogenase is the equivalent of an ATPase and represents the (small) metabolic cost of the sensitivity achieved by such regulation.

Inspection of the properties of kinase and phosphatase suggests that an increase in the ratio ATP/ADP should favor the kinase: this follows not only from the fact that ADP inhibits the kinase (Hucho *et al.*, 1972), and that this inhibition will be diminished, but also from the fact that ATP binds Mg^{2+} ions more tightly than ADP, which will lower the activity of the phosphatase more than that of the kinase (Hucho, 1974). Equally, an increase in the ratio $NADH/NAD^+$, or in the ratio acetyl-CoA/CoA, should favor the kinase over the phosphatase and lead to a lower content of PDH_a. To what extent are these predictions fulfilled in studies with intact mitochondria and intact tissues?

There is a considerable body of work establishing an inverse relation between the mitochondrial ATP/ADP content and the content of PDH_a.

The experimental designs involved the comparison of respiratory states 3 and 4 (Portenhauser and Wieland, 1972, 1977; Hansford, 1977), the use of hexokinase to generate progressive changes in ATP/ADP ratio (Wieland and Portenhauser, 1974), and the use of uncoupling agents, with and without oligomycin, the latter to allow generation of ATP by substrate-level phosphorylation (Wieland and Portenhauser, 1974; Walajtys et al., 1974; Chiang and Sacktor, 1975; Taylor et al., 1975). In general, the correlation was impressive: for instance, Taylor et al. (1975) showed a linear inverse relationship between PDH_a content and the mitochondrial ATP/ADP ratio when the latter parameter was varied over two orders of magnitude. However, there were anomalies. Thus, Taylor et al. (1975) showed that inclusion of octanoate lowered the PDH_a content of liver mitochondria oxidizing succinate in state 3, without a change in the ATP/ADP ratio. Equally, 3-hydroxybutyrate lowered PDH_a content in the same system, whereas acetoacetate raised it. This led to the supposition of an effect of the $NADH/NAD^+$ ratio on pyruvate dehydrogenase interconversion. Similar conclusions, based on similar anomalies, were reached by Kerbey et al. (1976), who also provided suggestive evidence for a role of the acetyl-CoA/CoA ratio in mediating the powerful effect of octanoate oxidation in lowering PDH_a content. These results were understandable in the light of the findings by Pettit et al. (1975) and Cooper et al. (1975) of the effect of $NADH/NAD^+$ and acetyl-CoA/CoA ratios on kinase and phosphatase activity. These findings at the same time offered an attractive mechanism for the inhibitory effect of fatty acid oxidation on pyruvate dehydrogenase (see later) and clouded the earlier results establishing a predominant role for the ATP/ADP ratio in modulating interconversion. The reason is that ATP/ADP and $NADH/NAD^+$ ratios normally shift in the same sense in intact, respiring mitochondria and were probably both changing in the earlier studies. The acetyl-CoA/CoA ratio may well have been changing, too, in a less predictable sense. The effect of these three ratios, altered singly, was studied by Hansford (1976), using nonrespiring heart mitochondria and suitable hydrogen and acetyl-group donors and acceptors. As seen in Fig. 8, the alteration of the $NADH/NAD^+$ ratio, in the absence of changes in the other effector ratios, produces reversible changes in PDH_a content—the inactivation, reflecting excess kinase over phosphatase activity, being very rapid. Figure 9 presents an experiment of similar design, in which only the ratio acetyl-CoA/CoA is changed, with a similar reversible effect on PDH_a content. Finally, Fig. 10 presents the effect of changing the ATP/ADP (as ADP/ATP) ratio, in the absence of changes in the other effectors (cf. Taylor et al., 1975; Kerbey et al., 1976). These studies necessarily involved the use of inhibitors of well described properties to aid in the dis-

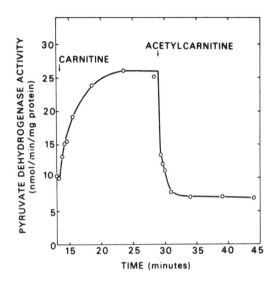

FIG. 9. The effect of changing the acetyl-CoA/CoA ratio on the active, nonphosphoryl-ated pyruvate dehydrogenase (PDH_a) content of heart mitochondria. The acetyl-CoA/CoA ratio was measured to be 0.22 after the addition of carnitine and 8.3 after the addition of ace-tylcarnitine. Other effector ratios were stabilized during the course of the experiment. From Hansford (1976), by permission of the copyright holder.

section of a complex system, in an intact organelle. To this extent, they were model studies and one must extrapolate the results to more intact systems with care. Thus, the criticism offered by Kerbey *et al.* (1977) is appropriate, as it is to all studies that use inhibitors. However, the other criticisms of this work raised by Kerbey *et al.* (1977) are quite groundless, as proton electrochemical activity was already fully equilibrated across the membrane in the earlier study by the use of uncoupling agent and thus was not sensitive to any further slight uncoupling effect of the substrate acetylcarnitine. Nor was an active adenine nucleotide translocase re-quired in mitochondria that were not phosphorylating external ADP. In fact, the attainment of true equilibrium in the effector ratios is the major advantage of respiration-inhibited studies (Hansford, 1976) and is difficult to achieve with respiring mitochondria (Batenburg and Olson, 1976; Kerbey *et al.*, 1976, 1977).

It is clear that the transition from state 4 to state 3 results in an in-creased content of PDH_a in isolated mitochondria (Portenhauser and Wie-land, 1972, 1977; Wieland and Portenhauser, 1974; Hansford, 1977). It is also clear that increasing the work load of isolated perfused hearts in-creases the PDH_a content (Illingworth and Mullings, 1976) and that

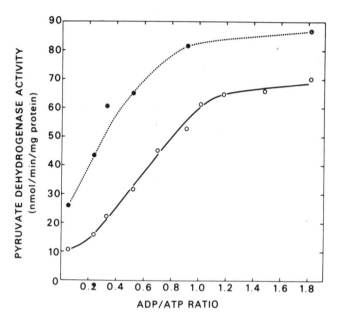

FIG. 10. The effect of the ADP/ATP ratio on the content of active, nonphosphorylated pyruvate dehydrogenase (PDH$_a$) of heart mitochondria in the absence of changes in other known effectors. Mitochondria were respiration-inhibited and incubated in the presence of oligomycin and carbonyl cyanide p-trifluoromethoxyphenylhydrazone. Experiments marked by an open circle symbol (○) included isobutyrate, an inhibitor of pyruvate dehydrogenase kinase. From Hansford (1976), by permission of the copyright holder.

KCl-induced arrest of the heart, with its consequent decrease in mechanical work, results in a decrease in PDH$_a$ content (Hiltunen and Hassinen, 1976). Whether the predominant mechanism is a change in the mitochondrial ATP/ADP or in the NADH/NAD$^+$ ratio, however, is not so clear. Thus, the mitochondrial matrix ATP/ADP ratio may not change much with respiratory state (Davis and Lumeng, 1975; see also Soboll *et al.*, 1978), possibly owing to a direct interaction between the F$_1$-ATPase and the adenine nucleotide translocase (Vignais *et al.*, 1975). Equally, heart tissue ATP/ADP ratios alter only very slightly with work (see Hiltunen and Hassinen, 1976, and Section I of this review). In this context, a decreased mitochondrial NADH/NAD$^+$ ratio may be very important in generating an increased PDH$_a$ content in states of high flux, as this ratio is normally conceded to decrease with increased work load (Moravec *et al.*, 1974; Illingworth *et al.*, 1975; though cf. Nishiki *et al.*, 1978). The reviewer feels that too much emphasis has been placed in the past on control by ATP/ADP ratios, engendered partly by mitochondrial studies in which changes in ATP/ADP ratio have been beyond physiological bounds (e.g., Taylor *et al.*, 1975), and that changes in both the ATP/ADP and NADH/NAD$^+$ ratios are important in the response of muscle tissue PDH$_a$ content to changes in work load, as well as possibly changes in Ca^{2+} ion concentration (Denton *et al.*, 1972; Pettit *et al.*, 1972; Hansford and Cohen, 1978) and citrate concentration (Taylor and Halperin, 1973).

   The mechanism of the response of PDH$_a$ content to the altered availability of fatty acid substrates has been a matter of some controversy. Thus, Wieland and Portenhauser (1974) suggested that fatty acid oxidation might lead to a decrease in PDH$_a$ content via a rise in the tissue content of long-chain acyl-CoA and the well described inhibition of the adenine nucleotide translocase by the latter species (Shug *et al.*, 1971; Pande and Blanchaer, 1971; see Wojtczak, 1976, for a review). Addition of long-chain acyl-CoA compounds to isolated mitochondria was indeed shown to give rise to elevated matrix ATP/ADP ratios and a decreased content of PDH$_a$ (Löffler *et al.*, 1975). The question arises of whether such a mechanism exists in the intact cell or tissue. Siess and Wieland (1976), studying isolated hepatocytes, found that there was a relation between PDH$_a$ content and mitochondrial ATP/ADP ratio when the latter was varied by addition of fructose, sorbitol, glycerol, or ethanol and was measured after digitonin fractionation of the cells (Zuurendonk and Tager, 1974). However, addition of oleate, which is effective in decreasing the PDH$_a$ content of perfused liver (Patzelt *et al.*, 1973), did not elevate the mitochondrial ATP/ADP ratio at the expense of the cytosolic ratio, as would be expected if the adenine nucleotide translocase were indeed made rate-limiting. In addition, hepatocytes from starved or diabetic rats had a much lower PDH$_a$ content yet unchanged mitochondrial ATP/ADP ratios when compared to cells from fed rats. Along similar lines, Akerboom *et al.* (1977), also using hepatocytes and the digitonin-fractionation technique, showed that addition of oleate caused only a very small inhibition in the amount of ATP exported to the cytosol (cf. 2 mM and 3 mM oleate) and no detectable change in mitochondrial ATP or cellular ATP content. A later study from the same group, using the same methodology, was in substantial agreement, although there was perhaps a minimal rise in the mitochondrial ATP/ADP ratio in the presence of oleate (Akerboom *et al.*, 1978). Thus, the idea that long-chain acyl-CoA generated from fatty acids raises the mitochondrial ATP/ADP ratio in intact cells is open to doubt. The apparent discrepancy between these studies and those in which long-chain acyl-CoA is added to dilute suspensions of isolated mitochondria (see, e.g., Löffler *et al.*, 1975) may reflect a lowering of the free acyl-CoA concentration by binding to the much higher concentration of protein in the intact cell. However, it is also possible that the digitonin fractionation technique fails to quench the mitochondrial adenine nucleotide sufficiently quickly and that fatty acid does in fact result in a raised mitochondrial ATP/ADP ratio *in vivo*. This would be in accord with the results of Soboll *et al.* (1978), who showed, using a nonaqueous solvent extraction of isolated perfused liver, that the cytosolic phosphorylation potential exceeded that of the mitochondrial matrix by 2.6 kcal/mol for the fed animal, but only by 0.72 kcal/mol for the starved. If the former difference is in near equilibrium with the mitochondrial membrane potential, $\Delta\psi$ (see Klingenberg and Rottenberg, 1977), then the latter is nonequilibrium, suggesting that the translocase may indeed limit flux through oxidative phosphorylation in the liver from the starved animal. The matter thus remains open. However, it would seem clumsy to control pyruvate dehydrogenase at the level of the adenine nucleotide translocase, the cytosolic ATP/ADP ratio presumably falling to maintain the rate of translocation, with inevitable consequences for ATP-requiring activities in the cytosol and plasma membrane. Such a decreased extramitochondrial ATP/ADP ratio has indeed recently been observed in *in vitro* experiments on the effect of long-chain acyl-CoA compounds on the ADP-limited respiration of liver mitochondria (Christiansen and Davis, 1978).

Be that as it may, it is clear that the effect of fatty acid oxidation on PDH_a content can be explained without reference to inhibition of the adenine nucleotide translocase. Thus, the oxidation of octanoate by liver mitochondria greatly depresses PDH_a content without involving inhibitory long-chain acyl-CoA compounds or affecting the mitochondrial ATP/ADP ratio (Taylor *et al.*, 1975; Batenburg and Olson, 1976), and the oxidation of octanoate or acetate diminishes the PDH_a content of perfused, isolated heart (Olson *et al.*, 1978a). Similarly, palmitoylcarnitine oxidation reduces the content of PDH_a in heart mitochondria without a change in mitochondrial (Kerbey *et al.*, 1977; Olson *et al.*, 1978b) or whole suspension ATP/ADP ratio (Hansford, 1977). The mechanism of these effects, and quite possibly of all the effects of fatty acid oxidation on PDH_a content, is suggested to be the elevation of the $NADH/NAD^+$ and acetyl CoA/CoA ratios seen quite clearly with isolated mitochondria (Batenburg and Olson, 1975, 1976; Kerbey *et al.*, 1976, 1977; Hansford, 1977).

B. Control of Pyruvate Dehydrogenase by End-Product Inhibition and Its Relation to Control by Covalent Modification

Active, nonphosphorylated pyruvate dehydrogenase (PDH_a) is subject to inhibition by the end products NADH and acetyl-CoA (Garland and Randle, 1964; Bremer, 1969; Tsai *et al.*, 1973). Thus, an elevation of the ratios $NADH/NAD^+$ and acetyl-CoA/CoA will be expected to diminish flux through the pyruvate dehydrogenase reaction both by stimulating phosphorylation (see above) and by inhibiting that fraction of the enzyme present as PDH_a. The question arises as to which process is quantitatively the more important.

In the intact heart, PDH_a content changes in response to work load, but the ratio of PDH content to enzymic flux remains essentially unchanged (Hiltunen and Hassinen, 1976; Illingworth and Mullings, 1976). This suggests a predominant role for interconversion in the adjustment of enzyme activity, and a rather constant degree of end-product inhibition. A similar result emerged from studies with isolated heart mitochondria (Hansford and Cohen, 1978), in which the transition from state 4 pyruvate oxidation to a respiratory activity equal to 50% of state 3 led to a large increase in both flux and PDH_a content, the former remaining at 40–50% of the latter. This proportion then expresses the degree to which the PDH_a present in the mitochondrion is not exposed to optimal (V_{max}) conditions and will reflect both end-product inhibition and, possibly, an absolute limitation by CoA availability. These latter mechanisms cannot be separated using intact mitochondria, but such a separation is possible using mitochondrial extracts (see Olson et al., 1978b). Further stimulation of pyruvate oxidation by ADP results, however, in a flux equal to near 100% of the PDH_a content (Hansford, 1977, and unpublished) indicating very little end-product inhibition in state 3.

The introduction of a fatty acid substrate drastically changes the picture presented above. The degree of end-product inhibition is much increased, and this is especially true for state 4 respiration (Portenhauser and Wieland, 1977; Hansford and Cohen, 1978). However, even in state 3, the presence of palmitoylcarnitine as well as 50 μM pyruvate as substrate for heart mitochondria decreases the flux through pyruvate dehydrogenase to 45% of the PDH_a content (calculated from data in Hansford, 1977).

Figure 11 presents some of these relations between covalent modification and end-product inhibition, merely as an example of one kind of approach to assigning relative importance. The PDH_a content of heart mitochondria is increased with dichloroacetate, a nonmetabolizable carboxylate that inhibits the kinase (Whitehouse et al., 1974). PDH_a values are still declining slightly over the period 5–10 minutes but are near enough constant for the disappearance of pyruvate between 5 and 10 minutes to give an approximation of flux that can fairly be compared with the PDH_a content. In the left-hand panel (A), flux is invariant: this is not surprising as pyruvate is the only oxidizable substrate and total dehydrogenase activity is limited by the respiratory chain (state 4 conditions). Accordingly, flux decreases from 29 to 18% of PDH_a with increasing dichloroacetate

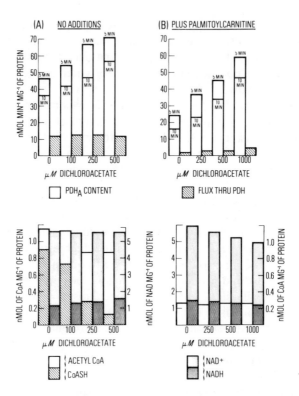

FIG. 11. Comparison of the flux through the pyruvate dehydrogenase (PDH) reaction with the content of active, nonphosphorylated PDH (PDH$_a$). Heart mitochondria were incubated with 50 μM pyruvate (A) or 50 μM pyruvate plus 50 μM palmitoylcarnitine (B) as substrate, and various concentrations of dichloroacetate. Flux was determined by pyruvate consumption, as described in the original work. The lower panels present the mitochondrial contents of CoA, acetyl-CoA, NAD$^+$, and NADH measured under conditions identical to those of the experiments directly above. Data on flux and PDH$_a$ content are mean values derived from three experiments, each using a different mitochondrial suspension; for errors, see the original work. Redrawn from Hansford and Cohen (1978), by permission of the copyright holder.

concentration. Correspondingly, the NADH/NAD$^+$ ratio increases from 0.24 to 0.38, and the acetyl-CoA/CoA ratio from 0.28 to 6.3. Clearly, PDH$_a$ in the mitochondrial environment cannot be very sensitive to inhibition by acetyl-CoA. On the other hand, the acetyl-CoA/CoA ratio is found to vary widely in this and other experiments (Hansford and Cohen, 1978), whereas the NADH/NAD$^+$ ratio is more tightly conserved in keeping with its role in oxidative phosphorylation. Perhaps the most interesting aspect of this experiment is the way in which flux is maintained constant, as dictated by the respiratory chain, in the presence of increased active enzyme protein, by allowing the development of higher concentrations of end-product inhibitors. In the right-hand panel (B), the presence of palmitoylcarnitine decreases the PDH_a content and gives rise to a greater inhibition of PDH_a. This inhibition is rather constant with dichloroacetate concentration, however, such that flux is 7–9% of PDH_a. in keeping with this, the $NADH/NAD^+$ ratio is unchanged with dichloroacetate, at 0.32 to 0.34, and the acetyl-CoA content is unchanged also.

Very recently Dennis et al. (1979) have also used dichloroacetate as a tool in studies of pyruvate dehydrogenase control, in perfused heart. They demonstrated that acetate or octanoate may give an inhibition of flux without a change in PDH_a content, when the latter is "fixed" at maximal levels with dichloroacetate or high concentrations of pyruvate. Moreover, under some circumstances, inhibition of flux may be attributed to changes in the acetyl-CoA/CoA ratio, as the $NADH/NAD^+$ ratio is invariant.

In a sense, it is not surprising that one form of control of pyruvate dehydrogenase can be made to predominate over the other under somewhat extreme conditions (Hansford and Cohen, 1978; Dennis et al., 1979). It is clear that the balance of importance of covalent modification vis-à-vis end-product inhibition can be altered drastically by effectors of the interconversion system, net protein phosphorylation not occurring at all if the pyruvate concentration (Hucho et al., 1972; Hansford, 1977; but cf. Olson et al., 1978b) or the Ca^{2+} ion concentration (Denton et al., 1972; Hansford and Cohen, 1978) are high enough. Under more physiological conditions, there will be an infinite variety in the interplay between these two different forms of metabolic control.

V. Some Concluding Remarks

This review has emphasized control of oxidative metabolism by ADP availability in both isolated mitochondria and perfused organs. In many cases the state 3 to 4 transition (Chance and Williams, 1956) of a suspension of mitochondria seems very analogous to a high-work to low-work transition at the organ level. For instance, the intermediate changes reported by Hiltunen and Hassinen (1977) for the KCl arrest of a perfused heart are very similar to those presented by Johnson and Hansford (1975) for the transition from state 3 to state 4 pyruvate oxidation by isolated mitochondria from another muscle. However, this analogy may lead to the ignoring of other changes occurring in vivo. Thus, there is now a compelling body of evidence that the Ca^{2+} ion also acts as a signal to increase the activity of several mitochondrial dehydrogenases during muscular work. Increased intramitochondrial Ca^{2+} ion concentration in the range 0.1 to 10 μM will lead to an increased PDH_a content via an activation of the phosphatase (Denton *et al.*, 1972) and an inhibition of the kinase (Cooper *et al.*, 1974). The same change will lead to an activation of NAD-isocitrate dehydrogenase by a lowering of the apparent K_m for isocitrate (Denton *et al.*, 1978) and an activation of 2-oxoglutarate dehydrogenase by a lowering of the apparent K_m for 2-oxoglutarate (McCormack and Denton, 1979). That Ca^{2+} sensitivity is not confined to contractile tissues but is found also in liver and adipose tissue (Denton *et al.*, 1978) raises the possibility of a role of Ca^{2+} ions in mediating the hormonal control of dehydrogenase activity, as discussed for the effect of insulin on adipose tissue pyruvate dehydrogenase by Severson *et al.* (1976). This mode of control has recently been queried by Nicholls (1978), who maintains on thermodynamic grounds that the intramitochondrial Ca^{2+} ion concentration never falls as low as the control range defined by Denton *et al.* (1972, 1978) and McCormack and Denton (1979). The resolution of this issue awaits the measurement of mitochondrial free Ca^{2+} ion concentrations. In the meantime it is noted that there may well be entirely distinct, parallel mechanisms for adjusting the activities of pyruvate, isocitrate, and 2-oxoglutarate dehydrogenases to an increased work load upon the tissue. The mechanism dealt with at length in this review involves control by the $NADH/NAD^+$ and ATP/ADP ratios, directly or indirectly, and is the manifestation of respiratory control at the dehydrogenase level. That involving Ca^{2+} ions has not been emphasized, but could provide an important additional control of these three nonequilibrium enzymes. This would be flexible in the sense that mitochondrial Ca^{2+} ion concentration is not directly linked to adenine nucleotide phosphorylation potential, unlike the mitochondrial $NADH/NAD^+$ ratio. Instead, it may be presumed to largely follow the cytosolic Ca^{2+} ion concentration and reflect the activities of ion transport at the sarcoplasmic reticulum and sarcolemma. However, in a contractile tissue, an increased cytosolic Ca^{2+} ion concentration would be associated with an increased availability of ADP to the mitochondrion, and the two mechanisms of control of these three key catabolic enzymes would be expected to reinforce one another.

Substrate availability may also limit respiration and has not been discussed in any detail. Thus, for example, Akerboom *et al.* (1978) showed with hepatocytes that the inclusion of oleate as substrate increased the rate of O_2 uptake by 35%, without any change in cytosolic ATP/ADP ratio, a clear case of substrate limitation. Presumably, in this instance, the mitochondrial $NADH/NAD^+$ ratio increased, thereby driving respiration in the absence of a change in phosphorylation potential (van der Meer *et al.*, 1978; Wilson *et al.*, 1977). Tightly linked to substrate availability is the question of mitochondrial permeability, which cannot be ignored in any broad sketch of the control of mitochondrial metabolism. Permeability has been suggested to limit substrate oxidation by isolated mitochondria (e.g., Palmieri *et al.*, 1967; Harris *et al.*, 1967), and there are many instances in which the dependence of the mitochondrial rate of respiration upon substrate concentration is consistent with the known kinetic properties of the substrate carrier system, derived from direct transport experiments. There are many difficulties, however, in relating these *in vitro* experiments to the physiology of the cell. Thus, the direct measurement of transport normally requires low temperatures (see, e.g., Palmieri *et al.*, 1972; Coty and Pedersen, 1974), and the extrapolation to 37°C is uncertain. Equally, the experimental system is normally set up to avoid "futile exchanges", for instance, the exchange carnitine (in) : carnitine (out) that will occur *in vivo* and lower the effective net flux (Ramsay and Tubbs, 1976). The interpretation of substrate-oxidation experiments in turn is complicated, as most experiments with mitochondria employ a single substrate, whereas *in vivo* the dehydrogenase systems share the load more evenly, with reduced demands on the rate of permeation of any one substrate.

The most telling criterion of whether substrate permeation limits metabolic fluxes *in vivo* is the determination of whether or not substrate species attain equilibrium across the mitochondrial membrane. This will involve not an equality of concentrations, but an equilibration with the ΔpH across the membrane, according to the general relationship log (S mito/S cyt) = $n\Delta$pH, where S is the total concentration of an acidic substrate with p$K \ll$ pH, dissociating to give an anion of charge n (see Palmieri *et al.*, 1970). This follows from the electroneutral exchange of di- and tricarboxylates for phosphate and of phosphate for OH⁻ (see Chappell, 1968). At the moment such evidence from whole cells and tissues is equivocal. Thus, there is some evidence for nonequilibration of dicarboxylates across the mitochondrial membrane, when their distribution is calculated from measured whole-liver metabolite contents and assumptions of equilibrium at several NAD-linked dehydrogenases and transaminases (Parrilla and Ayuso-Parrilla, 1976). On the other hand, direct measurements following a mechanical separation of mitochondrial and cytosolic compartments of hepatocytes indicate a substantial equilibration of the gradients of citrate, isocitrate, 2-oxoglutarate, glutamate, and malate with the ΔpH (Tischler *et al.*, 1977). Thus, steady-state metabolic fluxes do not seem to be limited by the permeation of these compounds. Aspartate distribution is different, owing to the electrogenic nature of aspartate : glutamate exchange (LaNoue *et al.*, 1974). Evidence has been discussed earlier in this review of a transient rate limitation by the activity of aspartate:glutamate exchange during the adjustment of the tricarboxylate cycle and the malate:aspartate cycle to substrate transitions in the heart (Safer and Williamson, 1973; Achs and Garfinkel, 1977).

Finally, it should be said that control of substrate permeation is not really the province of this review, which is the phenomenon of respiratory control, in its broadest sense. This is because the overwhelming evidence is that adjustment of flux through the mitochondrial anion-transport systems occurs by adjustment of substrate concentration. As such, the only transport systems that respond directly to the drop in adenine nucleotide phosphorylation potential, which is the messenger of respiratory control, are the carriers for phosphate and adenine nucleotides. The former seems to be of very high activity (Coty and Pedersen, 1974) and presumably capable of maintaining equilibrium; the latter was discussed extensively earlier in this review. There are reviews of the metabolic implications of mitochondrial substrate transport by Meijer and Van Dam (1974) and by Williamson (1976).

Returning to the state of substrate sufficiency, it is clear that the increase in oxidative flux that occurs during a state 4 to 3 transition must involve activation of the dehydrogenases, as well as the increase in respiratory chain activity described by Chance and Williams (1956). The interplay between the two may be complex and tissue specific. In one case, increased dehydrogenase flux may follow from a decreased $NADH/NAD^+$ ratio in state 3, itself a consequence of facilitated electron transfer by the respiratory chain. This approximates the picture in heart, where the pyruvate dehydrogenase, citrate synthase, and NAD-isocitrate dehydrogenase reactions, for example, are all critically dependent on the $NADH/NAD^+$ ratio, either directly or indirectly, as documented above. In another case, that of insect flight muscle, a primary activation of NAD–isocitrate dehydrogenase by a decreased ATP/ADP ratio gives an enhanced flux through the tricarboxylate cycle, despite a rise in $NADH/NAD^+$ ratio (Hansford, 1975; Johnson and Hansford, 1975). At the same time, activation of the flavoprotein glycerol-3-phosphate dehydrogenase by micromolar concentrations of Ca^{2+} ions released with increased muscle activity (Hansford and Chappell, 1967) contributes to the reduction of flavoprotein and coenzyme Q. Because of the near equilibrium relations between ΔG ATP and ΔEh for the span $NAD^+/NADH$ to cytochrome c Fe^{3+}/Fe^{2+} (Erecińska et al., 1974; Owen and Wilson, 1974), the cytochrome c couple becomes more reduced in the state of high flux, raising the flux through the final, irreversible, step of electron transport. The success of the model of Chance and Williams (1956) has tended to lead to the neglect of this phenomenon of dehydrogenase activation, which was, however, foreshadowed many years ago when Keilin (1925) wrote of another insect—the wax moth, *Galleria mellonella:* "In specimens of males and females which began to struggle constantly, vibrating their wings in efforts to detach themselves from the slides, the bands of cytochrome gradually appeared. When these specimens ceased to move and stopped the vibration of the wings, the bands became very faint and hardly detectable." The increased absorption, of course, corresponded to reduction.

ACKNOWLEDGMENTS

I wish to thank Dr. Bertram Sacktor for his interest in the work from the author's laboratory; Drs. D. G. Nicholls, D. F. Wilson, and J. R. Williamson for permission to reproduce portions of their work; and Dr. D. Garfinkel for allowing me to see several of his manuscripts prior to publication.

REFERENCES

Achs, M. J., and Garfinkel, D. (1977). *Am. J. Physiol.* **232,** R175–R184.
Akerboom, T. P. M., Bookelman, H., and Tager, J. M. (1977). *FEBS Lett.* **74,** 50–54.
Akerboom, T. P. M., Bookelman, H., Zuurendonk, P. F., van der Meer, R., and Tager, J. M. (1978). *Eur. J. Biochem.* **84,** 413–420.
Azzone, G. F., Pozzan, T., Massari, S., and Bragadin, M. (1978a). *Biochim. Biophys. Acta* **501,** 296–306.
Azzone, G. F., Pozzan, T., and Massari, S. (1978b). *Biochim. Biophys. Acta* **501,** 307–316.
Batenburg, J. J., and Olson, M. S. (1975). *Biochem. Biophys. Res. Commun.* **66,** 533–540.
Batenburg, J. J., and Olson, M. S. (1976). *J. Biol. Chem.* **251,** 1364–1370.
Borst, P. (1963). *Wiss. Konf. Ges. Dtsch. Naturforsch. Aerzte* **1,** 137.
Brand, M. D., Reynafarje, B., and Lehninger, A. L. (1976). *J. Biol. Chem.* **251,** 5670–5679.
Brand, M. D., Harper, W. G., Nicholls, D. G., and Ingledew, W. J. (1978). *FEBS Lett.* **95,** 125–129.
Bremer, J. (1969). *Eur. J. Biochem.* **8,** 535–540.
Cha, S., and Parks, R. E. (1964). *J. Biol. Chem.* **239,** 1968–1977.
Chance, B., and Hollunger, G. (1961). *J. Biol. Chem.* **236,** 1534–1543.
Chance, B., and Williams, G. R. (1956). *Adv. Enzymol.* **17,** 65–134.
Chappell, J. B. (1968). *Br. Med. Bull.* **24,** 150–157.
Chen, R. F., and Plaut, G. W. E. (1963). *Biochemistry* **2,** 1023–1032.
Chiang, P. K., and Sacktor, B. (1975). *J. Biol. Chem.* **250,** 3399–3408.
Christiansen, E. N., and Davis, E. J. (1978). *Biochim. Biophys. Acta* **502,** 17–28.
Cooper, R. H., Randle, P. J., and Denton, R. M. (1974). *Biochem. J.* **143,** 625–641.
Cooper, R. H., Randle, P. J., and Denton, R. M. (1975). *Nature (London)* **257,** 808–809.
Coty, W. A., and Pedersen, P. L. (1974). *J. Biol. Chem.* **249,** 2593–2598.
Davis, E. J., and Davis-van Thienen, W. I. A. (1978). *Biochem. Biophys. Res. Commun.* **83,** 1260–1266.
Davis, E. J., and Lumeng, L. (1975). *J. Biol. Chem.* **250,** 2275–2282.
Davis, R. A., and Fraenkel, G. (1940). *J. Exp. Biol.* **17,** 402–407.
Dennis, S. C., Padma, A., DeBuysere, M. S., and Olson, M. S. (1979). *J. Biol. Chem.* **254,** 1252–1258.
Denton, R. M., and Hughes, W. A. (1978). *Int. J. Biochem.* **9,** 545–552.

Denton, R. M., Randle, P. J., and Martin, B. R. (1972). *Biochem. J.* **128**, 161–163.

Denton, R. M., Randle, P. J., Bridges, B. J., Cooper, R. H., Kerbey, A. L., Pask, H. T., Severson, D. L., Stansbie, D., and Whitehouse, S. (1975). *Mol. Cell. Biochem.* **9**, 27–52.

Denton, R. M., Richards, D. A., and Chin, J. G. (1978). *Biochem. J.* **176**, 899–906.

Duszynski, J., Mueller, G., and LaNoue, K. (1978). *J. Biol. Chem.* **253**, 6149–6157.

Dynnik, V. V., and Temnov, A. V. (1977). *Biokhimia* **42**, 1030–1044.

England, P. J., and Robinson, B. H. (1969). *Biochem. J.* **112**, 8p.

Erecińska, M., Veech, R. L., and Wilson, D. F. (1974). *Arch. Biochem. Biophys.* **160**, 412–424.

Erecińska, M., Wilson, D. F., and Nishiki, K. (1978). *Am. J. Physiol.* **234**, C82–C89.

Garland, P. B. (1964). *Biochem. J.* **92**, 10C–12C.

Garland, P. B., and Randle, P. J. (1964). *Biochem. J.* **91**, 6c–7c.

Garland, P. B., Shepherd, D., and Nicholls, D. G. (1967). *In* "Mitochondrial Structure and Compartmentation" (E. Quagliariello, S. Papa, E. C. Slater, and J. M. Tager, eds.), pp. 424–441. Adriatica Editrice, Bari.

Gimpel, J. A., De Haan, E. J., and Tager, J. M. (1973). *Biochim. Biophys. Acta* **292**, 582–591.

Goebell, H., and Klingenberg, M. (1964). *Biochem. Z.* **340**, 441–464.

Greville, G. D. (1969). *Curr. Top. Bioenerg.* **3**, 1–78.

Gutman, M. (1977). *In* "Bioenergetics of Membranes" (L. Packer *et al.*, eds.), pp. 165–175. Elsevier/North-Holland Biomedical Press, Amsterdam.

Gutman, M. (1978). *Mol. Cell. Biochem.* **20**, 41–60.

Gutman, M., and Silman, N. (1975). *Mol. Cell. Biochem.* **7**, 51–58.

Gutman, M., Kearney, E. B., and Singer, T. P. (1971a). *Biochemistry* **10**, 2726–2733.

Gutman, M., Kearney, E. B., and Singer, T. P. (1971b). *Biochemistry* **10**, 4763–4769.

Hackenbrock, C. R., and Hammon, K. M. (1975). *J. Biol. Chem.* **250**, 9185–9197.

Hansford, R. G. (1968). Ph.D. Thesis, University of Bristol.

Hansford, R. G. (1972a) *Biochem. J.* **127**, 271–283.

Hansford, R. G. (1972b). *FEBS Lett.* **21**, 139–141.

Hansford, R. G. (1974). *Biochem. J.* **142**, 509–519.

Hansford, R. G. (1975). *Biochem. J.* **146**, 537–547.

Hansford, R. G. (1976). *J. Biol. Chem.* **251**, 5483–5489.

Hansford, R. G. (1977). *J. Biol. Chem.* **252**, 1552–1560.

Hansford, R. G. (1978). *Comp. Biochem. Physiol. B* **59**, 37–46.

Hansford, R. G., and Chappell, J. B. (1967). *Biochem. Biophys. Res. Commun.* **27**, 686–692.

Hansford, R. G., and Cohen, L. (1978). *Arch. Biochem. Biophys.* **191**, 65–81.

Hansford, R. G., and Johnson, R. N. (1975). *J. Biol. Chem.* **250**, 8361–8375.

Harris, E. J., Höfer, M. P., and Pressman, B. C. (1967). *Biochemistry* **6**, 1348–1360.

Hassinen, I. E., and Hiltunen, J. K. (1975). *Biochim. Biophys. Acta* **408**, 319–330.

Heldt, H. W. (1969). *In* "Inhibitors, Tools in Cell Research" (T. Bücher and H. Sies, eds.), pp. 301–317. Springer-Verlag, Berlin and New York.

Heldt, H. W., and Klingenberg, M. (1968). *Eur. J. Biochem.* **4**, 1–8.

Heldt, H. W., and Pfaff, E. (1969). *Eur. J. Biochem.* **10**, 494–500.

Heldt, H. W., Klingenberg, M., and Milovancev, M. (1972). *Eur. J. Biochem.* **30**, 434–440.

Hiltunen, J. K., and Hassinen, I. E. (1976). *Biochim. Biophys. Acta* **440**, 377–390.

Hiltunen, J. K., and Hassinen, I. E. (1977). *Int. J. Biochem.* **8**, 505–509.

Hirashima, M., Hayakawa, T., and Koike, M. (1967). *J. Biol. Chem.* **242**, 902–907.

Holian, A., Owen, C. S., and Wilson, D. F. (1977). *Arch. Biochem. Biophys.* **181**, 164–171.

Hucho, F. (1974). *Eur. J. Biochem.* **46**, 499–505.

Hucho, F., Randall, D. D., Roche, T. E., Burgett, M. W., Pelley, J. W., and Reed, L. J. (1972). *Arch. Biochem. Biophys.* **151**, 328–340.

Hughes, W. A., and Denton, R. M. (1976). *Nature (London)* **264**, 471–473.

Hull, F. E., Cheney, H., and Baker, L. (1973). *J. Mol. Cell. Cardiol.* **5**, 319–339.

Illingworth, J. A., and Mullings, R. (1976). *Biochem. Soc. Trans.* **4**, 291–292.

Illingworth, J. A., Ford, W. C. L., Kobayashi, K., and Williamson, J. R. (1975). *Recent Adv. Stud. Card. Struct. Metab.* **8**, 271–290.

Johnson, R. N., and Hansford, R. G. (1975). *Biochem. J.* **146**, 527–535.

Johnson, R. N., and Hansford, R. G. (1977). *Biochem. J.* **164**, 305–322.

Keilin, D. (1925). *Proc. R. Soc. London, Ser. B* **98**, 312–339.

Kemp, A., Jr., Groot, G. S. P., and Reitsma, H. J. (1969). *Biochim. Biophys. Acta* **180**, 28–34.

Kerbey, A. L., Randle, P. J., Cooper, R. H., Whitehouse, S., Pask, H. T., and Denton, R. M. (1976). *Biochem. J.* **154**, 327–348.

Kerbey, A. L., Radcliffe, P. M., and Randle, P. J. (1977). *Biochem. J.* **164**, 509–519.

Klingenberg, M. (1970). *Essays Biochem.* **6**, 119–159.

Klingenberg, M. (1976). *In* "The Enzymes of Biological Membranes" (A. Martonosi, ed.), Vol. 3, pp. 383–438. Plenum, New York.

Klingenberg, M., and Bücher, T. (1961). *Biochem. Z.* **334**, 1–17.

Klingenberg, M., and Rottenberg, H. (1977). *Eur. J. Biochem.* **73**, 125–130.

Kohn, M. C., Achs, M. J., and Garfinkel, D. (1979). *Am. J. Physiol.* **237**, R159–166.

Kosicki, G. W., and Lee, L. P. K. (1966). *J. Biol. Chem.* **241**, 3571–3574.

Küster, U., Bohnensack, R., and Kunz, W. (1976). *Biochim. Biophys. Acta* **440**, 391–402.

LaNoue, K., Nicklas, W. J., and Williamson, J. R. (1970). *J. Biol. Chem.* **245**, 102–111.

LaNoue, K. F., Bryla, J., and Williamson, J. R. (1972). *J. Biol. Chem.* **247**, 667–679.

LaNoue, K. F., Walajtys, E. I., and Williamson, J. R. (1973). *J. Biol. Chem.* **248**, 7171–7183.

LaNoue, K., Meijer, A. J., and Brouwer, A. (1974). *Arch. Biochem. Biophys.* **161**, 544–550.

LaNoue, K., Mizani, S. M., and Klingenberg, M. (1978). *J. Biol. Chem.* **253**, 191–198.

Lehninger, A. L. (1946). *J. Biol. Chem.* **164**, 291.

Leiter, A. B., Weinberg, M., Isohashi, F., Utter, M. F., and Linn, T. (1978). *J. Biol. Chem.* **253**, 2716–2723.

Lemasters, J. J., and Sowers, A. E. (1979). *J. Biol. Chem.* **254**, 1248–1251.

Lenartowicz, E., Winter, C., Kunz, W., and Wojtczak, A. B. (1976). *Eur. J. Biochem.* **67**, 137–144.

Lerner, E., Shug, A. L., Elson, C., and Schrago, E. (1972). *J. Biol. Chem.* **247**, 1513–1519.

Linn, T. C., Pettit, F. H., and Reed, L. J. (1969a). *Proc. Natl. Acad. Sci. U.S.A.* **62**, 234–241.

Linn, T. C., Pettit, F. H., Hucho, F., and Reed, L. J. (1969b). *Proc. Natl. Acad. Sci. U.S.A.* **64**, 227–234.

Löffler, G., Bard, S., and Wieland, O. H. (1975). *FEBS Lett.* **60**, 269–274.

Lopes-Cardozo, M., and Van den Bergh, S. G. (1972). *Biochim. Biophys. Acta* **283**, 1–15.

McCormack, J. G., and Denton, R. M. (1979). *Biochem. J.* **180**, 533–544.

McElroy, F. A., Wong, G. S., and Williams, G. R. (1968). *Arch. Biochem. Biophys.* **128**, 563–565.

McMinn, C. L., and Ottaway, J. H. (1976). *J. Theor. Biol.* **56**, 57–73.

Meijer, A. J., and Van Dam, K. (1974). *Biochim. Biophys. Acta* **346**, 213–244.

Meisner, H., Palmieri, F., and Quagliariello, E. (1972). *Biochemistry* **11**, 949–955.

Mitchell, P. (1961). *Nature (London)* **191**, 144.

Mitchell, P. (1966). *Biol. Rev. Cambridge Philos. Soc.* **41**, 445–501.

Mitchell, P. (1979). *Eur. J. Biochem.* **95**, 1–20.

Mitchell, P., and Moyle, J. (1969). *Eur. J. Biochem.* **7**, 471–484.

Moravec, J., Corsin, A., Owen, P., and Opie, L. H. (1974). *J. Mol. Cell. Cardiol.* **6,** 187–200.

Neely, J. R., Denton, R. M., England, P. J., and Randle, P. J. (1972a). *Biochem. J.* **128,** 147–159.

Neely, J. R., Rovetto, M. J., and Oram, J. F. (1972b). *Prog. Cardiovasc. Dis.* **15,** 289–329.

Neely, J. R., Whitmer, K. M., and Mochizuki, S. (1976). *Circ. Res.* **38,** Suppl. 1, I-22–I-30.

Nicholls, D. G. (1974a). *Eur. J. Biochem.* **49,** 573–583.

Nicholls, D. G. (1974b). *Eur. J. Biochem.* **50,** 305–315.

Nicholls, D. G. (1978). *Biochem. J.* **176,** 463–474.

Nicholls, D. G., and Bernson, V. S. M. (1977). *Eur. J. Biochem.* **75,** 601–612.

Nicholls, D. G., and Garland, P. B. (1969). *Biochem. J.* **114,** 215–225.

Nicholls, D. G., Shepherd, D., and Garland, P. B. (1967). *Biochem. J.* **103,** 677–691.

Nishiki, K., Erecińska, M., and Wilson, D. F. (1978). *Am. J. Physiol.* **234,** C73–81.

Nohl, H., and Klingenberg, M. (1978). *Biochim. Biophys. Acta* **503,** 155–169.

Olson, M. S., and Williamson, J. R. (1971). *J. Biol. Chem.* **246,** 7794–7803.

Olson, M. S., Dennis, S. C., DeBuysere, M. S., and Padma, A. (1978a). *J. Biol. Chem.* **253,** 7369–7375.

Olson, M. S., Dennis, S. C., Routh, C. A., and DeBuysere, M. S. (1978b). *Arch. Biochem. Biophys.* **187,** 121–131.

Opie, L. H., and Owen, P. (1975). *Biochem. J.* **148,** 403–415.

Owen, C. S., and Wilson, D. F. (1974). *Arch. Biochem. Biophys.* **161,** 581–591.

Padan, E., and Rottenberg, H. (1973). *Eur. J. Biochem.* **40,** 431–437.

Palmieri, F., Cisternino, M., and Quagliariello, E. (1967). *Biochim. Biophys. Acta* **143,** 625–627.

Palmieri, F., Quagliariello, E., and Klingenberg, M. (1970). *Eur. J. Biochem.* **17,** 230–238.

Palmieri, F., Stipani, I., Quagliariello, E., and Klingenberg, M. (1972). *Eur. J. Biochem.* **26,** 587–594.

Pande, S. V., and Blanchaer, M. C. (1971). *J. Biol. Chem.* **246,** 402–411.

Parks, R. E., Jr., and Agarwal, R. P. (1973). *In* "The Enzymes" (P. D. Boyer, ed.), 3rd ed., Vol. 8, pp. 307–333. Academic Press, New York.

Parrilla, R., and Ayuso-Parrilla, M. S. (1976). *Pfluegers Arch.* **362,** 49–54.

Passarella, S., Palmieri, F., and Quagliariello, E. (1978). *FEBS Lett.* **90,** 61–68.

Patzelt, C., Löffler, G., and Wieland, O. H. (1973). *Eur. J. Biochem.* **33,** 117–122.

Pettit, F. H., Roche, T. E., and Reed, L. J. (1972). *Biochem. Biophys. Res. Commun.* **49,** 563–571.

Pettit, F. H., Pelley, J. W., and Reed, L. J. (1975). *Biochem. Biophys. Res. Commun.* **65,** 575–582.

Pfaff, E., Heldt, H. W., and Klingenberg, M. (1969). *Eur. J. Biochem.* **10,** 484–493.

Plaut, G. W. E. (1970). *Curr. Top. Cell. Regul.* **2,** 1–27.

Plaut, G. W. E., and Aogaichi, T. (1968). *J. Biol. Chem.* **243,** 5572–5583.

Portenhauser, R., and Wieland, O. H. (1972). *Eur. J. Biochem.* **31,** 308–314.

Portenhauser, R., and Wieland, O. H. (1977). *Hoppe Seyler's Z. Physiol. Chem.* **358,** 647–658.

Ramsay, R. R., and Tubbs, P. K. (1976). *Eur. J. Biochem.* **69,** 299–303.

Randle, P. J., England, P. J., and Denton, R. M. (1970). *Biochem. J.* **117,** 677–695.

Reynafarje, B., and Lehninger, A. L. (1978). *J. Biol. Chem.* **253,** 6331–6334.

Reynafarje, B., Brand, M. D., and Lehninger, A. L. (1976). *J. Biol. Chem.* **251,** 7442–7451.

Rich, T. L., and Williamson, J. R. (1978). *In* "Frontiers of Biological Energetics" (P. L. Dutton, J. S. Leigh, and A. Scarpa, eds.), Vol. 2, pp. 1523–1532. Academic Press, New York.

Rolleston, F. S. (1972). *Curr. Top. Cell. Regul.* **5**, 47–75.

Rowan, A. N., and Newsholme, E. A. (1979). *Biochem. J.* **178**, 209–216.

Sacktor, B., and Hurlbut, E. C. (1966). *J. Biol. Chem.* **241**, 632–634.

Safer, B., and Williamson, J. R. (1973). *J. Biol. Chem.* **248**, 2570–2579.

Schaffer, S. W., Safer, B., Ford, C., Illingworth, J., and Williamson, J. R. (1978). *Am. J. Physiol.* **234**, H40–H51.

Scherer, B., Grebe, K., Riccio, P., and Klingenberg, M. (1973). *FEBS Lett.* **31**, 15–19.

Schuster, S. M., Olson, M. S., and Routh, C. A. (1975). *Arch. Biochem. Biophys.* **171**, 745–752.

Severson, D. L., Denton, R. M., Pask, H. T., and Randle, P. J. (1974). *Biochem. J.* **140**, 225–237.

Severson, D. L., Denton, R. M., Bridges, B. J., and Randle, P. J. (1976). *Biochem. J.* **154**, 209–223.

Shepherd, D., and Garland, P. B. (1969). *Biochem. J.* **114**, 597–610.

Shepherd, D., Yates, D. W., and Garland, P. B. (1965). *Biochem. J.* **97**, 38c.

Shug, A., Lerner, E., Elson, C., and Shrago, E. (1971). *Biochem. Biophys. Res. Commun.* **43**, 557–563.

Siess, E. A., and Wieland, O. H. (1976). *Biochem. J.* **156**, 91–102.

Slater, E. C., Rosing, J., and Mol, A. (1973). *Biochim. Biophys. Acta* **292**, 534–553.

Sluse, F. E., Meijer, A. J., and Tager, J. M. (1971). *FEBS Lett.* **18**, 149–151.

Smith, C. M., and Williamson, J. R. (1971). *FEBS Lett.* **18**, 35–38.

Smith, C. M., Bryla, J., and Williamson, J. R. (1974). *J. Biol. Chem.* **249**, 1497–1505.

Soboll, S., Scholz, R., and Heldt, H. W. (1978). *Eur. J. Biochem.* **87**, 377–390.

Srere, P. A. (1972). *In* "Energy Metabolism and the Regulation of Metabolic Processes in Mitochondria" (M. A. Mehlman and R. W. Hanson, eds.), pp. 79–91. Academic Press, New York.

Srere, P. A. (1974). *Life Sci.* **15**, 1695–1710.

Stubbs, M., Vignais, P. V., and Krebs, H. A. (1978). *Biochem. J.* **172**, 333–342.

Taylor, S. I., Mukherjee, C., and Jungas, R. L. (1975). *J. Biol. Chem.* **250**, 2028–2035.

Taylor, W. M., and Halperin, M. L. (1973). *J. Biol. Chem.* **248**, 6080–6083.

Thayer, W. S., and Hinkle, P. C. (1973). *J. Biol. Chem.* **248**, 5395–5402.

Tischler, M. E., Friedrichs, D., Coll, K., and Williamson, J. R. (1977). *Arch. Biochem. Biophys.* **184**, 222–236.

Tsai, C. S., Burgett, M. W., and Reed, L. J. (1973). *J. Biol. Chem.* **248**, 8348–8352.

Van Dam, K., Wiechmann, A. H. C. A., and Hellingwerf, K. J. (1977). *Biochem. Soc. Trans.* **5**, 485–491.

Van den Bergh, S. G., and Slater, E. C. (1962). *Biochem. J.* **82**, 362–371.

van der Meer, R., Akerboom, T. P. M., Groen, A. K., and Tager, J. M. (1978). *Eur. J. Biochem.* **84**, 421–428.

Vercesi, A., Reynafarje, B., and Lehninger, A. L. (1978). *J. Biol. Chem.* **253**, 6379–6385.

Vignais, P. V. (1976). *Biochim. Biophys. Acta* **456**, 1–38.

Vignais, P. V., Vignais, P. M., and Doussiere, J. (1975). *Biochim. Biophys. Acta* **376**, 219–230.

Walajtys, E. I., Gottesman, D. P., and Williamson, J. R. (1974). *J. Biol. Chem.* **249**, 1857–1865.

Whitehouse, S., Cooper, R. H., and Randle, P. J. (1974). *Biochem. J.* **141**, 761–774.

Wiechmann, A. H. C. A., Beem, E. P., and Van Dam, K. (1975). *In* "Electron Transfer Chains and Oxidative Phosphorylation" (E. Quagliariello, S. Papa, F. Palmieri, E. C. Slater, and N. Siliprandi, eds.), pp. 335–342. North-Holland Publ., Amsterdam.

Wieland, O. H., and Portenhauser, R. (1974). *Eur. J. Biochem.* **45**, 577–588.

Wieland, O. H., and Weiss, L. (1963). *Biochem. Biophys. Res. Commun.* **13,** 26–31.

Williamson, J. R. (1976). *In* "Gluconeogenesis" (M. A. Mehlman and R. W. Hanson, eds.), pp. 165–220. Wiley, New York.

Williamson, J. R. (1979). *Annu. Rev. Physiol.* **41,** 485–506.

Williamson, J. R., Smith, C. M., LaNoue, K. F., and Bryła, J. (1972). *In* "Energy Metabolism and the Regulation of Metabolic Processes in Mitochondria" (M. A. Mehlman and R. W. Hanson, eds.), pp. 185–210. Academic Press, New York.

Wilson, D. F., and Brocklehurst, E. S. (1973). *Arch. Biochem. Biophys.* **158,** 200–212.

Wilson, D. F., Stubbs, M., Oshino, N., and Erecińska, M. (1974). *Biochemistry* **13,** 5305–5311.

Wilson, D. F., Owen, C. S., and Holian, A. (1977). *Arch. Biochem. Biophys.* **182,** 749–762.

Wojtczak, L. (1976). *J. Bioenerg. Biomembr.* **8,** 293–311.

Wojtczak, L., Wojtczak, A. B., and Ernster, L. (1969). *Biochim. Biophys. Acta* **191,** 10–21.

Yeaman, S. J., Hutcheson, E. T., Roche, T. E., Pettit, F. H., Brown, J. R., Reed, L. J., Watson, D. C., and Dixon, G. H. (1978). *Biochemistry* **17,** 2364–2370.

Zuurendonk, P. F., and Tager, J. M. (1974). *Biochim. Biophys. Acta* **333,** 393–399.

Electrochemistry of Nitrogenase and the Role of ATP

ROBERT V. HAGEMAN[1] AND R. H. BURRIS

Department of Biochemistry
College of Agricultural and Life Sciences
University of Wisconsin—Madison
Madison, Wisconsin

I. Introduction

The nitrogenase enzyme system catalyzes the ATP-dependent reduction of N_2 to $2NH_3$, a process requiring the transfer of six electrons. Multielectron processes such as this are rare in either chemistry or biochemistry and as such are of considerable interest. Although the overall reaction ($N_2 + 3H_2 \rightarrow 2NH_3$) is thermodynamically favorable, both the chemical and biochemical reactions require a large energy input. The industrial reaction utilizes high temperature and high pressure to overcome the activation energy barrier, whereas the biological reaction requires the energy from at least 12 molecules of ATP for each N_2 reduced. Little is known about how the nitrogenase enzyme system effects the reduction of N_2,

---

[1] Present address: Department of Chemistry, Stanford University, Stanford, California 94305.

although the overall outline of the reaction sequence has been defined, and some of the prosthetic groups of the enzyme have been identified. We will concentrate on how the electrons destined for the reduction of N_2 are processed and what role MgATP performs in the reaction. The role of MgATP is particularly interesting, as it represents the coupling of the hydrolysis energy of ATP to an electron transfer reaction occurring in a soluble system.

II. Nitrogenase and the Nitrogenase Reaction

A. NITROGENASE COMPONENTS

The nitrogenase enzyme system consists of two proteins: dinitrogenase, which is an enzyme containing molybdenum and iron, and dinitrogenase reductase, which is an enzyme containing iron. Dinitrogenase contains 2 atoms of molybdenum, about 30 atoms of iron and 30 atoms of acid-labile sulfur per $\alpha_2\beta_2$ tetramer of molecular weight 200,000–240,000. The molybdenum and some of the iron and sulfur are contained in a small cofactor that is responsible for the unusual electron paramagnetic resonance (EPR) signal of dinitrogenase. Dinitrogenase reductase is an α_2 dimer with a molecular weight of about 60,000. It contains a single $Fe_4S_4^*$ cluster (Winter and Burris, 1976; Zumft, 1976; Mortenson and Thorneley, 1979).

B. THE NITROGENASE REACTION

The reaction of biological importance catalyzed by the nitrogenase enzyme system is the six-electron reduction of dinitrogen to ammonia. The electrons are donated *in vivo* by ferredoxin or flavodoxin, whereas *in vitro* the most commonly used reductant is sodium dithionite. The electrons pass through dinitrogenase reductase and thence to dinitrogenase. Dinitrogenase acts as a storage sink for electrons, and passes the electrons in multiples of 2 to substrates. In addition to the reduction of N_2, dinitrogenase will reduce a number of other substrates; the most studied of these reactions are the reduction of acetylene to ethylene and the reduction of protons to H_2. Nitrous oxide, azide, cyanide, methyl isocyanide, cyclopropene, and some of their analogs also are reduced. All the reductions catalyzed by the nitrogenase system are accompanied by the hydrolysis of a large amount of MgATP. The minimum MgATP hydrolysed appears to be four MgATPs per two electrons transferred to substrate ($4 \text{ ATP}/e_2^-$), much larger numbers being observed under some conditions

(Winter and Burris, 1976; Zumft, 1976; Mortenson and Thorneley, 1979). The function of the MgATP hydrolysis will be considered later in this chapter.

C. Intermediates and Energy

The reduction of N_2 to 2 NH_3 by H_2 is a thermodynamically favorable reaction; however, the formation of possible intermediates, such as N_2H_2 or N_2H_4, is unfavorable. The most reasonable reaction sequence thus appears to be one in which the partially reduced intermediates are avoided. In spite of the logic of this argument, all available evidence points to the reduction of N_2 by two e^- steps. Indeed, a tightly bound intermediate at the reduction level of N_2H_4 has been chemically trapped and shown to exist in a stoichiometric relationship to dinitrogenase (Thorneley et al., 1978). Additionally, N_2H_2 has been implicated in the formation of HD by the nitrogenase system (Newton et al., 1977). These intermediates, however, are not released into solution by the enzyme.

D. Electron Donors and Potentials

The in vivo electron donor to the nitrogenase system appears to be either ferredoxin or flavodoxin (Yates, 1977). Ferredoxin has a midpoint potential approximately equal to that of the H_2 electrode at pH 7 (-403 mV: Stombaugh et al., 1976), whereas flavodoxin is considerably more negative (-495 mV: Mayhew, 1978). The biological reductants thus

TABLE I

Thermodynamics for the Reduction of N_2[a]

Reaction	Gas phase		Aqueous $G°$
	$H°$	$G°$	
$N_2 + 3H_2 \rightarrow 2NH_3$	-92	-33.4	-100
$N_2 + H_2 \rightarrow N_2H_2$	$+150$	$+213$	$+150$
$N_2 + 2H_2 \rightarrow N_2H_4$	$+95$	$+159$	$+96$
$N_2H_2 + H_2 \rightarrow N_2H_4$	-56	-54	-54
$N_2H_4 + H_2 \rightarrow 2NH_3$	-187	-192	-194
$C_2H_2 + H_2 \rightarrow C_2H_4$	-175	-141	—
$MgATP + H_2O \rightarrow MgADP + P_1$	—	—	-37

[a] Gas phase values were calculated from data in Stiefel (1977); aqueous phase values are from Leigh (1977). Values are expressed as kilojoules.

TABLE II

REDUCTION POTENTIALS

FOR NITROGENASE REACTIONS[a]

Reaction	$E^{\circ\prime}$ (mV)
$N_2 + 2e^- + 2H^+ \rightarrow N_2H_2$	-1050
$N_2H_2 + 2e^- + 3H^+ \rightarrow N_2H_5^+$	-350
$N_2H_5^+ + 2e^- + 3H^+ \rightarrow 2NH_4^+$	$+550$
$N_2 + 4e^- + 5H^+ \rightarrow N_2H_5^+$	-695
$N_2 + 6e^- + 8H^+ \rightarrow 2NH_4^+$	-280
$C_2H_4 + 2e^- + 2H^+ \rightarrow C_2H_4$	$+320$

[a] Data from Stiefel (1977).

can be equated to H_2 for the purpose of comparing the thermodynamics of the reactions. The *in vitro* electron donor, dithionite, has a midpoint potential even more negative than flavodoxin at pH 7 (Mayhew, 1978). Table I shows the gas phase thermodynamic constants for a number of reactions of possible interest in the reduction of N_2 (Leigh, 1977; Stiefel, 1977). The constants for the reduction of C_2H_2 are included. It is apparent that the barrier in the reduction of N_2 lies in the formation of N_2H_2. Once this product is formed, the further reduction to NH_3 is exothermic. A process that would form N_2H_4 as the first intermediate would be much more favorable thermodynamically than one in which N_2H_2 was formed. It is evident that the reduction of C_2H_2 by the nitrogenase system can be quite exothermic. Table II compares the reduction potentials of the reactions shown in Table I (Stiefel, 1977). If the hydrolysis energy of the 4 ATP/e_2^- is converted to a change in electrode potential, it could decrease the potential of dinitrogenase reductase by approximately 700 mV (from its value of about -400 mV), which would give a reduction potential comparable to that necessary to form diimide (diazene) as an intermediate.

III.   Oxidation–Reduction of Nitrogenase Components

A.   DINITROGENASE REDUCTASE

The $Fe_4S_4^*$ cluster of dinitrogenase reductase is in the reduced state as isolated in the presence of dithionite, and it can be oxidized electrochemically (Zumft *et al.*, 1974), chemically with dyes (Thorneley *et al.*, 1976), and biochemically with dinitrogenase plus MgATP (Ljones and Burris, 1978a). In the reduced state, dinitrogenase reductase has a ferredoxin-type EPR signal, and this disappears upon oxidation (Zumft, 1976). By comparison with ferredoxins and synthetic $Fe_4S_4^*$ clusters (Holm and Ibers, 1977), the oxidation states of the $Fe_4S_4^*$ cluster in dinitrogenase reductase can be assigned as the $Fe_4S_4^*(SR)_4^{3-}$ state[2] in the reduced protein, and the $Fe_4S_4^*(SR)_4^{2-}$ state in the oxidized protein. In the biological reaction, each $Fe_4S_4^*$ cluster functions as a one-electron donor to dinitrogenase (Ljones and Burris, 1978b). As is true with the ferredoxins and the synthetic tetramers, the absorption of dinitrogenase reductase in the 400–500 nm region increases upon oxidation. Both optical and EPR spectroscopy can be used to monitor the oxidation level of dinitrogenase reductase.

Effect of MgATP on Potential

Potentiometric titrations of dinitrogenase reductase have been performed and have been monitored with changes in the EPR signal (Zumft *et al.*, 1974). In the absence of MgATP, the midpoint potential (E_m) of *Clostridium pasteurianum* dinitrogenase reductase is about -290 mV. The binding of two MgATPs to the enzyme molecule lowers the potential to -400 mV. A change in the midpoint potential is also induced by MgADP and some of the analogs of ATP, but the change is less (Mortenson *et al.*, 1976). In contrast to this behavior, it is reported that dinitrogenase reductase from *Rhodospirillum rubrum* does not exhibit a change in its midpoint potential upon the addition of MgATP. This protein had an E_m of about -260 mV in either the presence or the absence of MgATP (Carithers *et al.*, 1979). Although this experiment was performed with an inactive form of the *R. rubrum* dinitrogenase reductase, it does raise a question about the assumed universality of the change in the potential observed with *C. pasteurianum* dinitrogenase reductase.

It is uncertain what meaning the observed change in potential has, as it is not the result of the hydrolysis of ATP; MgATP is not hydrolyzed by purified dinitrogenase reducase in the absence of dinitrogenase (Winter and Burris, 1976; Zumft, 1976; Mortenson and Thorneley, 1979). The observed change in potential of dinitrogenase reductase could be the result of a tighter binding of MgATP to oxidized dinitrogenase reductase than to reduced dinitrogenase reductase. As the reductants for the nitrogenase system, all have potentials more negative than -400 mV, any change in potential of dinitrogenase reductase is likely to be of little importance in the functioning of the nitrogenase system.

[2] The convention $(SR)_4^{3-}$ indicates bonding of the $Fe_4S_4^*$ through 4 thiol (SR) groups and indicates the net charge is minus 3.

B. POTENTIALS AND REACTION RATES

The rate of the nitrogenase-catalyzed reaction has been measured as a function of the potential applied to the system (Evans and Albrecht, 1974; Scherings *et al.*, 1977). This has been done both electrochemically (Evans and Albrecht, 1974) and by monitoring the oxidation state of the flavodoxin electron donor to the nitrogenase system (Scherings *et al.*, 1977). In all cases, the nitrogenase-catalyzed reaction essentially halts near − 460 mV, a potential that is more negative than that required to keep the dinitrogenase reductase MgATP complex in the reduced state. This may be caused by a tighter binding of oxidized than of reduced dinitrogenase reductase to dinitrogenase, but such an explanation may be too simplistic.

C. DINITROGENASE

Dinitrogenase is present in a more reduced state during the steady-state turnover of the nitrogenase system than it is in the resting state (Zumft, 1976). To date, however, no one has succeeded in reducing dinitrogenase and retaining its catalytic activity by utilizing any chemical, electrochemical, or biochemical reductant other than the natural system of dinitrogenase reductase plus MgATP. Reported electrochemical experiments have dealt with the oxidation of dinitrogenase from the resting state rather than with what is considered to be the physiological reduction. The experiments have been designed to yield structural information, not information on the chemistry of the reduction of substrates by dinitrogenase. Early oxidative titrations were monitored by measuring the protein absorption at 460 nm, and thionine was utilized as an oxidant (Walker and Mortenson, 1973). These experiments indicated that there were four electrons removed from *C. pasteurianum* dinitrogenase in conversion from the resting state to the oxidized state. Rawlings *et al.* (1980) later performed titrations with thionine on *C. pasteurianum* dinitrogenase, but they monitored oxidation–reduction by changes in the EPR signal of the protein. They found that the first four electrons were removed from the protein without any change in the EPR signal, whereas removal of the next two electrons completely eliminated the EPR signal (Rawlings *et al.*, 1978; Zimmerman *et al.*, 1978). The two methods of monitoring the reaction also yielded two different midpoint potentials for the reaction; the optical titration gave an E_m of − 70 mV for the first four electrons, whereas the EPR titration gave an E_m of 0 mV for the next two electrons. It seems likely that there are at least two types of centers within dinitrogenase, and that the first four electrons arise from one type of center that does not have an observable EPR signal, whereas the next two electrons arise from a different type of center, the center responsible for the characteristic EPR signal of dinitrogenase. This interpretation agrees well with Mössbauer and cluster extrusion experiments, which have identified four $Fe_4S_4^*$ clusters per dinitrogenase molecule in addition to two other cofactors (responsible for the EPR signal of dinitrogenase) containing six Fe atoms apiece (Zimmerman et al., 1978; Rawlings et al., 1978; Huynh et al., 1979). O'Donnell and Smith (1978) have performed electrochemical titrations of dinitrogenase from a variety of different organisms and have monitored the EPR signal as a measure of the oxidation state. They found that the midpoint potential for the disappearance of the EPR signal varied over the range of 0 to -250 mV, depending on the source of the dinitrogenase.

D. BINDING AND ACTION OF MgATP

Although MgATP is not thermodynamically required for the reduction of N_2, it is an absolute requirement for all nitrogenase-catalyzed reactions. MgATP binds to dinitrogenase reductase, and in so doing it changes the physical properties of the protein. In the presence of MgATP the reduction potential of dinitrogenase reductase shifts approximately 100 mV more negative (Zumft et al., 1974), and the sulfhydryl groups of the protein become more reactive (Thorneley and Eady, 1973). The iron in the $Fe_4S_4^*$ clusters becomes more reactive toward chelators (Ljones and Burris, 1978a), and the symmetry of the EPR signal changes from rhombic to axial (Mortenson et al., 1973; Orme-Johnson et al., 1972). The most accurate measurements of the binding constant of MgATP to dinitrogenase reductase probably are those derived from a gel equilibration technique (Tso and Burris, 1973) and from the reaction of the iron chelator bathophenanthroline disulfonate (BPS) with the iron of dinitrogenase reductase in the presence of MgATP (Ljones and Burris, 1978a). With C. pasteurianum dinitrogenase reductase the gel equilibration method gives a value of $17-50$ μM (Tso and Burris, 1973; Emerich et al., 1978) for the dissociation constant, whereas the BPS method gives 85 μM (Ljones and Burris, 1978a). With dinitrogenase reductase from Azotobacter vinelandii only the BPS method has given reproducible results, and values of 220 and 430 μM have been reported for each of the two MgATP molecules that are bound to dinitrogease reductase (Hageman, 1979). Two MgATP molecules also bind to the dinitrogenase reductase from C. pasteurianum (Tso and Burris, 1973). The binding of both molecules of MgATP is required for the reaction of the iron with BPS (Ljones and Burris, 1978a) and for the change in the reduction potential of dinitrogenase reductase (Zumft et al., 1974) or the change in the symmetry of the EPR signal (Mortenson et al., 1973).

E. ELECTRON TRANSFER BETWEEN COMPONENTS AND THE ROLE OF MgATP

A ternary complex between dinitrogenase, dinitrogenase reductase, and two MgATP can form rapidly and apparently in a random order. After the formation of this complex, an electron is transferred from dinitrogenase reductase to dinitrogenase (Smith *et al.*, 1973; Thorneley, 1975). This reaction has been studied by Thorneley (1975) and by Hageman (1979). Thorneley (1975) reported that the reaction is dependent on one MgATP with a K_m of 400 μM. Hageman (1979), on the other hand, has concluded that the electron transfer reaction is dependent on the presence of two MgATP molecules, with K_m's comparable to the K_d for binding of MgATP to dinitrogenase reductase, i.e., 970 μM and 220 μM. Hageman also suggested an explanation for the failure of Thorneley to observe the dependence on two MgATPs, i.e., that Thorneley (1975) did not extend his studies to sufficiently low concentrations of MgATP and that he neglected the participation of a back reaction in his analysis of the experimental data.

Eady *et al.* (1978) demonstrated that MgATP hydrolysis is coupled to the initial electron transfer between the proteins. They observed an identical pre-steady-state time course for the hydrolysis of MgATP and for the electron transfer from dinitrogenase reductase to dinitrogenase. Although Eady *et al.* (1978) did not establish the stoichiometry of the reaction, Burris and Hageman (1980) have demonstrated that two MgATPs are hydrolyzed for each electron transferred during the pre-steady-state reaction. As the minimum requirement for MgATP in the nitrogenase-catalyzed reaction is 4 ATP/e_2^-, the pre-steady-state results indicate that the ATP-coupled hydrolysis can be all accounted for as occurring in a reaction coupled directly to electron transfer between the two nitrogenase proteins.

Studies have been directed at the effect of MgATP dependence on the rate of initial electron transfer from dinitrogenase reductase to dinitrogenase (Hageman, 1979; Thorneley, 1975; Thorneley and Cornish-Bowden, 1977). Thorneley (1975) has found that there is a kinetic dependence upon one MgATP for the electron transfer to occur. The K_m for this MgATP was 400 μM, and the maximum rate at saturating MgATP concentrations was 200 sec^{-1}. The reaction was independent of the order of mixing of the reactants, and the rate of electron transfer was independent of the concentration of dinitrogenase reductase and dinitrogenase; this indicates that the formation of the ternary complex is fast relative to the rate of electron transfer. By premixing MgADP with dinitrogenase reductase, Thorneley and Cornish-Bowden (1977) demonstrated that the dissociation of MgADP from dinitrogenase reductase occurs at a

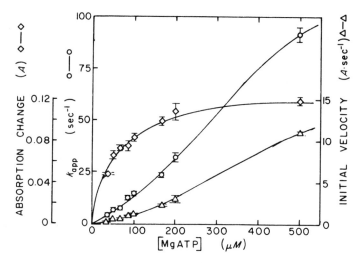

FIG. 1. Dependence on MgATP of the pre-steady-state oxidation of dinitrogenase reductase by dinitrogenase. Final reaction conditions were 50 mM buffer, pH 7.4, 10 mM creatine phosphate, 1 mM magnesium acetate, 0.5 mg of creatine kinase per milliliter, 5 mM dithionite, 9.6 μM dinitrogenase, 23.7 μM dinitrogenase reductase with MgATP as indicated. ○——○, k_{app}, the apparent first-order rate constant for oxidation of dinitrogenase reductase by dinitrogenase; ◇——◇, the extent of total oxidation of dinitrogenase reductase as measured by the absorbance change from time zero to infinity; △——△, the initial velocity of the oxidation of dinitrogenase reductase as measured by the initial rate of change of the absorption.

rate comparable to electron transfer (200 sec^{-1}); therefore dissociation of MgADP from the enzyme is not rate limiting in the overall turnover of the enzyme system.

Figure 1 shows the dependence of the rate of the initial electron transfer on the MgATP concentration. By extending the studies to sufficiently low concentrations of MgATP, it was possible to demonstrate that there is a clearly sigmoidal dependence of the rate of electron transfer on the MgATP concentration. The sigmoidal dependence indicates that two molecules of MgATP are required for the reaction, and the analysis of the data indicates that the K_m's for these two MgATP molecules are 970 μM and 220 μM. The discrepancy between these results and those of Thorneley (1975) most likely arise from the use of a lower concentration of MgATP in our studies and from differences in the method of analyzing the data. In particular, we have taken account of the existence of a back reaction leading to the reduction of oxidized dinitrogenase reductase by dithionite, a condition that complicates analysis of the data. Thorneley's (1975) neglect of this back reaction does not lead to significant errors at high concentrations of MgATP, but it does introduce significant errors in the analysis at low concentrations of MgATP.

The dependence of the electron transfer reaction on two molecules of MgATP, and the hydrolysis of two molecules of MgATP/e$^-$ at the time of the electron transfer, suggests that the only role for MgATP is in the electron transfer reaction from dinitrogenase reductase to dinitrogenase. A kinetic dependence on two MgATPs for the H_2 evolution reaction has been demonstrated previously (Watt and Burns, 1977), and the minimal hydrolysis of two MgATP/e$^-$ has been observed frequently (Winter and Burris, 1976; Zumft, 1976). Although more complicated ATP kinetics (of order greater than 2) have been observed (Kennedy, 1970), these likely arose from specific substrate effects, as the H_2 evolution reaction is quite clearly dependent on only two MgATPs (Hageman, 1979; Burris and Hageman, 1980; Watt and Burns, 1977). Observed hydrolysis of more than two MgATP/e$^-$ occurs only under conditions of suboptimal electron transfer rates (Winter and Burris, 1976; Zumft, 1976). At least two mechanisms have been proposed to account for this "excess" ATP hydrolysis, both of which involve the high steady state concentration of the oxidized form of dinitrogenase reductase (Hageman and Burris, 1978a; Orme-Johnson and Davis, 1977).

IV. Model for Nitrogenase-Catalyzed Electron Transfer

Figure 2 shows a schematic model for the nitrogenase-catalysed electron transfer and H_2 evolution reactions. The model shows the transfer of electrons one at a time into dinitrogenase, whereas H_2 evolution is shown to occur only after the accumulation of two or more electrons in dinitrogenase (Hageman and Burris, 1978b). Thus the cycle shown must be completed at least twice before H_2 evolution (or other substrate reduction) can occur. The cycle starts with the formation of a ternary complex between dinitrogenase, dinitrogenase reductase, and two MgATPs. For the sake of simplicity, this complex formation is shown as occurring in an ordered manner, whereas the actual reaction is probably random, as both MgATP (Tso and Burris, 1973) and dinitrogenase (Thorneley et al., 1975) can form complexes with dinitrogenase reductase independently of the presence of the other component. Following the formation of the ternary complex, an electron is transferred from dinitrogenase reductase to dinitrogenase (Thorneley, 1975), and this is accompanied by the hydrolysis of two MgATPs (Hageman, 1979; Burris and Hageman, 1980). After the electron transfer, the rate-limiting step in the nitrogenase turnover occurs. This step is not the dissociation of MgADP from the enzyme, as this has been shown to occur at a rate comparable to the rate of electron

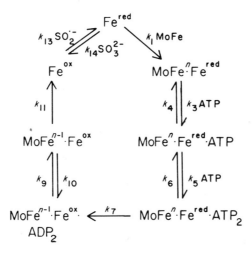

FIG. 2. A simplified scheme for the functioning of the nitrogenase system. The steps in the electron transfer from dinitrogenase reductase to dinitrogenase are shown; not shown are the steps leading to H_2 evolution after dinitrogenase has been around the cycle at least twice. The exact oxidation state of dinitrogenase is not defined, as the steps are presumably the same regardless of how many times the dinitrogease has been through the cycle.

transfer (200 sec^{-1}) (Thorneley and Cornish-Bowden, 1977), whereas turnover of the enzyme occurs at only about 10 sec^{-1}. It has been suggested that the slow step is the dissociation of the two proteins from each other (Mortenson and Thorneley, 1979), and this is consistent with what is known about the association constant between the two proteins (Thorneley, 1975; Thorneley et al., 1975). The slow step must occur before the reduction of dinitrogenase reductase by dithionite, as the protein is largely oxidized in the steady-state reaction (Orme-Johnson et al., 1972; Smith et al., 1973). Additional data have been presented that the two proteins do, in fact, dissociate before the reduction by dithionite occurs (Hageman and Burris, 1978b). The final step in the proposed cycle is the reduction of oxidized dinitrogenase reductase by dithionite, a reaction that is known to proceed rapidly (Thorneley et al., 1976).

REFERENCES

Burris, R. H., and Hageman, R. V. (1980). In "Molybdenum and Molybdenum-Containing Enzymes" (M. Coughlan, ed.), pp. 403–426. Pergamon Press, Oxford, New York.
Carithers, R. P., Yoch, D. C., and Arnon, D. I. (1979). J. Bacteriol. 137, 779–789.
Eady, R. R., Lowe, D. J., and Thorneley, R. N. F. (1978). FEBS Lett. 95, 211–213.
Emerich, D. W., Ljones, T., and Burris, R. H. (1978). Biochim. Biophys. Acta 527, 359–369.

Evans, M. C. W., and Albrecht, S. L. (1974). *Biochem. Biophys. Res. Commun.* **61**, 1187–1192.
Hageman, R. V. (1979). Ph.D. Thesis, University of Wisconsin-Madison.
Hageman, R. V., and Burris, R. H. (1978a). *Biochemistry* **17**, 4117–4124.
Hageman, R. V., and Burris, R. H. (1978b). *Proc. Natl. Acad. Sci. U.S.A.* **75**, 2699–2702.
Holm, R. H., and Ibers, J. A. (1977). *In* "Iron-Sulfur Proteins" (W. Lovenberg, ed.), Vol. 3, pp. 205–281. Academic Press, New York.
Huynh, B. H., Münck, E., and Orme-Johnson, W. H. (1979). *Biochim. Biophys. Acta* **576**, 192–203.
Kennedy, I. R. (1970). *Biochim. Biophys. Acta* **222**, 135–144.
Leigh, G. J. (1977). *In* "Recent Developments in Nitrogen Fixation" (W. Newton, J. R. Postgate, and C. Rodriguez-Barrueco, eds.), pp. 1–24. Academic Press, New York.
Ljones, T., and Burris, R. H. (1978a). *Biochemistry* **17**, 1866–1872.
Ljones, T., and Burris, R. H. (1978b). *Biochem. Biophys. Res. Commun.* **80**, 22–25.
Mayhew, S. G. (1978). *Eur. J. Biochem.* **85**, 535–547.
Mortenson, L. E., and Thorneley, R. N. F. (1979). *Annu. Rev. Biochem.* **48**, 387–418.
Mortenson, L. E., Zumft, W. G., and Palmer, G. (1973). *Biochim. Biophys. Acta* **292**, 422–435.
Mortenson, L. E., Walker, M. N., and Walker, G. A. (1976). *In* "Proceedings of the First International Symposium on Nitrogen Fixation" (W. E. Newton and C. J. Nyman, eds.), pp. 117–149. Washington State Univ. Press, Pullman.
Newton, W. E., Bulen, W. A., Hadfield, K. L., Stiefel, E. I., and Watt, G. D. (1977). *In* "Recent Developments in Nitrogen Fixation" (W. Newton, J. R. Postgate, and C. Rodriguez-Barrueco, eds.), pp. 117–130. Academic Press, New York.
O'Donnell, M. J., and Smith, B. E. (1978). *Biochem. J.* **173**, 831–838.
Orme-Johnson, W. H., and Davis, L. C. (1977). *In* "Iron-Sulfur Proteins" (W. Lovenberg, ed.), Vol. 3, pp. 15–60. Academic Press, New York.
Orme-Johnson, W. H., Hamilton, W. D., Ljones, T., Tso, M.-Y. W., Burris, R. H., Shah, V. K., and Brill, W. J. (1972). *Proc. Natl. Acad. Sci. U. S. A.* **69**, 3142–3145.
Rawlings, J., Shah, V. K., Chisnell, J. R., Brill, W. J., Zimmerman, R., Münck, E., and Orme-Johnson, W. H. (1978). *J. Biol. Chem.* **253**, 1001–1004.
Rawlings, J., Henzl, M. T., and Orme-Johnson, W. H. (1980). *In* "Nitrogen Fixation" (W. E. Newton and W. H. Orme-Johnson, eds). University Park Press, Baltimore. In press.
Scherings, G., Haaker, H., and Veeger, C. (1977). *Eur. J. Biochem.* **77**, 621–630.
Smith, B. E., Lowe, D. J., and Bray, R. C. (1973). *Biochem. J.* **135**, 331–341.
Stiefel, E. I. (1977). *In* "Recent Developments in Nitrogen Fixation" (W. Newton, J. R. Postgate, and C. Rodriguez-Barrueco, eds.), pp. 69–108. Academic Press, New York.
Stombaugh, N. A., Sundquist, J. E., Burris, R. H., and Orme-Johnson, W. H. (1976). *Biochemistry* **15**, 2633–2641.
Thorneley, R. N. F. (1975). *Biochem. J.* **145**, 391–396.
Thorneley, R. N. F., and Cornish-Bowden, A. (1977). *Biochem. J.* **165**, 255–262.
Thorneley, R. N. F., and Eady, R. R. (1973). *Biochem. J.* **133**, 405–408.
Thorneley, R. N. F., Eady, R. R., and Yates, M. G. (1975). *Biochim. Biophys. Acta* **403**, 269–284.
Thorneley, R. N. F., Yates, M. G., and Lowe, D. J. (1976). *Biochem. J.* **155**, 137–144.
Thorneley, R. N. F., Eady, R. R., and Lowe, D. J. (1978). *Nature (London)* **272**, 557–558.
Tso, M.-Y. W., and Burris, R. H. (1973). *Biochim. Biophys. Acta* **309**, 263–270.
Walker, M., and Mortenson, L. E. (1973). *Biochim. Biophys. Res. Commun.* **54**, 669–676.

Watt, G. D., and Burns, A. (1977). *Biochemistry* **16**, 264–270.

Winter, H. C., and Burris, R. H. (1976). *Annu. Rev. Biochem.* **45**, 409–426.

Yates, M. G. (1977). *In* "Recent Developments in Nitrogen Fixation" (W. Newton, J. R. Postgate and C. Rodriguez-Barrueco, eds.), pp. 219–270. Academic Press, New York.

Zimmermann, R., Münck, E., Brill, W. J., Shah, V. K., Henzl, M. T., Rawlings, J., and Orme-Johnson, W. H. (1978). *Biochim. Biophys. Acta* **537**, 185–207.

Zumft, W. G. (1976). *Struct. Bonding* **29**, 1–65.

Zumft, W. G., Mortenson, L. E., and Palmer, G. (1974). *Eur. J. Biochem.* **46**, 525–535.

Index